Praise for
The Embodied Healing Workbook

"As signals of threat permeate our world, we become aware of the need to feel safe enough in our body to function successfully in both our work and social environments. In this challenging world, we need to be aware of our innate reactions to threat and when threat shifts us from a species of benevolence to one locked in a state of defense. In *The Embodied Healing Workbook*, Dr. Cook-Cottone provides a toolkit with easy-to-follow exercises that enable us to be safe enough to honor and explore our bodily feelings. Through this journey, an awareness of feelings emerges that both honors and respects the body's foundational survival reactions and frees the individual to express a more resilient and flexible strategy with others."

—**Stephen Porges, PhD,** author of *The Polyvagal Theory*
and *Clinical Applications of the Polyvagal Theory*

"Speaking from professional and personal experience, the legacy of posttraumatic problems is a miserable, unhealthy, and stultifying mixture of Eriksonian developmental problems: mistrust, shame, doubt, guilt, inferiority, isolation, disintegration, stagnation, and despair. Each of these self-defeating, self-perpetuating experiences, let alone their negative effects on each other, is grounded in and expressed through disconnections with the vitality, power, and wisdom of one's body. It all *feels* hopeless. In *The Embodied Healing Workbook*, Dr. Cook-Cottone demonstrates that there is more than hope, that it is possible to be with and honor this great ball of negativity AND take specific steps to transform your relationships with your body, the people in your life, and your potential for connection, joy, and meaning. I suspect you are thinking that in order to do this you would need, somehow, to find a guide who understands trauma AND who is also compassionate, knowledgeable, flexible, patient, experienced, extremely skilled, encouraging, and trustworthy. Moreover, this guide would need, somehow, to offer specific steps you can take to escape the black hole of trauma while providing the wisdom and other support necessary for you to move between the fundamental human needs for safety/comfort and challenge/growth. Believe me, I know and feel in my head and heart this pessimistic skepticism. AND I know we need look no further than Dr. Cook-Cottone and *The Embodied Healing Workbook* to find this guide."

—**Michael P. Levine, PhD,** fellow, Academy for Eating Disorders

"In an approachable, innovative, and masterful way, Dr. Cook-Cottone gives voice to the often silenced and ignored holder of trauma—the body. She brilliantly supports readers in discovering their body's intentions, needs, and inner resources, providing a roadmap for embarking safety on the journey within and finding one's way home through the body. Through science-backed strategies, loving yet practical instruction, and a wealth of reflective and experiential practices, she shows readers how to uncover their inner resources and transform their relationship with themselves after trauma. This workbook is informed by decades of Cook-Cottone's personal wisdom and experience as a psychotherapist, yoga teacher, and researcher. If there was one guide to trauma healing from a body-based perspective that I would recommend, this would be it."

—**Esther E. E. Estey, PhD,** psychologist and senior instructor at Harvard
Medical School and the Center for Mindfulness and Compassion

"In this wise guide to embodied healing, Dr. Cook-Cottone invites us to systematically explore our feelings and sensations to heal from the diverse bodily responses to trauma. This well-organized book provides a structured approach to discovering a new level of understanding of the story of the soma. Designed for the trauma survivor/ thriver to do at home as a self-paced process, the therapist can also use these exercises with clients directly, during individual sessions or in mind-body groups. The exercises are accessible and rich in detail, enabling a self-designed pace that promises a new level of embodiment and healing. This book is a must for everyone's shelf—for who among us will not benefit from a more comfortable, embodied way of being?"

—**Leslie Korn, PhD, MPH, LMHC,** author of *The Brainbow Blueprint: A Clinical Guide to Integrative Medicine and Nutrition for Mental Well-Being*

"*The Embodied Healing Workbook* might just be the most in-depth and comprehensive resource on trauma recovery available. I am blown away by the amount of exercises and accessible practices that this workbook contains. Indeed, Catherine Cook-Cottone shows us that 'your body [is] your most valuable resource in recovery.' This workbook is written and designed beautifully and thoughtfully. And you get to 'move at the speed of trust.' I will be using this workbook as my new go-to resource for myself and my clients."

—**Joanne Spence, MA, C-IAYT,** author of *Trauma-Informed Yoga Toolbox for Therapists* and *Trauma-Informed Yoga Card Deck*

"In *The Embodied Healing Workbook*, Dr. Cook-Cottone combines her personal journey, academic research, deep spiritual beliefs, and her years of experience as a healing practitioner into a practical guide for those recovering from trauma. Her exercises go beyond the superficial to provide gentle, meaningful experiences in a very accessible format. This workbook takes the theoretical and provides the reader with unique, creative experiences that heal body and soul. Keep this book at your bedside and find your path to healing. It is indispensable for those who suffer the wounds of trauma."

—**Celia Spacone, PhD,** coordinator, Suicide Prevention Coalition of Erie County

"With exceptional warmth and words which invite the reader in as if to open arms, Catherine Cook-Cottone provides accessible explanations to the lay person as to why trauma is embodied as it is, and then offers practical approaches to accepting and gradually reshaping that embodiment with love and self-acceptance. This is a treasure trove of resources for both trauma survivors and the therapists who work with them."

—**Dori Marshall, MD,** associate professor of psychiatry, University at Buffalo

"Dr. Cook-Cottone has expertly filled a gap in the clinical world. She has created an engaging, concise, and inspiring workbook for all levels. She beautifully describes accessible techniques that the individual can embrace in any context and caresses the participant with reminders about how to lead a calm, thoughtful, reflective, and meaningful life filled with self-love and compassion. She gracefully inhabits the embodied practices that she offers with expertise and common sense to make this an essential guide for every healing process."

—**Nan Herron, MD, RYT,** board-certified psychiatrist

Over 100
Healing
Practices

The
Embodied
Healing
Workbook

The Art and Science of
Befriending Your Body
in Trauma Recovery

Catherine Cook-Cottone, PhD, C-IAYT

THE EMBODIED HEALING WORKBOOK
Copyright © 2023 by Catherine Cook-Cottone

Published by
PESI Publishing, Inc.
3839 White Ave
Eau Claire, WI 54703

Cover and interior design by Emily Dyer
Editing by Jenessa Jackson, PhD

ISBN 9781683736936 (print)
ISBN 9781683736950 (ePDF)
ISBN 9781683736943 (ePUB)

PESI Publishing
pesipublishing.com

Dedication

This book is dedicated to my two daughters, Chloe and Maya Cottone.

I was able to find my own embodiment, befriend my own body—
a path that brought me to motherhood—and find the capacity
to find joy in loving two very beautiful humans.

I love you more.

Table of Contents

~

List of Embodied Practices

Introduction:
Getting Started in Embodied Healing

Trauma can change the way you feel about, and in, your body. That's because trauma shifts how your body functions. In the midst of a traumatic experience, your body does the very best it can to keep you safe. It courageously and imperfectly attempts to manage the unmanageable by activating your stress response system, which functions to separate you from danger and pain. And when the traumatic event is over, your body holds onto the memory of what happened so it can make sure you never hurt in this way again.

Therefore, trauma not only resides in your thoughts—as memories, images, and fears about what might happen—but also in your body. While it's true that we *think* about traumatic experiences after the fact, the truth is we also feel them deeply: in our hearts, nervous systems, muscles, and so often, in our bones. When trauma happens, it is our minds, hearts, *and* bodies that are overwhelmed, incapacitated, and ultimately traumatized. And when the trauma is over, it can feel like our bodies are no longer our partner in being in this world. Our bodies can become defensive, become unpredictable, and feel out of control or shut down.

That means that even if you have a really good understanding of why something happened, how it happened, and what to do if it happens again, it can still be difficult to move on because your body remembers the trauma. As Dr. Bessel van der Kolk (2014) says, "The body keeps the score." Or as Nikki Myers—an accomplished yoga teacher who works in addiction recovery—says, "The issues live in the tissues." You simply can't think your way out of trauma. I can tell you that the years of my own personal work, as well as my decades of work as a researcher and therapist, have demonstrated that any attempts to use logic or reason alone will fall short when your body is holding on to memories and trying hard to keep you safe.

Considering this, your body may be your most valuable resource in recovery. It is for this reason that I wrote *The Embodied Healing Workbook*: to help you work through your trauma, reconnect to your body, and begin thinking about what is next in your embodied path forward. This book was written to empower you to work through those moments that your body is afraid to forget. When I say *you*, I am referring to the embodied you. The embodied self—you as you are right now in this moment—holds all of what is happening inside of you: your awareness and intentions, your body states and sensations (e.g., calm, defensive, reactive), your feelings, and your thoughts, beliefs, and stories. Your embodied self is also shaped by your family and friends, your school or work, and your culture and traditions. In any given moment, you are all these things. Your embodiment is made up of all of it.

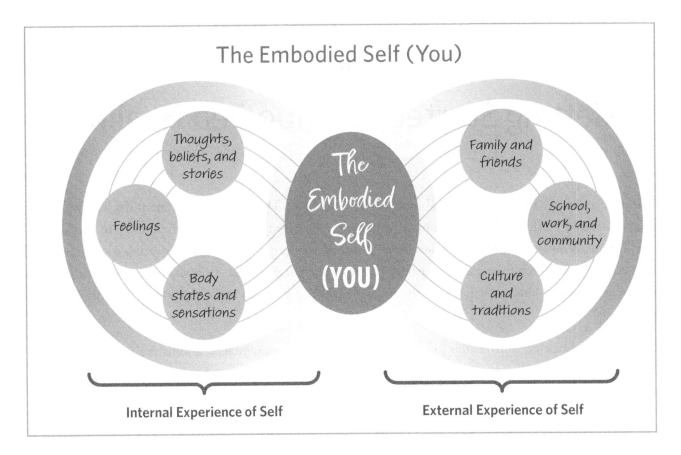

The Embodied Self (You)

Thoughts, beliefs, and stories

Feelings

Body states and sensations

The Embodied Self (YOU)

Family and friends

School, work, and community

Culture and traditions

Internal Experience of Self   **External Experience of Self**

Now add trauma to the mix. When you experience trauma, any one or more of those aspects of who you are can be disrupted. And this always includes the body. As you try to function day to day, the deeply physical symptoms of trauma challenge your attempts to balance what is happening on the inside of you with what is expected and needed from you on the outside. You might try and get a sense of it all—to understand what is happening—and, still, you might be startled easily, have difficulty sleeping, and pendulate from feeling shutdown or numb to feeling overactivated and agitated.

Sometimes it can feel like the answer is to drink alcohol or take another substance to "settle the nerves" or more reliably numb your dysregulated body and emotions. I've worked with people so exhausted and overwhelmed by their trauma symptoms that they have adopted self-destructive behaviors in an attempt to cope. Some examples include eating disorders, substance abuse, or self-harm. One patient whose body and emotions were feeling unmanageable told me that these types of behavior were hell, "but at least it's a hell I can control."

While these self-destructive behaviors can have a temporary numbing effect, they only put your body in more danger. I have heard it said that the way out is through. I agree and I'd add more: The way out is in. One of my graduate students, Carly Pershyn, shared a metaphor with me recently: "Be like a buffalo." She explained that on the Great Plains there are cows and buffalo. When a storm comes, the cows start running away from it, but they aren't fast enough to outrun the storm. They end up running with it, staying in the storm longer. When the buffalo sense the storm, they run toward it—getting through it and into clear and peaceful weather on the other side. True healing comes from reconnecting with the body and from being with and working with trauma as it resides in the body. It is courageous work that requires commitment and practice over time to, in essence, create a new way of being with all that you have been through.

How to Use This Book

In this workbook, you'll find a step-by-step, sequential process for embodied healing that begins with reconnecting to your body and developing your inner resources as well as your support system. It includes working with your sensations, feelings, intuition, and relationships in partnership with your body; processing trauma (if it's right for you); and then exploring what is possible in your embodied life going forward. Each step provides a foundation for the next step, one chapter at a time. I recommend that you mindfully work through the workbook, chapter by chapter, revisiting previous chapters as needed, without jumping ahead.

I also recommend identifying and reaching out to your support people now, at the very start of your journey. This might be a go-to friend, your therapist, or a support group. If a chapter or part of the process feels like a lot, this is the perfect time to reach out to your designated support system, slow the process down, and take care of you and your body. *Just move at the speed of trust.* There are several PAUSE prompts included throughout the book that remind you to **P**ause, **A**ssess, and **USE** your resources and supports.

This process, at its core, is about you and your body getting back to trusting each other and then taking that trust out into your relationships and the world. The pace matters—a lot. If you go too fast, your body will know. It might sound contradictory, but healing from trauma can be triggering. Healing is not a straightforward path, it is filled with forward movements, plateaus, and sometimes regressions. You might feel like you are losing ground. Just like each one of us, every path is unique and has its own trajectory. It can be helpful to consider that your goal is not to get somewhere called *recovered* or *better*. Rather, your goals may look more like this:

- To heal your relationship with yourself.
- To be a better friend with, and a partner to, your own body.
- To commit to listening to your body and heart with love and compassion.
- To learn how to be in relationship with your trauma(s).

What Is in This Book

In order to support you, your healing, and your growth, this book is divided into a three-part process:

Part I: Connecting to and Befriending Your Embodied Self provides you with guidance for facing and working through your trauma safely. It is here that you take the first steps toward befriending your body. You will learn the neuroscience behind your body's attempts to keep you safe and connected to others and how stress affects you and this process. It will also help you balance your efforts out in the world with your own mindful self-care. You will shore up your coping skills and build what are called *resources*. You will also be guided on how to secure needed supports.

Part II: Embodying Your Life is designed to help you build foundational layers of positive embodiment. Throughout each layer—sensations, emotions, cognitions, and relationships—you will develop competencies and skills for being with and working with the experiences of your body. You will learn ways in which your body helps you function effectively as you reconfigure what you'd like to do going forward. You will work through the layers of your experiential body—sensing (inside your body and out in your environment) and feeling. In this section, you will also explore ways to connect (or reconnect) to your body's wisdom, or *embodied decision-making*. Next, you will explore how the body can help you engage in healthy and supportive relationships and keep you safe in the midst of difficult or harmful ones.

In **Part III: Processing Trauma with and through the Body**, you will engage in practices that help you do embodied trauma work. In this work, you will detail your trauma and then intentionally and effectively connect with your body as you remember your trauma using your coping skills and inner resources. The last chapter helps you integrate what you have learned and prepare for continued healing and growth.

In each chapter, you will be provided with additional tools that can help the thinking or intellectualizing part of you stay on track in the form of *need-to-know* sections and a series of *embodying self-statements*. The need-to-know sections give you the rationale, theory, and science that supports what you are learning and practicing, while the embodying self-statements are powerful phrases based on trauma research that are known to be true. For this introductory chapter, I offer you three basic truths that are perhaps my favorite:

- Embodiment is a fundamental human right.

- I am worth the effort.

- My body can be a resource for recovery and growth.

When things get difficult, you can orient your thoughts to one of these statements. For example, if you begin to doubt your worthiness in this endeavor, remind yourself of this first truth: that embodiment— or living life in and through your body in a positive and fulfilling way—is a fundamental human right. You do not need to earn it. It is something that we all deserve from the very moment we are born.

Next, remind yourself of the second truth: that you are worth the effort. Say to yourself, *[Your name here], you are worth the effort and do not forget that—ever.* Then, step into that effort. The truth is, no matter what someone has been through or has done, they are worth the effort. Similarly, you are worthy of healing, growth, and change.

Last, remind yourself of this third truth: that your body can be a resource for recovery and growth. Even if it might seem difficult to believe that this can be true right now, I have seen it accomplished through my own work with people lost in addiction, disordered eating, and dissociation. They have found that by taking one small step at a time and with repetition and practice, they were able to shift their bodies from a source of pain to a source of solace. As author Will Durant (1926) said when summarizing the teachings of Aristotle, "We are what we repeatedly do" (p. 87). It will be your work and your practices that will make the difference. You can and will practice your way into knowing, for sure, that your body can be a resource in your recovery and growth.

I wish I could stand here in these pages with open arms and welcome you in. I can do the next best thing and let these words hold you. This book is for you. Your recovery is possible. You are worth the effort.

Letter to Therapists

Dear Therapist,

I am so excited you bought this workbook. I wrote it because I needed a resource like this to support my work with my own patients. I also felt like patients needed easier access to the concepts and practices I present here, which are often embedded in intellectually compelling and conceptually rich texts that are interesting to read yet too saturated with academic vernacular to be helpful for most people.

In this workbook, I provide an integrated set of practices that I have developed through my years of clinical practice and through my experience creating and implementing trauma-informed yoga methods. The foundations for these practices are rooted in polyvagal theory and well-developed methodologies such as sensorimotor psychotherapy, somatic experiencing, eye movement desensitization and reprocessing, emotional freedom techniques, and dialectical behavioral therapy. You can easily apply these tools and practices as adjunct methods as you work with more traditional treatments, or you can use them as standalone methods.

Although patients can use this workbook on their own, it is best used with the support of a mental health professional like you. However, there are many patients who are either resistant or otherwise lack access to therapy due to finances, geographical constraints, or a fear of (or negative history with) the system. For those patients, I hope this workbook becomes an access point—a pathway to the realization of how powerful working with a well-trained mental health professional can be in supporting their personal work toward healing and well-being.

I am very excited for you to explore these practices. Welcome to the world of embodiment!

Sincerely,

Catherine Cook-Cottone, PhD

Embodying Self-Statements by Chapter

Introduction
- Embodiment is a fundamental human right.
- I am worth the effort.
- My body can be a resource for recovery and growth.

Part I: Connecting to and Befriending Your Embodied Self

Chapter 1
- I can be aware of and connected to my body.
- What we practice, we become.
- I can listen to my body.
- My body is a source of grounding, connection, and support.
- I am taking time to thank you and know you, breath and body.

Chapter 2
- Working with my brain and body, change is possible.
- My body is my source of experience in this world.
- My body needs to feel connected and protected.

Chapter 3
- My body tells me what it needs and wants.
- My choices can make the effects of stress better or worse.
- Growing can feel uncomfortable.
- I can be uncomfortable and still be safe.
- I can notice my body, thoughts, and emotions and make changes.

Chapter 4
- My body requires and is worthy of care.
- I deserve to feel safe and loved.
- Self-love is a practice.

- Routine and structure help my body feel safe and regulated.
- I am worth the effort.

Chapter 5
- My body is my inner protector.
- I can connect to my body to relax and release.
- I have within me an inner resource of strength and calm.
- My body is a powerful resource for me in this world.

Chapter 6
- My life has meaning.
- My embodiment gives form to my values and dreams.
- My "why" will help me remember what matters.

Part II: Embodying Your Life

Chapter 7
- My body senses internal and external experiences.
- I can work to create the space I need to find my growth and my freedom.
- My body speaks to me through sensations, and I can listen.
- I can be intentionally and mindfully aware.

Chapter 8
- I can choose my response.
- I don't need to hold everything all of the time.
- My sensations are complex, beautiful, and varied.
- I can be intentionally and mindfully aware.

Chapter 9
- My body feels emotions.
- I can learn to befriend my emotions.

- My feelings are an important source of information.
- I feel so that I can heal.

Chapter 10

- I can build my capacity to be with and work with my emotions.
- Feeling difficult emotions is challenging and important to my growth.
- I can work to be open to the messages my emotions are sending me.
- I can feel my emotions and stay connected to myself and others.
- My emotions can move me, and I can move through my emotions.

Chapter 11

- My body is a source for knowing about my relationships.
- I will not abandon myself or my well-being in my relationships.
- I am worthy and my needs matter.
- My boundaries honor my relationships with myself and others.
- Working on my boundaries is a form of tending to my energetic and creative self.
- Boundary work is a pathway to knowing what I want and need.

Chapter 12

- My body is a means for connection with others.
- *Yes* and *no* are two of the most powerful words I can use.
- I can communicate my boundaries with my body.

Chapter 13

- I am more than my thoughts.
- My intuitive instincts are valid.
- My integrated, embodied self is wise.
- Embodiment is a human right that is critical to our relationship with ourselves, others, and our world.

Part III: Processing Trauma with and through the Body

Chapter 14

- I can move at the speed of trust.
- I can take breaks.
- I can choose.
- I can ask for help.
- Remembering can be a way to honor my past.
- I can honor my body's resilience and strength.

Chapter 15

- My body knows how to heal.
- It is okay to pause and take care of myself.
- I am right here, right now.
- I am partnering with my body to integrate my then and my now.
- I can be with and work with my experience within this moment.

Chapter 16

- I have the resources and skills I need.
- I can be activated and stay within my window of tolerance.
- My body can feel happiness and joy.
- I am always learning and growing.
- My embodiment is a journey toward integrated and attuned self-determination.

Part 1

Connecting to and Befriending Your Embodied Self

Chapter 1

Befriending Your Embodied Self

—*Embodying Self-Statement*—
I can be aware of and connected to my body.

Your embodied healing begins with a reintroduction to the body. Your body as it is right here, right now. Your body that has been through trauma and will be your ally as you heal and recover. Even though we spend every day with our bodies, many of us ignore, suppress, abuse, or otherwise disconnect from our bodies in an effort to get through the day. We may ignore overwhelming sensations, feelings, or memories and suppress unwanted reactions and behaviors. In this chapter, you will begin the basic practices of being with and working with the experiences of your body. Consider this a chance to dip your toe into the possibility of cultivating a meaningful and loving relationship with your body.

Being with entails connecting to, honoring, and listening to the experiences of your body as well as trusting your body's inherent ability to process information and heal. *Being with* practices counter the tendency many of us have to immediately attempt to fix what is making us uncomfortable. When you move to fixing before you try to be with what is, you can short circuit your own capacity to effectively integrate and manage your experiences.

Once you have spent time being with what is present, it can be very helpful to *work with* what is there. *Working with* is about exploring and enhancing your relationship with what has happened and what is happening, rather than trying to fix or repair. This process begins with understanding trauma and its impact on the embodied you.

—Embodying Practice—
Building a Place to Practice

Before you get started, take a moment to consider where you are doing this work. It will be important for you to create a safe haven, or sanctuary, to complete your reading, reflecting, and practicing. Some of the activities in this workbook will only require reading and reflecting. Others will invite you to meditate, imagine, and move your body, so you will want your space to be big enough for movement. Creating a safe space will help you more effectively practice being with and working with your body. This is one of your first steps for self-care.

Steps to creating your safe space or working sanctuary:

1. Find a room, or part of a room, in which you can experience privacy and a sense of safety. The best spaces are easy to visually scan, have a secure entrance to ensure others cannot come in unannounced, or are located in a private and secure setting outside.

2. Schedule time in which you can work and practice for 30 to 60 minutes with few, or no, interruptions. For example, it may be helpful to meditate and practice in the early mornings before others in your home are awake.

3. Gather supplies for your space. Helpful supplies in your safe space may include a cushion or seat, a yoga mat, a small pillow and blanket, and a box or container for other supplies that you may acquire as you work through the chapters (e.g., singing bowl, candles, a journal).

4. Personalize the space. Include objects or items that help you feel grounded or that inspire you (e.g., a gift or trinket from a safe person or time in your life, a stone or crystal that helps you feel grounded, a candle lit in a safe place).

Creating and cultivating this space is an important part of honoring your healing journey. Once you have set up your safe place, settle in and begin. If you do not have a consistent space, pull together a practice box within which you keep your supplies. When it's time to practice, pull out your box and claim a space.

—Embodying Practice—

A Commitment Letter to Your Body

Your body has been working hard to take care of you and to keep you safe. It might be difficult for your body to do this trauma work. It probably means changing the way you and your body relate to each other. So before you get started, consider writing a letter of commitment to your body. You might include a commitment to stay connected, to work as hard as your body works to keep you safe, and to be responsive and caring while you and your body go through this process. It's your letter, your body, and your relationship with your body.

Below is a sample letter of apology and commitment that I wrote to my body. Read it and consider what you might say to yours. You may use this sample letter as a template or come up with something completely different.

Dear Body,

I am writing to let you know that we are going to do something difficult. We have been through a lot together, some of the worst times of our life, me and you. We have been trying to manage it all, the memories and our own defensiveness, and I don't think we quite have it right.

For one, we are not getting along. I get impatient with you and your reactivity. I feel that we can never rest. When I try to do something new or fun, you hate it. You shake and struggle to breathe. When I try to speak out for what is right for me, your vocal cords fail me, trembling and weak. I have been ashamed of you. Then I withdraw, mad at you and mad at the world for hurting us.

I've tried leaving you. I hurt you. I focused on school. I ignored your wants and needs. Sometimes I drank alcohol to help me ignore you. Sometimes I ate too little or too much. Sometimes I ran too far and sometimes I lay in bed refusing to be with you or life. Ugh. And after, always, there you were. It seems I can't leave. It seems that no matter what I do to you, you don't leave me. It looks like we are going to have to sort this out.

I remember when we got along. I remember belly laughs, the smell of lilacs, how cuddly we felt in big blankets, diving into rivers, running in the fall, the smell of a campfire, painting, riding horses, eating the best foods, doing yoga, and dancing. Without you, there is none of this. I can't even hug my dog or cuddle my cat. Without you, there is no me. And when I let myself, I know in my heart that I love you.

I want us to sort out our past together. What happened to us wasn't either of our faults. We did the best we could. Sure, I wish it were better or different. I wish it never happened. But here we are and that's something. It's going to be hard work. We've been in protective mode for a while, and I am not sure if we even know how to get along or work together anymore. Still, we have to try.

I am going to make you a promise: I will work to not leave you or hurt you anymore. I will learn new ways of being together. I will practice and get support when I need it. We will get through this. On the other side of it, we will be partners again.

I feel your doubt. We have tried to get this right a lot of times. I know it might be hard to trust me because I have forgotten, fallen, and failed. To be honest, I am struggling to trust you too. We will just keep trying. If it takes 100 tries, then it takes 100 tries. Right here and right now, when I pause and breathe, I know the truth. You and I are worth every single try, every single time.

I know this will be difficult. And I will remind myself, over and over, that you—no, we—are worth the effort. I really do love you.

Love,
Me

Now, you write a letter to your body in the space here or on a separate piece of paper. It can be a letter of apology, a letter of friendship, or a promise of commitment to your body. You decide what the content should be based on your ongoing relationship with your body and the status of that relationship right now. You may want to include some of the positive and challenging history you and your body have shared together. Consider letting your body know the positive things it has done for you, even in the more difficult times. Write the letter that speaks your truth.

Embodying Practice
Your Resource Repository

For this practice, you will create a resource repository. A resource is something that helps you feel better, safer, calmer, grounded, and centered. It can be a thing, a person, a pet, a place, an experience, a thought, a practice, or even your own body. Here is a sample list of resources:

A cup of tea	My dog	My cat	Drawing
A TV show	My blanket	A best friend	Painting
Naps	Long runs	A walk	Porch swing
The gym	Parent/sibling	My bed	Meditating
Music	Baking	Yoga	Paddle boarding
My journal	Writing	Organizing	Sunshine

Using the space below, create your own resource repository. You might even consider dedicating a separate journal for this purpose. Create a label or title for your repository, such as Resource Repository, My Supports, Things That Help, or whatever you'd like. Get creative. Now, fill your repository with the resources you might already have.

Need-to-Know: What You and Your Body Control

Now that you have your space and you and your body are on the same page, let's dig in by talking about what you and your body can (and cannot) control. As humans, we can ultimately control very little of what is happening in any given moment. We can't control what other people think, feel, or do. In fact, when we speak to others, we often cannot control what they hear, which is why the Telephone Game is so funny. Of course, we can influence those around us and our environment, and there are many contexts in which we should (e.g., parenting and work). However, a very human error that we all can make is thinking that we can control much more than we can. This is why the serenity prayer, which is used in Alcoholics Anonymous, highlights the importance of having "the wisdom to know the difference" between what we can and cannot control. Trying to control more than is humanly possible is a very fast pathway to suffering.

When it comes to your body, emotions, and behaviors, there is also very little that you can intentionally control. For example, there are several physiological processes that your brain and body automatically control without conscious awareness, including your digestion, hormones, reproductive system, neurotransmitters, and more. There are valid evolutionary, genetic, and functional reasons for this: It would simply be too much for humans to monitor and control every single body function, which is why your brain and body work to make as many things as automatic as possible. However, since these processes function below conscious awareness, it also means you have less intentional control over them.

Table 1.1 Automatic vs. Intentional Control

What Your Body *Automatically* Controls	What You Can *Intentionally* Control
Aging Digestion Fight-or-flight response Growth Healing Hormones Neurotransmitters Reproductive system . . . and more	Mindful awareness ↓ Orientation ↓ Intention ↓ (Deliberate) Thoughts ↓ Muscles

In comparison, consider how little you can intentionally control. There are only five things you can truly control: (1) mindful awareness, (2) orientation, (3) intentions, (4) your (deliberate) thoughts, and (5) your muscles. Let's take a few moments and define each of these terms.

- *Mindful awareness* is your ability to be aware. Mindful awareness is present when you have a sense that you are paying attention, noticing, or witnessing what is happening in the present moment. This includes an awareness of what is happening internally (body, emotions, and thoughts), externally (family, community, culture), and existentially (your reason for being; Cook-Cottone, 2020).

- *Orientation* involves focusing your attention within you and on the world around you (Ogden & Fisher, 2016). For example, when meditating, you can be mindfully aware of your internal and external sensations and then orient your awareness toward your breath. Your breath becomes the focus of your attention. Or perhaps you meet your friend in a coffee shop with all the hustle and bustle. As they share a recent health scare or heartache, you orient your attention on them so deeply that it feels like there is no one else in the room.

- *Intentions* reflect your values and your sense of purpose. Your intentions give order and structure to how you relate with yourself, others, and the world. They are the foundations of goal-directed behavior and plans.

- *Thoughts* are the way you work with your cognitive or thinking self. Your thoughts allow you to anticipate, plan ahead, create, and more. As an important note, you *cannot* control the automatic thoughts that randomly pop into your head, nor can you control the feeling-based thoughts that are driven by strong emotions. However, you *can* control how you sit with these thoughts and rework them into more intentional and deliberate thoughts that are consistent with how you want to show up in life.

- *Muscles* are the sole way you can move your body. Working with your muscles, you can control your breath and mobilize and immobilize your body.

For example, when you notice—in other words, when you are *mindfully aware*—that you are stressed, you *orient* to the body sensations and thoughts aligned with the stress. You orient toward your tense muscles, sore shoulders, furrowed brow, and short and shallow breathing. Your *intentions* are to be responsive to your body when it is stressed. *Thinking deliberately*, you then decide to relax by listening to music, and your thinking brain commences a movement sequence in your body. Your *muscles* activate as you walk to get your headphones and phone. Your fingers pick up your phone and headphones, place your headphones in your ears, scroll through your phone to find your playlist, and press play. Then you use your mindful awareness, intentions, and diaphragm muscle to slow and deepen your breath as you relax into your favorite soothing song.

This is the essence of working with what you can control and using it to create positive change. You pay attention, orient and focus your brain, create intentional thoughts (e.g., *I am working toward a less reactive way of being*), and then practice. You practice new ways of being with and working with what comes up. By using your awareness, ability to orient, intentions, thoughts, and muscles, you can heal from trauma and develop healthier patterns of being and functioning. I love the saying "What we practice, we become." It is scientifically true. With practice, you can help your brain and body work together. You can influence, support, regulate, and enhance all of those functions that the body controls.

-Embodying Self-Statement-
What we practice, we become.

—Embodying Practice—

Working through What You Can Control

Think of the last time you were able to effectively handle something that was somewhat stressful. Perhaps you misplaced your house keys when you were already in a rush to leave the house. Perhaps your child accidentally overflowed the bathroom tub. Perhaps you were called upon to help with a last-minute work deadline. Whatever the situation, use the spaces below to identify what you recall at each stage of the process. By reflectively applying these concepts and practices to your lived experience, you can increase the likelihood that you will be able to access them in real time when you are stressed or feeling reactive.

Mindful awareness (In what ways did you notice your stress?)

_____

_____

_____

Orientation (What did you focus on that helped you be responsive to your stress?)

_____

_____

_____

Intentions (What intentions did you have that helped guide your thinking and movement?)

_____

_____

_____

(Deliberate) thoughts (What did you think in order to work through the situation?)

_____

_____

_____

Muscles (What did you do?)

_____

_____

_____

—Embodying Practice—

The Infinite Breath

This practice will help slow down your nervous system, move you into a less reactive state, and allow you to activate the part of you that is aware, oriented, intentional, and deliberate. From a more balanced state, it is much easier to make effective choices in how you'd like to be with or work with what is present.

To begin, find a comfortable seat, making sure you feel grounded and supported. Using your pointer finger, begin to inhale as you run your finger along the right side of the infinity symbol. Each arrow represents a count of one, for a total of eight counts per side.

When you reach the center of the symbol, pause and hold your breath for four counts.

Then, exhale as you run your ringer along the left side of the infinity circle for eight counts.

Pause again in the center for four counts.

Repeat this practice four to eight times, or as long as you'd like. If you find it helpful, you can add it to your resource repository, perhaps even making a photocopy or screenshot of the image for portable use. If you need help staying oriented during the exercise, try using your nondominant hand to trace the figure.

If you'd like to reinforce the concepts of awareness, orientation, intention, and deliberate thoughts and actions, you can repeat the mantras at the bottom of the figure after two breath cycles (i.e., inhale, pause, exhale, pause, inhale, pause, exhale, pause). Begin by stating to yourself, *I am aware of my breath.* Then complete two more breath cycles. Continue by stating, *I am focused on my breath.* Then complete two more breath cycles. Next try stating, *I care for my body.* Then complete two more breath cycles. Finally, bring the practice to a close by stating, *I am in creation of this breath.* Then complete two final breath cycles.

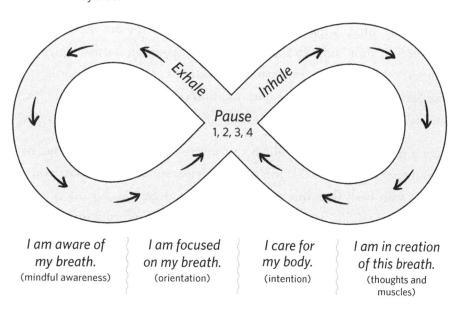

I am aware of my breath.	*I am focused on my breath.*	*I care for my body.*	*I am in creation of this breath.*
(mindful awareness)	(orientation)	(intention)	(thoughts and muscles)

Need-to-Know: Listening to Your Body

You might have noticed that the first thing on the list of what you can control is mindful awareness. One way that mindful awareness is developed is through the practice of listening to your body. You can listen to your body in three main ways: interoception, exteroception, and neuroception. Like healing from trauma, building up these skills is both challenging *and* worth the effort.

Interoception is the ability to notice, identify, understand, and respond to your inner experiences—to the signals from your body. It allows you to know when you're hot, cold, thirsty, full, tired, hungry, and more. This interoceptive awareness, in turn, allows you to take actions that return the system to balance. For example, when you notice the sensations of a grumbling stomach, you connect this with being hungry and use this as a cue to seek out nourishment. When your mouth is dry, you connect this with being thirsty and use this as a cue to take a drink. When your muscles feel heavy, you connect this with being fatigued and take some time to rest. Interoception is critical for self-regulation and self-care.

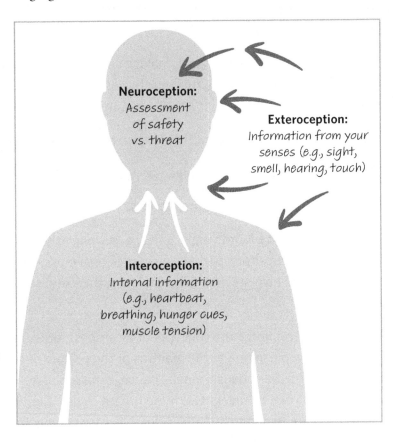

Neuroception: Assessment of safety vs. threat

Exteroception: Information from your senses (e.g., sight, smell, hearing, touch)

Interoception: Internal information (e.g., heartbeat, breathing, hunger cues, muscle tension)

Exteroception is your sensitivity to what is happening in your environment and the world outside your body. Befriending your body means learning to trust your five senses—sight, smell, hearing, touch, and taste—to give you accurate information about your surroundings. You can use both interoception and exteroception to connect to your body. To experience this for yourself, try placing your hand on your heart and see if you feel your heartbeat. Your hands use exteroception to feel your heart beating from the outside (sort of like taking your pulse), while interoception occurs when you notice the feeling of your heart beating from inside of your chest.

Finally, *neuroception* is the process through which your nervous system evaluates cues of safety and threat in your environment (Porges, 2017). It is the body's assessment of how safe you are in any given moment. Impressively, your body does this without requiring awareness. Neuroception is a reflexive process that uses both interoception and exteroception to integrate information from inside and outside of you. Although you may not be aware of the cues that are triggering neuroception, you may notice a shift in your heart rate or breathing in reaction to a perceived threat, or you might notice it through feelings of openness and connection when you feel safe.

However, traumatic experiences can affect interoception, exteroception, and neuroception by creating:

- heightened sensitivity to internal and external cues that appear to signal risk when there is none; or

- numbness, disconnection, and dissociation, preventing you from identifying cues that signal threat when there is risk.

For example, when your sense of interoception is interrupted, you might not have the desire to eat or drink even when hungry. You also might struggle to feel certain emotions, as you don't recognize the body sensations associated with those particular emotions (e.g., the muscle tension associated with anxiety, the feeling of heaviness in the chest associated with sadness). Your body might also feel like it is always triggered.

Your body will do the best it can to keep you safe regardless of your awareness. Your body is acting as your protector. Developing mindful awareness of these processes can help you better partner with your body to self-regulate, allowing it to know when it is best to protect and when it's best to self-nurture. Intentional, embodied practices support the development of all three types of self-awareness. As you learn to notice and experience your inner and outer worlds, your ability to respond to these signals will increase, allowing you to develop a connection to yourself—a connection to your body.

—Embodying Self-Statement—
I can listen to my body.

Embodying Practice
Grounded Breath and Centering

Grounding is the act of connecting to the earth beneath you and feeling the steadiness of its support. Centering is the act of orienting your awareness inward, toward your experience of you. The following practice supports both grounding and centering, which are foundational to the development of interoceptive awareness.

To begin, make sure you are settled into your safe place. Take a moment to scan your location, noticing the doors, windows, or landscape and addressing anything that might interfere with your practice. Find a comfortable seat, and support your legs and back as needed so you feel well supported by the earth below you. This is the grounding component of the practice. Your body is well grounded and you are safe in this space, in this moment.

Next, you will move into the centering component of the practice. Place one hand on your stomach and one hand over your heart as you focus on breathing in and out. Breathe using your typical breathing pattern for three breaths, then begin to slowly extend the inhalation and exhalation by counting—inhale 1, 2, 3, 4 . . . exhale 1, 2, 3, 4. Inhale 1, 2, 3, 4 . . . exhale 1, 2, 3, 4. Continue to take these deeper and longer breaths.

As you breathe deeply in and out, notice your hands as they move with your chest and your stomach. You might notice that as you inhale, your chest rises and your stomach expands, and as you exhale, your stomach contracts and your chest falls. Breathe here and simply notice.

Next, bring your awareness to your rib cage. You might feel your rib cage expanding with each inhalation and moving back to its neutral shape with each exhalation. Breathe here, noting your rib cage movement. Remember here to allow for the possibility that it may be difficult to notice sensations or that you might not notice anything. You are simply being with your breath and being aware.

Next, notice your nose and your nostrils. Notice the temperature of the cool air moving in and the warm air moving out. See if you notice the air moving down through your windpipe, into your bronchial tubes, and then into your lungs. Maybe open up to the possibility of noticing the air move into your lungs and back out. Breathe here and notice.

Continue breathing with a hand on your heart, and turn even deeper inward toward your heart. Perhaps you can feel a thump-thump of your heart beating with your hand, through the breath as you breathe, maybe in your chest. Remember here to allow for the possibility that it may be difficult to notice sensations or that you might not notice anything. You are simply being with your heart and noticing.

As you notice your breath and your heartbeat, perhaps say to yourself, *I can be aware of and connected to my body*. Breathe and repeat this statement to yourself: *I can be aware of and connected to my body*.

It can also be nice to add a message to your heart and your body, like *I am taking time to know you, breath* or *I am taking time to know you, heart*. Try different self-statements and see which ones align best with your embodied experience. Take as much time as you'd like there breathing, connecting to your heart.

When you are finished, use the space here, or write in your journal, to record what you noticed, including any inner and outer sensations, feelings, and thoughts.

—Embodying Self-Statement—
My body is a source of grounding, connection, and support.

Positive Embodiment Body Scan

This practice is more advanced and requires a more substantial capacity to be with the experiences and sensations in your body. Attempt this practice only after you can easily move through the previous **Grounded Breath and Centering** practice.

Begin by lying down in a comfortable and safe location. Make sure you are well supported, placing a small pillow under your head and maybe some type of support under your knees. If it is cool, cover yourself with a blanket, and if it is warm, crack a window or use a gentle fan.

When you are ready, breathe gently in and out and consider these two embodied self-statements:

- I will consider that my body is my source of experience in this world.

- I will consider that my body is a source of grounding, connection, and support.

Say these statements three times each: once out loud, once as a whisper, and once silently to yourself. This will help you activate your positive and supportive inner voice. If these statements begin to feel true to you, you can drop the *I will consider that . . .* section of the statements.

Next, for each section or part of the body, pause and follow this script. Begin with your lungs as offered here, then replace the word *lungs* with parts of the body in the table below. Note, pacing matters. *How* you do something is as important as *what* you do. You might work through this body scan one section at a time, allowing yourself time to work your way up to the full body scan. It can be helpful to rank the sections from least to most challenging and begin with those that are easiest.

1. Bring your awareness to your breath.

2. Breathe here, breathing into your [lungs], with each in-breath offering nourishment and each out-breath offering release.

3. Notice any tension or holding and give permission for release and relaxation.

4. Consider saying to your [lungs], *I am taking time to thank you and know you [lungs].*

Now follow the same script, moving from your toes to the crown of your head. Complete the process by offering awareness and attention to your lungs again, then your heart, and then your whole body.

Section 1	Section 2	Section 3	Section 4	Section 5
• Toes (1–5)	• Hips	• Shoulders	• Front of neck	• Crown of head
• Soles of feet	• Pelvis	• Elbows	• Back of neck	• Throat
• Heels	• Low belly	• Forearms	• Jaw	• Lungs
• Tops of feet	• Low back	• Wrists	• Mouth	• Heart*
• Ankles	• Belly	• Fingers (1–4)	• Nose	• Whole body
• Shins	• Chest	• Tops of arms	• Cheeks and eyes	
• Knees	• Mid back	• Thumbs	• Forehead	
• Thighs	• Upper back	• Palms of hands	• Back of head	
• Hips			• Scalp	

* Before completing the heart portion of this practice, rub your palms and place them on your heart. Then pause before moving to your whole body.

In closing, breathe gently in and out once again and consider these two embodied self-statements:

- I will consider that my body is my source of experience in this world.

- I will consider that my body is a source of grounding, connection, and support.

As before, express these statements three times each: once out loud, once as a whisper, and once silently to yourself. Remember that if these statements begin to feel true to you, you can drop the *I will consider that . . .* section of the statements.

When you are finished, use the space here, or write in your journal, to record what you noticed, including any inner and outer sensations, feelings, and thoughts. You can also use the image of the body on the next page to note which sections you worked on and perhaps anything you might have noticed as you worked through that area of the body.

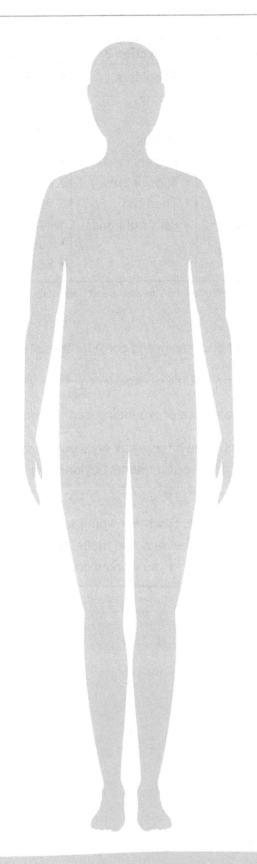

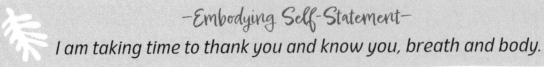

—Embodying Self-Statement—

I am taking time to thank you and know you, breath and body.

Embodying Practice
Awareness of Neuroceptive Cues

This practice will help you develop a better relationship with your body and support your work toward more positive embodiment and healing. Before you begin, you may want to have a journal nearby for reflection at the close of the practice.

Find a space that feels safe and comforting. Get into a comfortable seat, making sure you are well supported. It can help to sit on a small pillow or block, or in a chair. To begin, you might want to take a seat against a wall or with a wall behind you. Once you are comfortable, soften your eyes and orient your awareness toward your breath for four intentional breath cycles: breathing in and out, in and out, in and out, in and out.

Then turn your attention to your external surroundings, using your senses to gather information about the world around you. Look around you, starting at ground level, and scan the area from right to left. Use your eyes, ears, and even skin to notice your surroundings. You might see a sliding door open, hear the birds outside, or feel a slight breeze on your cheeks. Make a mental note of what you see by simply labeling each item (e.g., bookshelf, cat, art). Pause here and take four intentional breath cycles: breathing in and out, in and out, in and out, in and out.

Next, scan the area at midlevel, going in the same direction and noting anything you see, feel, or hear. Pause here and take four intentional breath cycles: breathing in and out, in and out, in and out, in and out. Finally, scan the highest level. If you are inside, scan the top edge of the walls to the ceiling. If you are outside, scan the skyline and sky. Again, use your eyes, ears, and skin to notice and mentally note or label what you observe.

Use what you have noticed to make any changes that would help you feel more comfortable. Perhaps you would like to change your location, shut a door, or place yourself against a wall or tree. If you make changes, return your attention to your external surroundings and rescan your environment using the same steps as before. If you have only made minor adjustments or no adjustments, it is time to shift to internal awareness.

Soften or close your eyes as you turn your attention inward. Take an overall scan of your body. Notice your feet, legs, hands, and arms first. Consider your muscles and make note of any tension, clenching, softness, or ease. Pause wherever you note tension or clenching and breathe gently, offering comfort. Take four intentional breath cycles: breathing in and out, in and out, in and out, in and out. Do not make an effort to change anything. Simply notice and offer comfort through your breath.

Next, notice your hips, shoulders, and jaw. These areas are often tense or clenched when you perceive danger or a lack of safety. If you notice this, offer your breath and consider that a part of you might not be feeling safe. Pause wherever you note tension or clenching and breathe gently, offering comfort. Take four intentional breath cycles: breathing in and out, in and out, in and out, in and out. If at any point you feel the signal *I am not safe*, honor the signal, breathe, and return your attention to your external surroundings by scanning your environment.

Now, notice your core and chest area. A more global signal of not feeling safe can be offered by these two areas. Bring your awareness to your chest, feeling your breath moving in and out of your body and your lungs. Feel your rib cage rise and fall and your lungs expand and contract with each breath. Notice any sensations around your heart and chest. This is where feelings of anxiety, anger, happiness, and love are often felt. Notice any clenching, heaviness, activation, expansion, radiating warmth, stillness, or quietness in this area. Simply name or describe what you notice gently, offering comfort. Take four intentional breath cycles: breathing in and out, in and out, in and out, in and out.

Last, notice your stomach area. This is the area where you might experience what is called a "gut feeling." Your gut feelings reflect your body's attempt to tell you that something is off or not safe. Notice any feelings and sensations here. If at any point you feel the signal, or gut feeling, of *I am not safe*, honor the signal, breathe, and return your attention to your external surroundings by scanning your environment. If you are feeling settled and safe, simply breathe here. With a focus on your gut, you might say, *I can listen to and honor the wisdom of my body* as you breathe.

To close, take four intentional breath cycles: breathing in and out, in and out, in and out, in and out. Slowly return your attention to your external environment, anchoring your gaze on one thing in your surrounding area first, then expand your awareness to take in the whole scene. Take a moment to jot down what you noticed in the space below, or in your journal, and thank yourself for taking the time to practice.

 Chapter 2

Understanding Your Protective Body: Trauma

Now that you have begun the work to be with and work with the sensations in your body, the next step is to learn about trauma and your body. Understanding your body and its role in your symptoms and your healing is critical.

Need-to-Know: What Is Trauma?

Trauma, or being traumatized, occurs at the intersection of two things: (1) an experience and (2) your in-the-moment capacity to manage or cope with it. Many different types of events can be traumatic, including one-time events (like an accident, assault, or natural disaster) and ongoing stressors that aggregate over time (like living in a violent neighborhood or home, being bullied or harassed, racism, or war). Trauma can result from things that you expect, like the death of a loved one, as well as things you don't expect, like betrayal or humiliation. The experience becomes traumatizing when your mind and body are overwhelmed and incapacitated.

The effects of trauma vary for everyone due to the complexities of our genetics, personal identities, past experiences, and level of social support. The intersection of historically marginalized identities will also impact the extent to which a person is impacted by trauma. No one thing will traumatize everyone. We are all just too different. What is similar, to some degree, is how trauma shows up in our minds and bodies afterward.

To illustrate how this can look, in this chapter I will introduce you to Mathilde, an 18-year-old college student studying the psychology of trauma. When she was 7 years old, she was in a car accident in which she was seriously injured and her sister was killed. Her recovery included two surgeries and a month-long hospital stay. In the wake of the accident, her parents began drinking more in the evenings, which often ended in them fighting and getting frustrated or angry with her. She did not remember much about the accident, her sister, or the years leading up to middle school.

Mathilde reported that in her middle school years, she had difficulty with her emotions. She was nearly always tense and anxious. She was also either agitated, quarrelsome, and hurtful to those closest to her or shutdown, withdrawn, and filled with shame and self-hatred. Sometimes she could feel nothing at all. She sensed that she was somehow different from her friends, and she spent her high school and early college years "trying to be normal" and learning all she could about trauma and recovery. She had learned and grown a lot but was still overcontrolling in relationships and frequently felt anxious and threatened by her partner's actions. However, after a terrifying argument with her partner in which Mathilde threatened her, grabbed her wrists, and wouldn't let go, Mathilde came for help. Despite all she had learned about psychology and trauma, her knowledge wasn't helping her with her self-regulation.

Like Mathilde, you might suffer from intense, rapid, unpredictable, and prolonged experiences where you feel dysregulated or out of control. You might find that certain environmental cues, body sensations, or thoughts trigger intense memories, pain, fear, and shame. When you're triggered, you might feel as if the trauma is happening again or that you are in danger right now. You might feel like you are always in defensive or protective mode. Why does this happen? Why do traumatic experiences have this effect? The difference lies in how memories of trauma are encoded in your brain and body.

Need-to-Know: Trauma Memories vs. Regular Memories

To help you understand the impact of trauma on your body, I'll start by reviewing how regular memories are stored. Typically, important day-to-day experiences are encoded as explicit memories in a part of the brain known as the neocortex, which is responsible for processing language, context, a sense of time, reason, and your life narrative. Explicit memories are those that you can consciously bring to mind, such as your graduation date, the name of your first pet, and the ingredients of your favorite recipe. These day-to-day memories are integrated into your brain in the form of rich stories that contain associated images, sensations, feelings, context, and a sense of how they fit into your larger life story.

Traumatic memories are much less likely to be stored in this way. As Bessel van der Kolk (2014) described in *The Body Keeps the Score*, traumatic memories are stored primarily in the limbic system in the form of implicit memories, which do not rely upon conscious recall. These traumatic memories are experienced as images, body sensations, and emotions, without any coherent story and without any strong connection with your explicit memory system. These memories lack an organized narrative, meaning that thoughts are often fragmented, have no sense of time or context, and can be primarily driven by emotions or reactions.

Because these implicit memories are not sufficiently linked to your conscious brain and your explicit memory system, two consequences ensue. First, these memories can be easily triggered, seemingly appearing out of nowhere as reactions and intense emotional experiences. For example, you might feel numb and shut down like Mathilde. You might carry chronic tension in your muscles, as your body is consistently in protection mode and ready to defend you or run. You might notice that in certain situations, you are hypervigilant to any possible threats in your environment. It can feel like you will never be able to know the difference between what you think is dangerous and what really is.

Second, these memories live within you in the places that words can't reach. When you try to share your trauma experiences, the words and sentences simply aren't there. This is why so many people with trauma feel isolated and alone. They are feeling so much that it's overwhelming, and at the same time, they feel incapacitated or incompetent when trying to find the words to ask for help.

—Embodying Self-Statement—
My body is my source of experience in this world.

Need-to-Know: Trauma and Your Body

You sense and feel the effects of trauma deeply, in your heart, nervous system, and muscles—and often in your bones. That's because the human body experiences it all—accidents, sexual and physical abuse, assault, neglect, community violence, natural disasters, sex trafficking, war, and medical trauma. Even traumas that happen in relationships or at the community and systems level deeply affect your body. Consider the feelings that accompany betrayal, infidelity, bullying, harassment, prolonged grief, refugee trauma, and systemic racism.

Your body remembers. Your body remembers in the form of bodily sensations, whether that's a lack of sensation (desensitization) or increased sensitivity to sensations (hypersensitization). Your body also remembers in the form of behaviors intended to keep you safe, whether you're continually scanning your environment for threats or reacting to perceived threats by immediately isolating yourself.

Because your body remembers, simply trying to understand your traumatic experience on a cognitive level isn't enough for whole-self, embodied healing. If treatment only addresses your "thinking brain" by focusing on your thoughts and thought patterns, you risk further alienating your body. Your thinking brain can get frustrated with, or intolerant of, your body's reactions, feelings, and challenges. In fact, the more you try to use your thinking brain to settle things in your body, the more likely you are to see your body as a complication, problem, or obstacle in your healing process. Worse, you may begin to see your own body as the enemy or threat. As a patient once lamented, "I thought all it would take is me getting it out and maybe understanding what happened. And here I am. I told my story. I get what happened. And I am still so triggered and afraid. I see now that just getting it out is not enough. I have more work to do."

It may be helpful to think of it this way: After a traumatic event, your body prioritizes making sure you are okay going forward. *Your body wants you safe.* To do this, your body goes into protection mode by shifting how you orient to your surroundings, respond to things you see and hear, react to stressors, experience emotions, and initiate behavior.

However, like I told Mathilde, it is possible to learn to tell the difference and to have a more effective and integrated relationship with your body and your trauma memories. Your work in this chapter is to continue developing a partnership with your body, to get better at listening to your body, and to further understand your body's response systems.

PAUSE

(P - Pause, **A** - Assess → **USE** your resources and supports)

☐ <u>P</u>ause, check in, and acknowledge how you are feeling. This is a chance to be kind to yourself. The pace of your work is very important. Press your feet into the earth and take four gentle breaths.

☐ <u>A</u>ssess by asking yourself, *Is this a good place for a break?* If the answer is *yes* or *I don't know*, then fold over the corner of the page and take a break. This workbook is here for you for as long as it takes and for as many breaks as you need.

☐ **USE** your resources. Take a rest. Connect to your trusted friends. Contact your therapist. Practice your favorite well-being strategies. Get back to work when YOU are ready.

—Embodying Practice—
How Are You Right Now?
What Are Your Symptoms of Trauma?

If you have been exposed to trauma, you may or may not have symptoms of posttraumatic stress disorder (PTSD). To get a good sense of how trauma has affected you, the following is a list of common symptoms people have experienced after trauma. Each section includes specific symptoms of PTSD as well as other symptoms you may notice. See if any of the symptoms below ring true for you. Check off any that you have experienced, star or highlight the ones that are strongest or most problematic, and add any additional symptoms you may be experiencing that are not listed here.

Domain of Embodiment	Symptom
Thinking	☐ Recurrent, unwanted, distressing memories of the trauma
	☐ Flashbacks where you relive the trauma as if it were happening again
	☐ Upsetting dreams or nightmares about the trauma
	☐ Attempts to avoid thinking or talking about the trauma
	☐ Inability to recall certain aspects of the trauma
	☐ Overly negative thoughts about yourself, others, and the world
	☐ Cycling between being overwhelmed by intrusive thoughts and having no thoughts at all
	☐ Blaming yourself or others for causing the trauma
	☐ Decreased interest in activities that were previously enjoyable
	☐ Difficulty with concentration and focus
	☐ Feeling as if things are not real
	☐ Other related symptoms: disbelief, denial, confusion, rumination, memory problems, obsessions, fear of going crazy or "losing it," no thoughts of the future, no sense of self (*Who am I?*)
Feeling	☐ Feeling emotionally triggered when something reminds you of the trauma
	☐ Attempts to avoid any feelings associated with the trauma
	☐ Cycling between feeling overwhelmed and feeling numb
	☐ Increased negative feelings
	☐ Decreased positive feelings
	☐ Feeling isolated
	☐ Easily irritated or agitated
	☐ Experience of being an outside observer or detached from yourself
	☐ Feeling nothing or empty

Feeling (cont.)	☐ Other related symptoms: anger, annoyance, anxiety, shock, panic attacks, guilt, shame, self-blame, sadness, hopelessness, emotional numbness, emotionally overwhelmed, short fuse, agitation, easily triggered, mood swings, worthlessness, distress
Body	☐ Severe physical reactions when something reminds you of the trauma (e.g., racing heart, hyperventilating) ☐ Risky or self-destructive behavior (e.g., substance use, self-harm) ☐ Heightened startle response ☐ Chronic body tension and activation ☐ Chronic experience of feeling shutdown ☐ Cycling between feeling tense and shutdown ☐ Difficulty sleeping ☐ Other related symptoms: racing heartbeat, sweating, body aches and pains, chronic muscle tension, panic attacks, sexual problems, eating problems, fatigue, exhaustion, weight changes, inability to rest, inability to feel in your body, feeling disconnected from your body, numbness, inability to feel hunger or fullness cues, chronic pain, headaches, feeling sick, digestion issues
Action	☐ Avoidance of places, activities, or people that remind you of the trauma ☐ Hypervigilant to your surroundings ☐ Feeling immobilized or unable to move ☐ Feeling mobilized (ready for fight or flight) in response to triggers ☐ Cycling between feeling immobilized and mobilized ☐ Unconsciously repeating aspects of the trauma in your day-to-day life (e.g., getting into fights with authority figures, spending time with unsafe or hurtful people) ☐ Other related symptoms: isolating or withdrawing from others, misusing substances, self-medicating, self-harm or self-destructiveness, aggression, compulsive behavior, inability to do "normal stuff," overworking, disordered eating, binge eating, restricting food intake, compulsive exercise, risk taking, gambling

Once you have completed the checklist, take some time to see what you notice. Look over the symptoms you have circled, starred, or highlighted. What stands out most? What patterns did you notice?

_____

_____

_____

_____

_____

PAUSE

(**P** - Pause, **A** - Assess ➔ **USE** your resources and supports)

☐ <u>P</u>ause, check in, and acknowledge how you are feeling. This is a chance to be kind to yourself. The pace of your work is very important. Press your feet into the earth and take four gentle breaths.

☐ **<u>A</u>ssess** by asking yourself, *Is this a good place for a break?* If the answer is *yes or I don't know*, then fold over the corner of the page and take a break. This workbook is here for you for as long as it takes and for as many breaks as you need.

☐ **<u>USE</u>** your resources. Take a rest. Connect to your trusted friends. Contact your therapist. Practice your favorite well-being strategies. Get back to work when YOU are ready.

Need-to-Know: This Can Be the Hardest Part

It is important to let you know that the work you did in learning about trauma and identifying your own trauma symptoms can be difficult and overwhelming. In their work on self-compassion, Kristin Neff and Chris Germer (2018) use the word *backdraft* to refer to this part of the process. This is a term firefighters use to describe what happens when the door to a burning house is opened. The oxygen enters the house and the flames grow. This is what happens when you open the door to your heart: Love enters and the pain begins to come out. You give your experience love, acknowledgment, and validation. You see it for what it is. It is this very acknowledgment and validation that is the foundation of healing. Yet the process can be overwhelming and at times painful.

When you are feeling overwhelmed, it is important that you take a break, pause, and go back to the **Grounded Breath and Centering** practice from the previous chapter. This simple and accessible practice can help you soothe your body, emotions, and thoughts. It also serves as a reminder that it can be very helpful to work through this book with a therapist or group therapy community. One of my biggest lessons in recovery is reflected in this statement: *When I am overwhelmed, I slow down, connect to the foundational practices, and find support.*

Need-to-Know: Your Nervous System and Connection and Protection

Humans need each other to survive. Throughout our lifespans, it is our connection to others that keeps us safe, secure, and thriving. Yet other humans are also most likely to be the cause of our pain and trauma. As much as we long for connection with other humans, we also need protection from them. This results in the ongoing dilemma of balancing our drive to survive with our longing for and need to connect (Dana, 2020). So how do we balance these opposing needs? Through our sense of interoception, exteroception, and neuroception, which work in concert with the autonomic nervous system to help us negotiate this very real, daily challenge. In the following section, I will share with you a bit of the science and theory behind this.

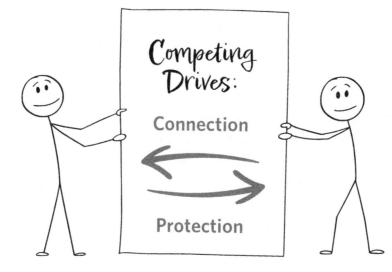

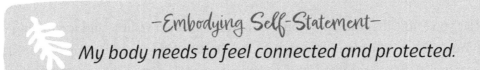

—Embodying Self-Statement—
My body needs to feel connected and protected.

The Autonomic Nervous System

The part of your nervous system that is primarily in charge of responding to safety (connection) and danger (protection) is the *autonomic nervous system*. Like its name implies, it works automatically, often below your awareness. Its functions are deeply impacted by trauma, which makes the autonomic nervous system more sensitive and reactive. To heal from trauma, it is necessary to understand, listen to, and befriend this part of your nervous system. To start, let's discuss the two branches of the autonomic nervous system: sympathetic and parasympathetic.

The *sympathetic nervous system* mobilizes you for action. You can think of it as your "get-going" system. It supports, responds to, and regulates physiological functions such as blood flow, heart rate, and body temperature. Overall, it helps you get alert and moving while also gearing you up in matters of passion and play. For this reason, it facilitates both connection and protection. When your senses of interoception, exteroception, and neuroception send signals that you are in danger or unsafe, the sympathetic nervous system mobilizes you to a state of fight or flight. It also works with the parasympathetic nervous system to elicit the freeze response, which is a state of attentive immobility in which you have an elevated sense of alertness that prepares you for fight or flight.

The *parasympathetic nervous system* used to be considered the immobilizing part of your nervous system that slows you down and facilitates a relaxation response. While this is still true, more recent research suggests that it is a bit more complicated than that. In particular, polyvagal theory proposes that the parasympathetic nervous system is actually divided into two circuits—a ventral vagal circuit and a dorsal vagal circuit—that operate in different manners (Porges, 2017). One way to understand the functions of these two circuits is to look deeper at the vagus nerve, which governs the parasympathetic nervous system. More than a single nerve, it is really a group of nerve fibers that wander, or extend, throughout the core of your body.

The *ventral vagal complex* (VVC) is the quicker, myelinated branch of the vagus nerve that is associated with the parts of your body above the diaphragm. Believed to have evolved when mammals diverged from our reptile ancestors, it is considered the face-heart connection, linking your heart, lungs, throat, vocal cords, inner ear, and facial muscles. It controls how you show emotions, the nature of your voice, the look in your eyes, and the subtle tilts in your head that help you connect and communicate with others. When the VVC is active, your nervous system is optimized to support health, growth, restoration, and connectedness. It is for this reason that the VVC is often called the "social engagement system." It is easier to make healthy choices, as well as to receive and give support to others, when the VVC is online. This vagal circuit is not active during fight or flight or reactive trauma responses.

In contrast, the *dorsal vagal complex* (DVC) is the slower, unmyelinated branch of the vagus nerve that connects to the organs below your diaphragm and sends a smaller number of nerve fibers to your heart. This vagal circuit is responsible for immobilization, allowing you to slow down and experience restful stillness. As you go through your day, the DVC runs in the background like a software program, supporting rest, digestion, and healing. However, when you are exposed to extreme stress or faced with an overwhelming life threat, the DVC activates a shutdown response, in which you may feel numb, dissociated, or collapsed. When there is perceived danger, the DVC can also work in combination with the sympathetic nervous system to elicit the freeze response, in which the DVC reduces motion, heart rate, and breathing while the sympathetic nervous system supports alertness and action preparation.

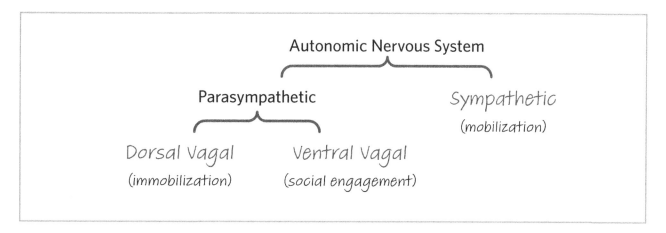

The sympathetic nervous system works together with the VVC and DVC to create distinct states of being, which are in service of either connection or protection. There are specific circumstances that determine when each system takes over and runs the show. The following table brings this science and theory together for you to illustrate how this works.

Table 2.1. States of Connection vs. Protection

	State of Embodiment	Body Experience
C O N N E C T I O N	**Rest and restoration**	**Safe and relaxed** Ventral vagal connection and intentional dorsal vagal immobilization
	Alert engagement	**Safe** Ventral vagal connection and intentional, mild sympathetic mobilization
	Active play, challenge, and growth	**Safe and activated** Ventral vagal connection and intentional, moderate sympathetic mobilization
P R O T E C T I O N	**Fight or flight**	**Unsafe and threatened** Strong sympathetic nervous system mobilization
	Freeze	**Unsafe and threatened** Dorsal vagal immobilization and sympathetic nervous system alertness and preparation
	Shutdown	**Overloaded and overwhelmed** Strong dorsal vagal immobilization in response to incapacitated sympathetic response

Therefore, when you are feeling safe, your body's connection mode activates to help you rest, restore, play, work, and grow. But when something threatening, dangerous, or traumatizing occurs, your body's protective system activates the fight, flight, freeze, or shutdown response. This happens automatically, below your consciousness. Your body assesses the situation and selects the option that it feels is safest for you. It is for this reason that connection and protection are competing drives. When you are in protection mode and feeling unsafe, it is extremely difficult to feel connected to yourself or others—even if you want to.

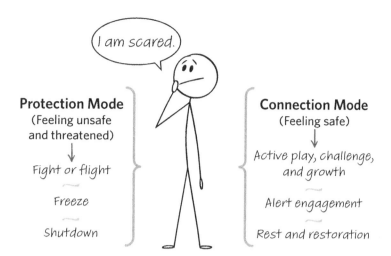

To explore your own states of connection and protection, consider the figure below. When you are feeling safe, you can experience both activation and deactivation, getting excited and settling down, all while feeling connected to yourself and others (right side of the figure). Having been through trauma, your body is sensitized and may react more strongly to stressors and triggers. As a result, your body is more likely to shift into a protective state more often than it needs and more than you want. That means you spend more time on the left side of the figure.

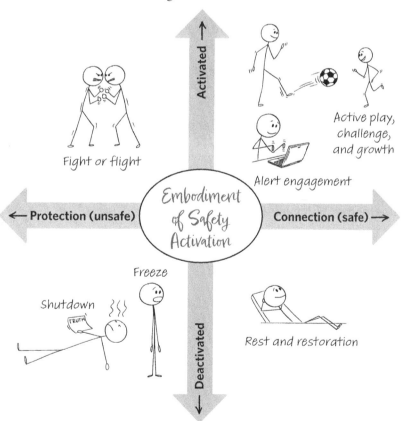

It can be helpful to explore what it feels like when you are open for connection versus when you are in survival mode. Getting to know your body and when you are in each of these states is an essential part of your recovery. To help you in this process, I am going to review each of the connection and protection states and their functions and features. I'll also share with you what each state is like for Mathilde.

Embodying Practice

Experiential Anchor: Deep Rest and Restoration

Rest and restoration are what happen during deeply relaxing moments, such as when you are lying in *savasana* at the end of yoga class. When this happens, your mind and body are responding to cues of safety, like the teacher's soft and gentle voice or the safe container of the yoga space. This can also happen when you cuddle on the couch with your dog or a safe person. You may even feel this while in a deeply meditative state and connected to yourself. Your system softens, you relax, and your restorative systems engage to promote rest, digestion, and healing. Your thoughts shift to *I am at peace* and *In this world, there are safe places to rest in and safe people to rest with*. You might feel restful, grateful, peaceful, or a sense of loving-kindness.

Mathilde asserted that she never felt this way. She had taken yoga classes, but during the resting pose at the end of class, she always kept her eyes open and made sure she could see the door. However, she could recall some moments when she felt deep rest and restoration before her sister died. They would play outside and when they were tired, they would lie down in the grass and watch the clouds. She said they would tell stories about the clouds and belly laugh. As Mathilde recalled this experience, she described feeling open, free, and "lazy in the best ways." Her muscles were relaxed. She could smell the grass and feel the sun on her skin.

To create an experiential anchor of what deep rest and restoration feel like to you, take a moment and soften or close your eyes, and imagine feeling very safe and deeply relaxed. If it is helpful, remember a time when you felt this way. Think about what information you received through your sense of interoception (inside listening), exteroception (outside listening), and neuroception (safety/danger listening). Describe the moment and what you notice here.

Embodying Practice
Experiential Anchor: Alert Engagement

When you are in a state of alert engagement, you feel safe and connected to others. You feel integrated and have increased access to the different aspects of being you, including your ability to sense, feel, and think. For example, the part of your brain that thinks and conceptualizes (neocortex) and the part of your brain that processes emotions (limbic system) can easily communicate with each other. Spending time in this state can strengthen these neural connections, making it easier to experience your emotions and learn from them. A state of alert engagement is the pathway to creativity, learning, and openheartedness. It is a state where healing can occur. Possibility lives here, but the key is feeling safe and connected. For many people, this is what day-to-day life feels like.

When Mathilde was in a state of alert engagement, she described feeling happier and being her "best self." Her heart felt open. Her muscles were relaxed. She didn't monitor what she said or did. She was able to sense and feel the experiences in her environment, whether it was the rhythm and lyrics of a song, her dog's heart beating, or the smell of banana bread in the oven. She described feeling this way when she was at home with her partner and they were talking about neutral topics or watching a show. She also felt this way with her rescue dog, who loved her unconditionally. However, Mathilde was rarely in this state.

To create an experiential anchor of what alert engagement feels like to you, take a moment and soften or close your eyes, and imagine feeling very safe. You are in a safe place and maybe with safe people. If it is helpful, remember a time when you felt this way. Think about what information you received through your sense of interoception (inside listening), exteroception (outside listening), and neuroception (safety/danger listening). Describe the moment and what you notice here.

Embodying Practice

Experiential Anchor: Active Play, Challenge, and Growth

In this state, you are engaged, connected, and challenged. You might be learning something new, playing a sport, or participating in some other lively activity. For example, imagine that it is your turn in kickball. You are safe though a bit nervous. You feel the thrill of the game, kick the ball, and run to first base. Your heart beats, you breathe deeply, and you move. You do not move into a state of fight or flight, but you are activated and engaged. I feel this way when taking horseback-riding lessons, speaking to a large group, or running with my friends. This is a state of mobilization without fear and is a healthy part of being a human.

Mathilde knew this state well. She was an avid lacrosse player who played with grace and respect for the game. She was fiercely competitive and loved the feeling of her heart practically beating out of her chest after a play. As she described it to me, "Sometimes the lacrosse field is the only place where I feel really alive." Although she was penalized for losing her temper on the field when she was younger, she was now able to engage, be challenged, compete, and manage herself effectively. In the game, she held the logic of each play well, knew where the other players were on the field, and moved her body in effective and powerful ways. Mathilde also remembered being in this state when her sister was alive. She reported that they would play all sorts of imaginary games and develop elaborate narratives in the backyard, where they were active, engaged, creative, and connected.

To create an experiential anchor of what a state of active play, challenge, and growth feels like to you, take a moment and soften or close your eyes, and imagine feeling engaged and connected to yourself and others. If it is helpful, remember a time when you felt this way. Think about what information you receive through your sense of interoception (inside listening), exteroception (outside listening), and neuroception (safety/danger listening). Describe the moment and what you notice here.

—Embodying Practice—

Experiential Anchor: Fight or Flight

When you perceive danger in your environment (whether real or imagined), your body can shift into a highly efficient state of fight or flight. In this state, your digestive and immune systems become suppressed so your body can prioritize the muscles that help you run away from or fight back against the threat—keeping you safe. Your brain functions differently in this state as well. The thinking part of your brain (neocortex) goes offline, and the feeling, or reactive, part of your brain (the limbic system) is activated. In this state, you act or speak without thinking. You may even say or do things you later regret. This is because it is impossible to be reasonable or thoughtful when your neocortex is offline. This combination of feeling shutdown and activated occurs much more frequently for people with trauma histories.

Mathilde unfortunately knew this state all too well. She frequently shifted into a state of fight or flight whenever she became anxious in her relationship. She would say and do things that she would never say or do if she was calm and centered. In this state, her thoughtful and loving self was unavailable; she literally felt hijacked by her emotions. Her muscles became tense, she started sweating, and her heart rate increased. She didn't have a sense of her body—just that she wanted to act out or run away. Mathilde did not like feeling this way because it reminded her of times when her parents would drink and yell at her, so she tried to avoid this state as much as possible.

To create an experiential anchor of what fight or flight feels like to you, take a moment and soften or close your eyes, and imagine feeling upset, triggered, or hijacked by your emotions. If it is helpful, remember a time when you felt this way. Think about what information you received through your sense of interoception (inside listening), exteroception (outside listening), and neuroception (safety/danger listening). Describe the moment and what you notice here.

Embodying Practice
Experiential Anchor: Freeze

Sometimes when you perceive threat or danger, your body reacts by freezing in place. You become very still and alert. Your muscles tense in case you need to run or fight. When you are immobilized in this way, it can feel like you are a deer in headlights. You can't engage anymore and have thoughts like *I can't* or even no thoughts at all. A patient once described to me how a man had sexually assaulted her at a concert, grabbing her inappropriately. Despite feeling violated, she said and did nothing. Instead, she stiffened in place and didn't move as he walked away, bought a beer, and casually left the area. It was not until he was safely away that her system came back online and she began to cry, shake, and run to her friends for support.

The experience of freezing sometimes happened to Mathilde too. Whenever she would hear or see people arguing or fighting, or someone would begin arguing with her, her body stopped moving and she felt stuck in place. Her muscles tensed up and her jaw clenched down tightly. In this state, she had trouble expressing herself and felt like the words wouldn't come out of her mouth.

To create an experiential anchor of what a freeze state feels like to you, take a moment and soften or close your eyes, and imagine feeling frozen, rigid, and still. If it is helpful, remember a time when you felt this way. Think about what information you received through your sense of interoception (inside listening), exteroception (outside listening), and neuroception (safety/danger listening). Describe the moment and what you notice here.

Experiential Anchor: Shutdown

Similar to a freeze state, a state of shutdown or behavioral collapse occurs when you are faced with a perceived threat from which there is no escape. In this situation, your brain and body determine that fighting or running away would not ensure your survival. However, unlike a freeze state (in which you become stiff), in a state of shutdown, you become limp. You may faint, lose consciousness, or dissociate. In this mode, your body decreases blood flow and oxygen to the large muscle groups, preserving it to send to the brain. As a result, you may feel unable to speak or act on your own behalf, or you might even experience a sense of complete incapacitation. There are no words or feelings.

When Mathilde's parents fought, she would shut down and hide in her room. Sometimes she became so terrified and missed her sister so badly that she felt completely incapacitated—in that there was nothing she could do to get her parents to stop or to bring her sister back. She would feel lightheaded, sleepy, and disconnected. Sometimes she felt like she was floating above her bed— watching herself cry and rock back and forth to stop the pain of missing her sister. Mathilde also felt this away after getting into a horrible fight with her partner. She collapsed on her bed just as she did as a child.

To create an experiential anchor of what a shutdown state feels like to you, take a moment and soften or close your eyes, and imagine going into a state of collapse or dissociation. If it is helpful, remember a time when you felt this way. Think about what information you received through your sense of interoception (inside listening), exteroception (outside listening), and neuroception (safety/danger listening). Describe the moment and what you notice here.

The Symphony of Your Protective Body: Bringing It Together

Healing from trauma requires forming a loving and kind relationship with all of the parts of you and understanding how your brain and body have tried to keep you safe by going into fight, flight, freeze, or shutdown mode.

Before you move forward, it might be helpful to look over your work in this chapter and journal about what you noticed. Were you able to recall more details about certain states of embodiment over others? Did you find it more difficult to anchor into states of connection or protection? Which states would you like to come back to later? What patterns did you see, if any? What do you want to remember about this chapter?

Take a deep breath and acknowledge the work you have done to better understand your body and how it works to support and protect you. Your next step is to learn how stress and your response to it can complicate or support the journey to healing and well-being.

If you really enjoy reading about polyvagal theory, I encourage you to seek out the work of Deb Dana, who does a wonderful job of explaining the theory in a way that is understandable. Both Stephen Porges's and Dana's work have helped me write about this for you.

Chapter 3

Stress and the Window of Tolerance

—Embodying Self-Statement—
My body tells me what it needs and wants.

Day-to-day life can be stressful. Whether it's sitting in traffic on your morning commute, keeping track of all the bills that need to be paid, or packing school lunches for your kids, there are innumerable stressors, some bigger than others, that you encounter in daily life. Even joyous or positive events, like starting a new relationship or getting promoted at work, can be considered stressful because they throw your system out of balance.

Fortunately, your body was designed to manage and adapt to stress. Throughout each day, it works hard to maintain *homeostasis* and get you back to balance. The body does this by attuning to and responding to your needs at any given moment. For example, if you go jogging, you need more oxygen, so your body automatically starts breathing faster so you have enough oxygen to fuel your muscles.

This process of adapting to stress and maintaining homeostasis is called *allostasis* (McEwen, 1998), or what I call stress-related workload. When your body takes on a stress-related workload, it prepares you to respond to the stressor by releasing stress hormones into your body, which increase your blood pressure and heart rate. Ideally, this allows you to effectively handle the stressor and move on, and your body then returns to its state of regular functioning (a process known as homeostatic self-regulation).

When your body encounters a repeated stressor, your body learns to gear up before anything happens. For example, if you always get in an argument with your partner after a long day at work, your body may begin getting you ready to fight before you pull in the driveway. Through your sense of interoception, you might notice your heart rate increase, your muscles tense, and your breath change. This is exactly the moment when it can be helpful to do something supportive and nurturing for your body to help bring yourself back to balance.

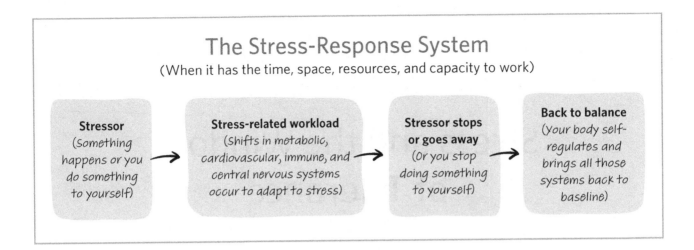

The Stress-Response System
(When it has the time, space, resources, and capacity to work)

Stressor
(Something happens or you do something to yourself)

Stress-related workload
(Shifts in metabolic, cardiovascular, immune, and central nervous systems occur to adapt to stress)

Stressor stops or goes away
(Or you stop doing something to yourself)

Back to balance
(Your body self-regulates and brings all those systems back to baseline)

However, many of us try to calm ourselves down by engaging in behaviors that stress our system out, such as drinking alcohol, misusing drugs, smoking, neglecting our nutritional habits, disinvesting in sleep hygiene, and failing to engage in other self-care behaviors. In the moment, it might feel like a night out drinking, a few glasses of wine, or an excessively long run is helping, but the truth is, it's not. It's making things worse.

As you learned in previous chapters, there is a limit to what your nervous system can tolerate before it moves into a state of fight, flight, freeze, or shutdown. In this chapter, you will get a better sense of how your actions in this world can shift your state of being from connection to protection mode. In particular, you will learn how your body self-regulates and responds to stress, how you might add to stress, and what it looks like when stress is too much for too long. You will also learn about your growth zone and your window of tolerance. Building on your mindful awareness, you will begin to identify what body sensations, thoughts, and feelings are present in each state of connection versus protection.

—Embodying Practice—
Subtle Breathing

Before you learn any more about stress, this subtle breathing practice will help you activate the calming part of your nervous system and deactivate any reactivity. This practice comes from Robin L. Rothenberg (2020), a breathwork expert in the field of yoga.

Find a seated position, making sure you feel grounded and well supported. Breathing normally, notice your breathing rate and heart rate before you begin. To begin, set a timer for two to three minutes, then place a hand on your chest and another on your belly, just below the front of the rib cage. Soften your shoulders and the muscles of your neck. Breathe through your nose, softening the muscles in your chest, working toward little or no movement of your upper rib cage. As you breathe, focus on allowing the lower ribs to expand outward with each inhale and to contract inward with each exhale.

Gradually and progressively, make your breath a little lighter, as if you could make your breath invisible. Imagine that with each inhale, your breath can enter and gently fill every cell within you. Consistently create lighter and lighter exhales until it feels as if you are connected to the exact amount of air your body needs. You might notice when it feels like too little, your body will want to breathe more and faster. Find a sustainable breath—very gentle, soft, and subtle.

Continue this way until your timer sounds. Then release your hands and take several rounds of your typical breath. When you are finished, take a moment to note your breathing and heart rates. If you'd like, you can add this subtle breathing practice to your resource repository.

Embodying Practice

Stressor Assessment

To gauge the extent to which you are handling stress in your life, look at your calendar and note the date six weeks ago. Since that date, what stressful experiences, increases in expectations, or changes have you encountered? This might include:

- Stressful behaviors that you engage in (e.g., excessive drinking or drug use, overexercising, overworking, overscheduling, sleep deprivation)

- Social stressors (e.g., fights with your partner, separation, divorce, breakup, a sick child, shifts in your social group or extended family)

- Larger social and community stressors (e.g., social or political unrest, worldwide pandemics, natural disasters, war, racism, or other forms of systemic bias or oppression)

Describe each of those stressors in the following table, or in your journal, and describe their impact.

Stressor	Description of Impact (Did you have a chance to recover? Did you adapt? How?)

When you are finished, look over the stressors you listed, and in your journal, write down any thoughts, reflections, or feelings about what you notice.

Need-to-Know: Allostatic Overload

Sometimes your body is able to adapt to the stressors you encounter, in which case the stress in your life doesn't go away—your behavior and systems essentially get used to it. Sometimes this works. For example, maybe you start a new role at work, but with a little extra effort and determination, you master the particulars of your new job responsibilities. Sometimes, though, this does not work. Maybe you start drinking too much to cope with stress at work. Maybe you begin working late into the evening and on weekends to try and get everything done.

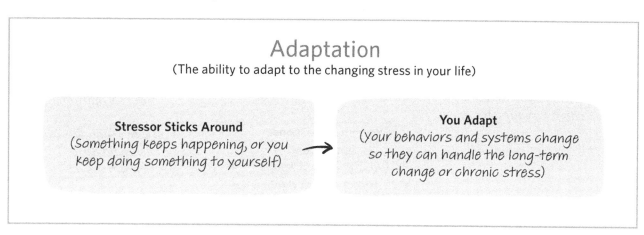

Adaptation
(The ability to adapt to the changing stress in your life)

Stressor Sticks Around
(Something keeps happening, or you keep doing something to yourself)

→

You Adapt
(Your behaviors and systems change so they can handle the long-term change or chronic stress)

When the stressors are too big, too numerous, and too frequent—and your adaptive response adds more stress to your system—stress begins to deplete your body. You simply do not have the time or resources to respond effectively anymore or to restore your physiological balance, and you may begin to experience a systemic overload. This is known as *allostatic overload* (Guidi et al., 2021), or what I call stress-related system overload. In this state, you are burnt out. When this happens, you may begin to show symptoms in three areas:

- **Self symptoms:** You may experience difficulty falling asleep, restless sleep, early waking, low energy, dizziness, anxiety, irritability, sadness, and a sense of demoralization. Your health is significantly affected, and you find yourself getting sick more frequently. In this state, you are at an increased risk for serious health problems.

- **Relationship and work symptoms:** You may experience impairments in social, academic, and occupational functioning. For example, you might fail to make deadlines, be chronically late, have a shorter fuse with others, and struggle with increased forgetfulness.

- **Can't-handle-everyday-life symptoms:** These are symptoms that relate to basic self-mastery. You may begin to feel overwhelmed by small everyday tasks, such as getting dressed for work, doing dishes, getting laundry done, or preparing meals. Everything simply feels too daunting.

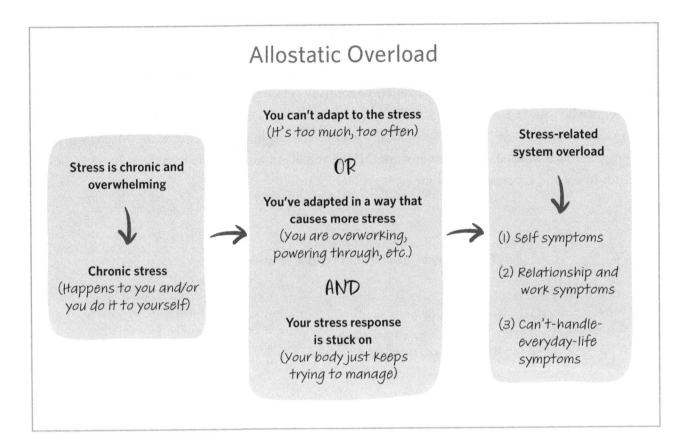

Building on your growing ability to be mindfully aware, consider your current state of stress and well-being. Think through your life experiences over the past few months. Have you had a recent stressful experience? Do you feel like you have had one stressful or challenging experience after another without time to adjust or cope? Does your schedule allow you the time you need to rest and nourish yourself before the next set of daily tasks?

Now, ask yourself those same questions again. However, this time, ask as if you were asking your body and not your brain: *Body, have you had a recent stressful experience? Body, do you feel like you have had one stressful and challenging experience after another without time to adjust or cope? Body, does your schedule allow you the time you need to rest and nourish yourself before the next set of daily tasks?* Your brain and body might be letting you know that you are at risk for (or are already in) allostatic overload. The following is a brief assessment to help you reflect on how you are feeling and consider if you are in allostatic overload.

—Embodying Practice—

Are You in Allostatic Overload?

To consider your experience of stress and possible stress-related system overload, put a check mark by any symptoms you've experienced in each category. Note, you might not have any symptoms or you might have quite a few. This is an opportunity to do a self-assessment and to reflect on where you are today.

Self symptoms

☐ Having difficulty falling or staying asleep

☐ Restless sleep

☐ Waking up early

☐ Having little or no energy

☐ Dizziness

☐ Anxiety or excessive worrying

☐ Feeling irritable and moody

☐ Feeling sad and down

☐ Feeling demoralized

☐ Getting sick very easily

☐ Having difficulty recovering from minor illness

☐ Feeling easily drained

☐ Other: _____

Relationship and work symptoms

☐ Not being there for the people in your life

☐ Needing more than you can give

☐ Your friends are frustrated with you

☐ Falling behind at school or work

☐ Making excuses for why things are not done

☐ Having a short fuse with others at home and at work

☐ Missing important deadlines

☐ Being late to meetings and engagements

☐ Forgetting about people and things that matter to you

☐ Feeling overwhelmed by relationships and work

☐ Wanting to avoid others and work

☐ Other: _____

Can't-handle-everyday-life symptoms

Feeling overwhelmed by:

☐ Getting out of bed

☐ Showering

☐ Getting dressed for the day

☐ Laundry

☐ Grocery shopping

☐ Preparing meals

☐ Doing dishes

☐ Going to work

☐ Paying bills and rent

☐ Picking up things around the house

☐ Taking care of pets

☐ Other: _____

This assessment might leave you with something to consider. Working on your trauma symptoms can be stressful. It requires exploring new ways of being while recalling and processing difficult and painful experiences. If you have determined that you are in allostatic overload, you may decide that you need to make some changes and secure support before going deeper into your trauma work. For example, you might need to:

- Get help for an addiction, eating disorder, or substance use problem

- Make changes in a relationship

- Step away from work or volunteer commitments for a while

- Join a support group, secure a therapist, or contact human resources at work

- Seek a less stressful or demanding job

—Embodying Self-Statement—
My choices can make the effects of stress better or worse.

—Embodying Practice—
The Second Arrow

There is an ancient Buddhist parable about the first and second arrows. The first arrows come from life and represent that which we cannot control. The second arrows stem from our self-destructive reactions to life's stressors and represent the unnecessary suffering we often add to life. I thought of this parable when I heard someone in recovery say the following: "There is no problem a drink [second arrow] won't make worse." It is so true. Life is full of first arrows, some big and some small. Some arrows nick our shins, and others feel like they hit us straight in the heart. When we get hit by a first arrow, the next moment is ours. Do we use our supports and tools to be with and work with what is present, or do we pick up the quiver of arrows and start shooting?

Consider your list of stressors from the earlier **Stressor Assessment**. Which ones can be considered first arrows, or stressors over which you have little control (e.g., a loved one getting sick, a moody boss, cutbacks at work, a project setback)? Which ones can be considered second arrows, or stressors you can control to some degree (e.g., bills from overspending, fatigue and dehydration from drinking too much, mounting deadlines from avoiding your work or overcommitting)?

You might have some that are a little of both. For example, let's say you agree to a project for which you thought you had time, but then something goes wrong (first arrow). Instead of dealing with it, you engage in finger-pointing and blame someone else (second arrow) and then go home to have a few glasses of wine (second arrow). You wake up the next day with a hangover and a delayed project. For these types of stressors, it's okay to use both boxes.

Considering First and Second Arrows
Stressors that can be considered first arrows (the ones over which you have little or no control):
Stressors that can be considered second arrows (the ones over which you have some control):

Once you have completed your list of first and second arrows, start thinking about how you can be a better partner to your nervous system so you don't create more suffering for yourself. Consider adding practices to your daily routine that support your nervous system as it works to manage stress. Offer your body something it can count on each day. Commit to going to your sanctuary for two to five minutes each day (or more), or spend a few minutes in your car listening to a meditation app or a script. Begin in small accomplishable steps. No amount of time is too small. These are hard changes to make. I have worked with people who initially feel more committed to having their daily glass of wine or beer after work than to the possibility of a daily meditation practice that could support their nervous system. To help you start this process, consider using any of the following three embodying practices.

The 4, 7, 8 Breathing Method

This yoga-based breathing practice can help slow down your nervous system and give you space for making more effective choices in your day-to-day life, especially when there are several stressors being thrown your way. It can also quiet your mind and help you sleep better if you are struggling to fall asleep.

Lie down or find a comfortable seat in which you feel well supported. Then place the tip of your tongue on the roof of your mouth on the ridge just behind your upper teeth.

Now exhale through your mouth, allowing the air to move around your tongue. Then close your mouth and gently inhale through your nose, counting 1, 2, 3, 4. Hold your breath, counting to 1, 2, 3, 4, 5, 6, 7. Finally, exhale through your mouth, around your tongue, for 1, 2, 3, 4, 5, 6, 7, 8.

Repeat this practice three to four times. If it is difficult to extend and hold your breath for the 4, 7, and 8 counts, reduce them all by one or two, keeping the overall ratio the same.

—Embodying Practice—
Grounding and Extended Exhale

This practice can be helpful in activating a state of connection and calming. It is especially helpful when you feel a spike in stress. For example, maybe your boss says something triggering at work or a loved one is upset with you. By connecting with the ground below you and slowing and extending your breath, you can reduce your overall stress response in the moment. Perhaps my favorite aspect of this practice is that you can practice without anybody knowing. This means you can use it anytime you need to, whether you're in a work meeting or in the middle of a disagreement.

Press your feet into the ground, establishing a sense of connection to the earth below you. Then soften your knees, legs, hips, shoulders, and arms. Soften your jaw. Soften your eyes. Press your feet into the ground again and simultaneously extend through the crown of your head.

Now bring your awareness up to your belly and heart area. Engage your breath, inhaling deeply for a count of 1, 2, 3, 4. Pause, then exhale completely for 1, 2, 3, 4, 5, 6. Pause. Repeat this breath cycle three more times, for a total of four cycles.

When you are finished, breathe normally, press your feet into the earth again, engage your core, and open your eyes fully as you lift your gaze.

Embodying Practice
Creating a Life in Which You Want to Be Present

This practice is a helpful reminder to consider what you can and cannot control when managing life's stressors. It is also designed to help you prioritize the actions and reactions you'd like to shift as you begin your trauma work. For example, you might want to work on establishing a short daily mediation practice (something you can control) while holding your worries about a loved one's illness (something you cannot control) in a beautiful container.

To begin, find a comfortable place to sit and take a moment to press your feet, legs, and sitting bones into the ground beneath you. Notice the connection. Breathe here. Next, orient your awareness toward your breath, noticing each inhale and exhale. As you breathe, say to yourself, *Breathing in, I know I am breathing in, and breathing out, I know I am breathing out.* As the words align with your actions, you might notice a settling of your body.

Now repeat to yourself, *I am committed to creating a life within which I want to be present and my nervous system can find peace and power. There will be things I can change and things I cannot. May I have the wisdom to know the difference and the courage, strength, and support to do what I need to do.*

Now, bring the things you feel like you cannot change to mind. If it seems like a lot, just focus on one or two things. Then say to yourself, *I accept and allow that these are things I cannot change. While I cannot change them, I can work on my relationship with them.* Pause here and breathe. See if there is one of these that you can let go. If so, pause here and breathe as you imagine letting that thing go, watching it slowly fade into the background.

For whatever things are left—things you cannot change—imagine creating a container to gently hold those things. Take time to build your container. Make it beautiful, strong, magical—whatever it needs to be to hold the boundary. Then imagine placing the things you cannot change in the container. Consider the separateness of the things in your container as you sit grounded and breathing. Breathe here for a while, being with the notion of separateness, boundaries, and release.

Now, bring to mind the things you feel like you can change. If there are a lot and it feels overwhelming, choose the most accessible one. Now say to yourself, *Within me, I have the courage, persistence, and strength to make this change. When this gets difficult, I will remind myself that I am working to create a life that I want to be present in. I am worthy of this effort.* If you prefer prayer, you might try *I am ready to change. When the moment and the challenge come, remind me of my courage and my worthiness.* Breathe here, offering your future self—the you who will need the strength and courage to change—everything you need. You might see this as energy you are sending forward or a prayer for the future you.

Close the meditation by reminding yourself, *I am committed to creating a life within which I want to be present and my nervous system can find peace and power. There will be things I can change and things I cannot. May I have the wisdom to know the difference and the courage, strength, and support to do what I need to do.*

Need-to-Know: The Window of Tolerance and the Growth Zone

Trauma is a sensitizing process (Perry & Winfrey, 2021), meaning that your trauma history can make you more sensitive to daily stressors and chronic stressors. That's because trauma narrows your window of tolerance (WOT) (Siegel, 1999), which is the current level of challenge or stress that you can manage as you get through the day. When you are outside of your window of tolerance, you lose your ability to effectively manage the stressors of day-to-day life. Instead, your body shifts into protection mode, meaning that your state of embodiment is fight, flight, freeze, or shutdown. Little to no learning can happen here. Being outside of your window of tolerance for too long can lead to allostatic overload and result in even more trauma.

So how can you translate what you have learned about allostatic load and overload into your everyday coping and healing processes? It begins with understanding your *comfort* and *growth zones*, in which you are solidly in connection mode and able to connect to yourself and others. The comfort and growth zones both exist within your window of tolerance. The difference is that in the comfort zone there are no challenges, and you feel safe. In your comfort zone, your body can rest, recover, and restore.

However, recovery from trauma requires practice moving outside of your comfort zone into what is called your growth zone. As its name suggests, the growth zone is where you can grow. This is where you can be with and work with your trauma memories and symptoms. Both the comfort and growth zones promote healing, each in their own way. Over time, you will help your nervous system become more resilient and you will begin feeling more connected to and grounded in your body even when facing challenges.

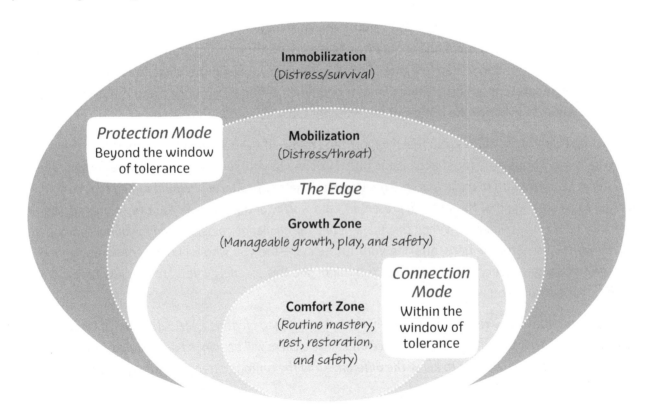

Let's take a moment to consider what each of these zones feels like for you. In the following section, I will describe each zone and its associated features. Then you will have a chance to reflect on what body sensations, emotions, and thoughts you experience when you're in each zone.

—Embodying Self-Statement—
Growing can feel uncomfortable.

Embodying Practice
Exploring the Comfort Zone

When you are in your comfort zone, you can embody any of the states associated with connection: deep rest and restoration, alert engagement, or active play, challenge, and growth. The main distinguishing feature of the comfort zone is that you feel a sense of freedom and ease. Here it is easier to be playful, laugh freely, belly breathe, create, explore, and work with focused attention. You have open access to your ability to connect in a loving and kind way to yourself and others. You feel comfortable, calm, safe, and relatively free of stress. You can move in a relaxed and engaged manner. You have a sense of mastery; you know how to do the things you are doing. There is predictability or routine in your life. You can rest deeply and restore here. Healing can happen here, but it is more restorative in nature.

Describe how you know when you are in the comfort zone. What body sensations, emotions, and thoughts do you experience here?

Body Sensations	Emotions	Thoughts (*I am . . . , People are . . . , The world is . . .*)

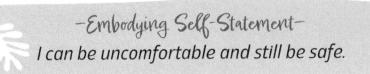

-Embodying Self-Statement-
I can be uncomfortable and still be safe.

Exploring the Growth Zone

Human beings long to be challenged by life, to have experiences that help them grow and learn. That is what happens in the growth zone. Here you are learning something new, and you are activated and mobilized. This can feel both comfortable and uncomfortable, but either way, you are safe in this zone. Despite being challenged, you are able to connect to yourself and others in a loving and kind way. You might notice your heart beating, your muscles working, and your lungs breathing. Still, you feel in control and have a solid sense that you can take a break when you need to. You might feel excited, a bit anxious, and even frustrated at times. Your feelings might intensify, but when they do, you are able to ground your feet and breathe. Your thoughts are aligned with your efforts as you remind yourself that you are worth the effort.

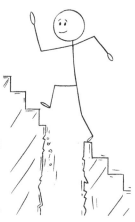

Describe how you know when you are in the growth zone. What body sensations, emotions, and thoughts do you experience here?

Body Sensations	Emotions	Thoughts (*I am . . . , People are . . . , The world is . . .*)

—Embodying Self-Statement—
I can notice my body, thoughts, and emotions and make changes.

Embodying Practice
Exploring Outside of the Window of Tolerance

When you are beyond the edge and pushed outside of your window of tolerance, you can go into a state of either hyperarousal or hypoarousal. When you are hyperaroused, your body is in fight-or-flight mode, which can be characterized by panic, overwhelm, agitation, racing thoughts, and the feeling of being out of control. Conversely, when you are hypoaroused, you feel shutdown, empty, dissociated, numb, or paralyzed. Trauma can narrow your window of tolerance, making it more likely that even seemingly minor stressors will throw you in a state of hyperarousal or hypoarousal. In this state, it is difficult to function and cope with daily life.

Describe how you know when you are outside of your window of tolerance. What body sensations, emotions, and thoughts do you experience here?

Body Sensations	Emotions	Thoughts (*I am . . . , People are . . . , The world is . . .*)

PAUSE

(**P** - Pause, **A** - Assess → **USE** your resources and supports)

☐ **P**ause, check in, and acknowledge how you are feeling. This is a chance to be kind to yourself. The pace of your work is very important. Press your feet into the earth and take four gentle breaths.

☐ **A**ssess by asking yourself, *Is this a good place for a break?* If the answer is *yes* or *I don't know*, then fold over the corner of the page and take a break. This workbook is here for you for as long as it takes and for as many breaks as you need.

☐ **USE** your resources. Take a rest. Connect to your trusted friends. Contact your therapist. Practice your favorite well-being strategies. Get back to work when YOU are ready.

Need-to-Know: Cycle between Great Effort and Great Rest

Learning about your own states and where you are within your window of tolerance can help you know what practices you need and what you are up for. The Self-Awareness Scale is one way to assess where you are and where you need to be within your window of tolerance. It's also a helpful way to communicate where you are with your therapist, or to rate where you are before and after different meditations, activities, and exercises.

For visual learners, the Self-Awareness Scale looks like this:

1 to 2 Comfort Zone	**3 to 6** Growth Zone	**7 to 10** Outside of the Window of Tolerance
My body, emotions, and thoughts are clear. I feel safe and competent. I can rest here.	My body, emotions, and thoughts are active and manageable. I can grow and be effective here.	My body, emotions, and thoughts are not manageable. I am overwhelmed, lost in reaction, or shutdown.

For more scientific learners, the Self-Awareness Scale looks like this:

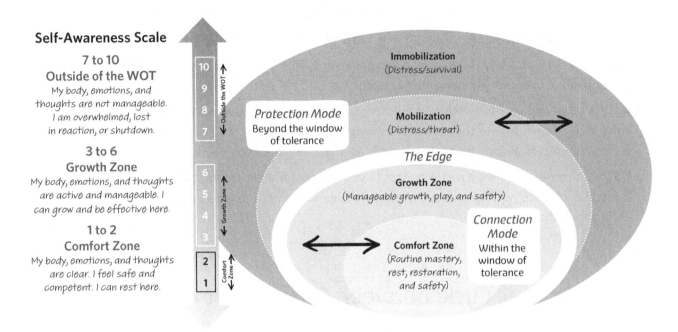

You can use the Self-Awareness Scale in conjunction with the following table, which provides some common examples of how your thoughts, emotions, and body might feel in each of the zones. Read over this table and circle any experiences that resonate with you. Add any new experiences that you identify to the previous set of embodying practices.

When you are doing your trauma work, you will be most effective if you cycle back and forth between the comfort zone and the growth zone, targeting Self-Awareness Scale scores from 1 to 6. Ultimately, you are working to expand both your comfort and growth zones without going into allostatic overload by pushing it too fast. That means that as you work, you want your score to move up from a 3 to 6 and then return to a 1 or 2 afterward to allow for rest.

If you find yourself at a 7 or even up to a 10, take a break until your body can come back to a 1 or 2 in your comfort zone. Then, secure some additional support (e.g., a therapist) or take the steps a bit slower before continuing. If you find yourself at or between scores of 6 to 10, the following **Sensate Focus for Distress** practice is a quick way to calm yourself. It can also be helpful to have a few supportive friends on speed dial. Do not use alcohol or nonprescribed substances to try to cope, as this will interfere with your healing work and prevent you from expanding outside of your comfort zone.

Table 3.1. States of Being in Each Zone*

Comfort Zone: Inside of the Window of Tolerance			
Self-Awareness Scale 1 2	**Body** My body is relaxed, my breath smooth, and heart rate slow. I feel calm. I feel open and connected.	**Emotions** My emotions are pleasant and positive. I feel safe, confident, peaceful, and happy. I feel good about other people. I feel trust.	**Thoughts** My thoughts are positive, clear, and reflective and come from a sense of safety. I may be more likely to give people the benefit of the doubt and be open to their ideas.
Growth Zone: Inside of the Window of Tolerance			
3 4 5 6	**Body** My body is active and alert. My muscles can easily engage and relax. My breath is steady and aligned with the task at hand. My heart rate reflects the work I am doing, and I can slow my heart rate when I slow my breath.	**Emotions** My emotions are aligned with the challenge with which I am engaged. They feel manageable and I can use my coping skills. I sometimes have mixed feelings, but I can work through these feelings.	**Thoughts** My thoughts are clear, supportive, and compassionate. I can see my strengths, efforts, and challenges clearly. I am aware of myself, my body, and my mind, and I am able to make effective choices. I can think rationally about the intentions and actions of others.
The Edge of the Window of Tolerance ↑ Engage in grounding and breathing practices as you begin ↑ to show signs of fight, flight, freeze, or shutdown.			
↓ **Outside of the Window of Tolerance** ↓			
Mobilization in Fight or Flight			
7 8	**Body** Mobilization is my system's priority. My body is highly activated and my muscles are ready to fight or run. My breath is rapid, and my heart rate is fast. I don't feel okay or safe.	**Emotions** My emotions are big, compelling, and overwhelming. They are often aligned with anger and fear. I can't cope. My interactions with others are clouded by anger, fear, and safety needs.	**Thoughts** I may have no thoughts at all, or they are aligned with fighting or escaping. My thoughts may be aggressive (*I need to fight back*) or oriented toward getting out (*I need to get out of here now*). I am biased by anger, fear, and concerns for safety.
Immobilization in Shutdown and Freeze			
9 10	**Body** My body feels immobilized. It feels numb, heavy, difficult, or impossible to move. I feel dissociated from my body.	**Emotions** I feel numb, hopeless, apathetic, overwhelmed, or despairing. I might feel inappropriately guilty or worthless. I have trouble feeling anything toward anybody, including myself.	**Thoughts** My thoughts are shut down. They seem foggy and confused. It is hard, if not impossible, to decide what to do next. I have no plans. I cannot connect with myself or others.

* Adapted from Cook-Cottone, 2020

As this chapter comes to a close, I want to commend you for completing this powerful learning about you, your body, and stress. The next chapter will help you create the foundation for heading into your trauma work from an unshakable base. It will help you feel more grounded in your comfort zone as an embodied sanctuary, or place from which you can grow.

—Embodying Practice—
Sensate Focus for Distress

This practice adds to your growing set of resources as an additional tool to shift your current state back into the window of tolerance. It helps you focus on your senses and orients you away from escalating thoughts and feelings. Use this practice when the **Grounding and Extended Exhale** practice is insufficient, or when you are feeling very escalated and triggered.

Before you start, think of something that really helps you feel grounded and that you know with certainty to be true, such as *I love my dog*, *The sun always shines behind the clouds*, *Right now, I can breathe and that matters*, or *I am worth the effort*. For this to work, the statement must be something that you 100 percent believe to be true.

My one positive, grounding thing that I know to be true is:

_____

_____

Once you have developed your grounding statement, make sure that your body is well grounded. Find a seat and press your feet into the floor and your sitting bones into your seat.

Then orient toward your breath, placing your hands on your belly to help you slow your breath, and take three cycles of a calming breath:
Breathe in 1, 2, 3, 4 . . . and out 1, 2, 3, 4, 5.
Breathe in 1, 2, 3, 4 . . . and out 1, 2, 3, 4, 5.
Breathe in 1, 2, 3, 4 . . . and out 1, 2, 3, 4, 5.

Once you are done with three breath cycles, continue by tuning into your senses:
Name five things you can see (pause).
Name four things you can hear (pause).
Name three things you can touch (pause).
Name two things you can smell (pause).
Say your one grounding, positive statement that you know to be true: "_____"

Developing a Signal for Support and a List of What You Need

The work you are doing to heal from trauma and reconnect with your body is not easy. Despite having the best plans, you might find yourself triggered into a state of fight or flight, or completely frozen or shutdown. To ensure you are well supported, prepare a signal you can use with your therapist, family members, or friends to communicate that you need support. Some ideas for signals are:

- Verbal phrases, like "connection time needed," "grounding needed," "hugs needed," or "emergency session needed"

- Physical gestures, like eye contact with a hand on your heart or a raised hand (which communicates that you need to stop)

- Artistic gestures, like having a drawing you place on the fridge or an image that you text to indicate it's a hard day

Use the space here to describe what signal you will use to indicate that you are not okay and that you need support.

_____

_____

_____

_____

Place a check mark by any sources of support that you might need when you give your signal:

☐ An emergency session with your therapist

☐ Quiet time with a loved one (no talking, just being)

☐ Body movement (e.g., practice yoga, go for a walk)

☐ A phone call with a loved one so you can share where you are at

☐ Someone to breathe with you

☐ Someone to walk you through one of the practices

☐ Other: _____

Now, let your support system know what your signal is, including how and when you might use it and, most importantly, what you need when you give the signal. Consider using the Self-Awareness Scale as you develop your plan. For example, you might commit to using this signal when you notice that you are at a 6 or higher on the Self-Awareness Scale and are unable to access or use your practices to self-regulate.

Chapter 4

Creating Safety and Caring for Your Body

—Embodying Self-Statement—
My body requires and is worthy of care.

After trauma, it is normal to feel constantly dysregulated and unsteady, which is why so many trauma survivors seek out quick relief and respite by using substances, overworking, or just getting lost in chaos. However, these habits only provide a temporary source of relief and end up accruing long-term consequences. To facilitate true healing, it is important to nurture and care for your body—to treat yourself and your body as if they are worthy of love. Interestingly, though, self-care often isn't viewed as a respite for many trauma survivors. It is often seen as an end goal, as something "healthy people do." This is the experience of many of my own patients, who often come to therapy with the notion that once they get themselves together—only once they heal from trauma—will they begin to take care of themselves.

For instance, Chandra was a patient of mine who had experienced extensive interpersonal trauma in her childhood, and she did not think that she deserved self-care until she stopped drinking. She thought self-care was something for people who had their lives "together" and whose drinking was under control. For Chandra, self-care was at the end of her healing journey. She was going to earn it. The problem, however, was that self-care was exactly what Chandra needed. She was drinking to feel a sense of comfort; it was a predictable way to lower her distress. Unfortunately, the drinking seemed to make things worse, not better. For example, she often skipped meals when drinking, sent angry texts to family members, lashed out at her partner, and was late for work because she was tired and hungover. She felt embarrassed by her behavior and noticed that it was beginning to affect her health and well-being. It most certainly wasn't helping her heal.

Over time, Chandra began to consider that self-care could possibly provide the comfort and predictability she craved. She began to integrate self-care into her routine in simple ways, by going for a walk after a stressful day at work or taking a bath on Sunday evenings. With time, she gradually built up a self-care routine that included mindfulness practices, regular walking, and the integration of relaxation and self-soothing practices as daily rituals. In turn, she became less reliant on alcohol to help her cope.

Similar to Chandra, self-care is one of the most important parts of your healing journey. In this chapter, I will take you through the process of cultivating safety and developing a routine of mindful self-care as a way to support your own embodied healing and well-being.

Need-to-Know: Mindful Self-Care

Self-care isn't a reward that you are only worthy of receiving once you learn how to manage your mental health. Rather, it's a necessary part of the pathway to achieving better mental health. It is the pathway to helping your body and mind feel safe, steady, and loved. No matter how much you might be struggling right now, you deserve to feel safe, and your body and mind are worthy of care and love.

—Embodying Self-Statement—
I deserve to feel safe and loved.

You might be wondering what self-care has to do with feeling safe. Consider that your body doesn't speak using words. Your body experiences *what you do and what you do not do*. In this way, you communicate with your body. If you feed it healthy food, your body experiences that. If you allow your body to rest each night around the same time, your body orients around that schedule and even anticipates it. If you hydrate your body throughout the day, your body feels replenished and relaxed. Caring for, nurturing, and nourishing your body is your body's love language. It is steady, routine, and predictable self-care that allows your body to relax and trust that it will be just that—predictably cared for. It is reliable and consistent self-love.

As you develop a practice of mindful self-care as a way to communicate with your body, you will begin to notice that your body also communicates with you through various sensations, such as a grumble in your stomach suggesting your body needs food or a whole-body feeling of radiating sunshine after a good night's sleep. Your body also communicates with you when you wake up with a hangover after drinking alcohol or binging on too many sugary foods. As you establish this communication system with your body, you can better attune and respond to your body's in-the-moment needs. This routine, predictable, and responsible self-care is the pathway to self-love. It is through a steady practice of mindful self-care that you give life to the part of you that loves and nurtures.

—Embodying Self-Statement—
Self-love is a practice.

I LOVE ME

For some people, the process of learning how to care for the self was developed through years of experiencing effective and loving parenting. Your caretakers are like self-care mentors. Within the context of a loving parent-child relationship, you learn to make sure you're rested enough during the day and get to bed at a reasonable hour so you get enough sleep. You learn to spend more time with people who are good to you and support you when you say no. You learn to spend less time with those who are hurtful or do not have your best interests in mind. You learn to fuel the body with nutritious food and hydrate it with water. You learn how to relax, move with awareness of your physical self, and carefully choose your actions based on the sensations, thoughts, and emotions you experience. Ultimately, you learn that your life has meaning and that in order to pursue that meaning, you must take care of the body that will get you there.

This process, however, is not automatic. In some cases, a person's own set of vulnerabilities and inclinations can impair their ability to develop and implement self-care skills. For those who are born as helpers and caretakers, focusing on the self can seem foreign and feel uncomfortable. For some, it might not even come to mind. For others, there may have been interruptions or failures in the parenting or mentoring process. Further, cultural beliefs can get in the way. In some cultures, self-care can be seen as an indulgence, while achieving and striving are held as the only true valuable pursuits. Work and school cultures can exacerbate this mindset, where the focus is on worker and student achievement above healing and well-being.

For Chandra, her inability to develop a healthy self-care practice stemmed from her childhood. Growing up, her parents were caught in substance use, so she went back and forth between various foster homes, depending on how her parents were doing. She did not consistently experience someone tucking her into bed when she was tired, noticing she was sad and helping her honor her feelings, or making sure she got to dance class. In fact, the thought of someone taking her to dance class when she was little was so far from her experience that the idea made her laugh—and then cry. For Chandra, beginning a self-care practice was a way to reparent herself. A way to give herself the structure, routine, and love she did not receive in childhood.

The healing work of self-care is well illustrated by Kim Chernin (1999) in her book, *The Woman Who Gave Birth to Her Mother*. In essence, through a series of case studies, this book shows that when we practice self-care, we become the person who mothers ourselves. With practice, taking care of yourself can become second nature. This is exactly the foundation the work of healing trauma can stand upon. In the chapters ahead, your work will include recalling, being with, and working with things that have happened. This work is difficult and dysregulating. A foundation of self-care offers the support you need to help meet these difficult memories.

Need-to-Know: Formal vs. Informal Self-Care

When most people think of self-care, they associate it with formal practices that require setting aside dedicated time each day. These include practices such as doing a yoga class, joining a volleyball league, taking a dance class, and going to the doctor for wellness visits. When people inadvertently believe that self-care only comprises these formal practices, it gets in the way of their ability to practice self-care. They will often say, "I don't have time."

The reality is that formal practices can be balanced with informal practices. Informal practices are those that you can weave into your day. They do not require allotted or dedicated time. For example, listening to soothing music as you work, taking a break from electronics, and surrounding yourself with friends who respect you when you say no are all examples of informal self-care that can greatly impact your life. These practices are so crucial because they are accessible for people with even the busiest of schedules.

To help you develop your own mindful self-care plan that incorporates both formal and informal practices, the following section explores 10 domains of self-care that you can integrate into your routine: nutrition and hydration, exercise, rest, physical and medical care, self-soothing, self-compassion, supportive relationships, environmental factors, spiritual practices, and self-awareness and mindfulness. Within each area, informal practices that can be woven into your day are indicated with an asterisk.

This mindful self-care plan is based on my work with Dr. Wendy Guyker, with whom I have developed an assessment tool called the Mindful Self-Care Scale (Cook-Cottone, 2015; Cook-Cottone & Guyker, 2018). There are three versions of the scale available, which are all easily accessible and available for free at www.catherinecookcottone.com.

As you explore each area and develop your self-care plan, ask yourself these three questions to ensure you are practicing the ART of self-care:

- **A**ttunement: Are you tuned in to what you really need?
- **R**esponsive: Is the self-care behavior going to serve what you need?
- **T**aking action: Did you engage in the self-care that you needed?

—Embodying Self-Statement—
Routine and structure help my body feel safe and regulated.

Embodying Practice
Nutrition and Hydration Assessment

How you fuel and hydrate your body directly relates to how you feel. Most of us have heard of the term "hangry" to describe the way a person can become agitated and irritable when their blood sugar is low. Alcoholics Anonymous even has a slogan called HALT, which means you are most at risk for making poor decisions if you are hungry, angry, lonely, or tired.

Hydration is equally as important. It is essential for skin health, neurological functioning, mood stability, digestive health, and more. Dehydration can stress your kidneys and body, causing headaches, fatigue, muscle cramps, food cravings, and reduced mental performance. In fact, severe dehydration can be fatal. That being said, too much water can be a problem as well. Balance is key. Generally speaking, adults should drink between six to eight large glasses of water per day.

The following assessment is designed to get you thinking about your nutrition and hydration goals. If you are struggling with disordered eating, or you feel like you may need more support, talk to your doctor for a referral to a nutritionist (or seek out one directly) who can help you traverse this difficult terrain.

This past week, how many days did you do the following?

1. I drank at least six to eight cups of water.*
   0 = never (0 days)   1 = rarely (1 day)   2 = sometimes (2 to 3 days)   3 = often (4 to 5 days)   4 = regularly (6 to 7 days)

2. Even though my stomach felt full enough, I kept eating.
   4 = never (0 days)   3 = rarely (1 day)   2 = sometimes (2 to 3 days)   1 = often (4 to 5 days)   0 = regularly (6 to 7 days)

3. I adjusted my water intake when I needed to (e.g., for exercise, hot weather).*
   0 = never (0 days)   1 = rarely (1 day)   2 = sometimes (2 to 3 days)   3 = often (4 to 5 days)   4 = regularly (6 to 7 days)

4. I skipped a meal.
   4 = never (0 days)   3 = rarely (1 day)   2 = sometimes (2 to 3 days)   1 = often (4 to 5 days)   0 = regularly (6 to 7 days)

5. I ate breakfast, lunch, dinner, and (when needed) snacks.
   0 = never (0 days)   1 = rarely (1 day)   2 = sometimes (2 to 3 days)   3 = often (4 to 5 days)   4 = regularly (6 to 7 days)

6. I ate a variety of nutritious foods (e.g., vegetables, protein, fruits, and grains).*
   0 = never (0 days)   1 = rarely (1 day)   2 = sometimes (2 to 3 days)   3 = often (4 to 5 days)   4 = regularly (6 to 7 days)

7. I planned my meals and snacks.
   0 = never (0 days)   1 = rarely (1 day)   2 = sometimes (2 to 3 days)   3 = often (4 to 5 days)   4 = regularly (6 to 7 days)

Add up your responses for each of the 7 questions. This is your total raw score. Your total raw score for this section can range from 0 to 28.

Total raw score: _____

Next, divide your total raw score by 7 to get your subscale score. Your subscale score should be a number between 0 and 4.

> The scoring key at the end of this chapter will help you interpret your scores.

Subscale score: _____

Embodying Practice
Exercise Assessment

Exercise supports well-being in a number of ways. It releases endorphins, promotes metabolism, strengthens the immune system, and combats stress. Regular exercise can also enhance cognitive performance, meaning it boosts your critical thinking skills. Not only can it help you mentally, but the lessons you learn on your yoga mat or in your running shoes can apply to your life too. For example, you can learn that persistence pays off, that your breath is a powerful tool in self-regulating, and that you can do difficult things. Exercise also provides you with an opportunity to mobilize your body without fear. It allows you to feel your heart beating, your body working, and your breath moving in service of your well-being, not just in reaction to trauma or traumatic memories. Just like nutrition and hydration, though, it's important to get the right amount of exercise—not too much and not too little. Most recommendations encourage about 30 to 60 minutes of exercise per day.

This past week, how many days did you do the following?

1. I exercised for at least 30 to 60 minutes.
   0 = never (0 days)   1 = rarely (1 day)   2 = sometimes (2 to 3 days)   3 = often (4 to 5 days)   4 = regularly (6 to 7 days)

2. I took part in scheduled physical activities (e.g., sports teams, dance classes).
   0 = never (0 days)   1 = rarely (1 day)   2 = sometimes (2 to 3 days)   3 = often (4 to 5 days)   4 = regularly (6 to 7 days)

3. I did sedentary activities instead of exercising (e.g., watched TV, worked on the computer).
   4 = never (0 days)   3 = rarely (1 day)   2 = sometimes (2 to 3 days)   1 = often (4 to 5 days)   0 = regularly (6 to 7 days)

4. I sat for periods of longer than 60 minutes at a time.
   4 = never (0 days)   3 = rarely (1 day)   2 = sometimes (2 to 3 days)   1 = often (4 to 5 days)   0 = regularly (6 to 7 days)

5. I did fun physical activities (e.g., danced, played active games, jumped in leaves).*
   0 = never (0 days)   1 = rarely (1 day)   2 = sometimes (2 to 3 days)   3 = often (4 to 5 days)   4 = regularly (6 to 7 days)

6. I overexercised (e.g., when I was tired, sleep deprived, or risking an injury).
   4 = never (0 days)   3 = rarely (1 day)   2 = sometimes (2 to 3 days)   1 = often (4 to 5 days)   0 = regularly (6 to 7 days)

7. I scheduled my exercise into my day.
   0 = never (0 days)   1 = rarely (1 day)   2 = sometimes (2 to 3 days)   3 = often (4 to 5 days)   4 = regularly (6 to 7 days)

Add up your responses for each of the 7 questions. This is your total raw score. Your total raw score for this section can range from 0 to 28.

Total raw score: _____

Next, divide your total raw score by 7 to get your subscale score. Your subscale score should be a number between 0 and 4.

> The scoring key at the end of this chapter will help you interpret your scores.

Subscale score: _____

—Embodying Practice—
Rest Assessment

Rest is a critical aspect of mindful self-care. It includes getting sufficient sleep, taking restorative breaks, and ensuring you have enough time in your schedule to rest and restore. Most guidelines recommend that you get between seven and nine hours of sleep per night. Both too much sleep and lack thereof can cause inflammation, suppress your immune system, disrupt your metabolism, exacerbate mental health problems, reduce cognitive functioning, and more.

Rest is also about taking breaks from work and other activities that require sustained attention or exertion. Rest can involve taking a 10-minute break to stretch your legs, staying in on the weekend to rejuvenate, or going away on a weeklong vacation. It is crucial to make time for rest as you dig into the more difficult aspects of trauma work. Cycling between trauma work and rest can support the development and installation of your new skills. Doing this work without allowing for rest can cause further trauma or exacerbate the trauma symptoms you already have.

This past week, how many days did you do the following?

1. I got enough sleep to feel rested when I woke up.

   0 = never (0 days)   1 = rarely (1 day)   2 = sometimes (2 to 3 days)   3 = often (4 to 5 days)   4 = regularly (6 to 7 days)

2. I planned rejuvenating breaks throughout my work or school day.

   0 = never (0 days)   1 = rarely (1 day)   2 = sometimes (2 to 3 days)   3 = often (4 to 5 days)   4 = regularly (6 to 7 days)

3. I rested when I needed to (e.g., when not feeling well, after a long workout).*

   0 = never (0 days)   1 = rarely (1 day)   2 = sometimes (2 to 3 days)   3 = often (4 to 5 days)   4 = regularly (6 to 7 days)

4. I took planned breaks at school or work.

   0 = never (0 days)   1 = rarely (1 day)   2 = sometimes (2 to 3 days)   3 = often (4 to 5 days)   4 = regularly (6 to 7 days)

5. I scheduled pleasant activities into my day that were not work or school related.

   0 = never (0 days)   1 = rarely (1 day)   2 = sometimes (2 to 3 days)   3 = often (4 to 5 days)   4 = regularly (6 to 7 days)

6. I took time away from electronics (e.g., turned off my phone and other devices).*

   0 = never (0 days)   1 = rarely (1 day)   2 = sometimes (2 to 3 days)   3 = often (4 to 5 days)   4 = regularly (6 to 7 days)

7. I made time in my schedule for enough sleep.

   0 = never (0 days)   1 = rarely (1 day)   2 = sometimes (2 to 3 days)   3 = often (4 to 5 days)   4 = regularly (6 to 7 days)

Add up your responses for each of the 7 questions. This is your total raw score. Your total raw score for this section can range from 0 to 28.

Total raw score: _____

> The scoring key at the end of this chapter will help you interpret your scores.

Next, divide your total raw score by 7 to get your subscale score. Your subscale score should be a number between 0 and 4.

Subscale score: _____

—Embodying Practice—
Physical and Medical Care Assessment

Physical and medical self-care involves going to the dentist and doctor for your annual exams, practicing daily hygiene, and adhering to medical advice. It also includes not hurting your body with alcohol or drugs. You are responsible for taking care of your beautiful body.

An important note here: If you are regularly using substances such as alcohol, cannabis, or other nonprescribed drugs, you should discuss your substance use with a mental health care provider before proceeding any further with trauma work. It is not recommended that you attempt to address your trauma while you are actively engaged in substance use.

This past week, how many days did you do the following?

1. I engaged in medical care to prevent or treat illness and disease (e.g., attended doctor visits, took prescribed medications and vitamins, remained up to date on screenings and immunizations, followed doctor recommendations).
   0 = never (0 days)   1 = rarely (1 day)   2 = sometimes (2 to 3 days)   3 = often (4 to 5 days)   4 = regularly (6 to 7 days)

2. I engaged in dental care to prevent or treat illness and disease (e.g., going to dental visits, brushing teeth, flossing).
   0 = never (0 days)   1 = rarely (1 day)   2 = sometimes (2 to 3 days)   3 = often (4 to 5 days)   4 = regularly (6 to 7 days)

3. I took recreational drugs.
   4 = never (0 days)   3 = rarely (1 day)   2 = sometimes (2 to 3 days)   1 = often (4 to 5 days)   0 = regularly (6 to 7 days)

4. I did not drink any alcohol.*
   0 = never (0 days)   1 = rarely (1 day)   2 = sometimes (2 to 3 days)   3 = often (4 to 5 days)   4 = regularly (6 to 7 days)

5. I did not drink alcohol in excess (i.e., more than 1 to 2 drinks [1 drink = 12 ounces beer, 5 ounces wine, or 1.5 ounces liquor]).*
   0 = never (0 days)   1 = rarely (1 day)   2 = sometimes (2 to 3 days)   3 = often (4 to 5 days)   4 = regularly (6 to 7 days)

6. I did not smoke or use tobacco products.*
   0 = never (0 days)   1 = rarely (1 day)   2 = sometimes (2 to 3 days)   3 = often (4 to 5 days)   4 = regularly (6 to 7 days)

7. I practiced good hygiene habits (e.g., showering, doing laundry, wearing clean clothes).*
   0 = never (0 days)   1 = rarely (1 day)   2 = sometimes (2 to 3 days)   3 = often (4 to 5 days)   4 = regularly (6 to 7 days)

8. I accessed the medical or dental care I needed.
   0 = never (0 days)   1 = rarely (1 day)   2 = sometimes (2 to 3 days)   3 = often (4 to 5 days)   4 = regularly (6 to 7 days)

Add up your responses for each of the 8 questions. This is your total raw score. Your total raw score for this section can range from 0 to 32.

Total raw score: _____

Next, divide your total raw score by 8 to get your subscale score. Your subscale score should be a number between 0 and 4.

Subscale score: _____

The scoring key at the end of this chapter will help you interpret your scores.

—Embodying Practice—
Self-Soothing Assessment

Self-soothing involves engaging in activities that help you feel calmer and more grounded when you are in a state of distress. These activities help you get back to your comfort zone, where you have a relaxed presence (a 1 or 2 on the Self-Awareness Scale). Many self-soothing practices draw on the five senses—sight, touch, hearing, smell, and taste—to help anchor your awareness in the present moment. You can use self-soothing practices in response to a trigger or an overwhelmed feeling, or you can use them as a prevention strategy to help your body feel supported and cared for. Some examples of self-soothing practices include giving yourself a massage, reading, coloring, and listening to music.

This past week, how many days did you do the following?

1. I used breathing practices to relax.*
   0 = never (0 days)   1 = rarely (1 day)   2 = sometimes (2 to 3 days)   3 = often (4 to 5 days)   4 = regularly (6 to 7 days)

2. I did not know how to relax.
   4 = never (0 days)   3 = rarely (1 day)   2 = sometimes (2 to 3 days)   1 = often (4 to 5 days)   0 = regularly (6 to 7 days)

3. I thought about calming things (e.g., nature, happy memories).*
   0 = never (0 days)   1 = rarely (1 day)   2 = sometimes (2 to 3 days)   3 = often (4 to 5 days)   4 = regularly (6 to 7 days)

4. When I got stressed, I couldn't calm down and stayed stressed for hours.
   4 = never (0 days)   3 = rarely (1 day)   2 = sometimes (2 to 3 days)   1 = often (4 to 5 days)   0 = regularly (6 to 7 days)

5. I did something physical to help me relax (e.g., took a bath, did yoga, went for a walk).
   0 = never (0 days)   1 = rarely (1 day)   2 = sometimes (2 to 3 days)   3 = often (4 to 5 days)   4 = regularly (6 to 7 days)

6. I used my mind to help me relax (e.g., read a book, wrote in a journal).
   0 = never (0 days)   1 = rarely (1 day)   2 = sometimes (2 to 3 days)   3 = often (4 to 5 days)   4 = regularly (6 to 7 days)

7. I drew upon my social supports to help me relax (e.g., called a friend, made plans to socialize).
   0 = never (0 days)   1 = rarely (1 day)   2 = sometimes (2 to 3 days)   3 = often (4 to 5 days)   4 = regularly (6 to 7 days)

8. I did something creative to help me relax (e.g., painted, played an instrument, did creative writing).
   0 = never (0 days)   1 = rarely (1 day)   2 = sometimes (2 to 3 days)   3 = often (4 to 5 days)   4 = regularly (6 to 7 days)

9. I sought out sounds to help me relax (e.g., listened to music, a podcast, rainforest sounds).*
   0 = never (0 days)   1 = rarely (1 day)   2 = sometimes (2 to 3 days)   3 = often (4 to 5 days)   4 = regularly (6 to 7 days)

10. I sought out comforting images to help me relax (e.g., looked at art, went window shopping, observed nature).*
    0 = never (0 days)   1 = rarely (1 day)   2 = sometimes (2 to 3 days)   3 = often (4 to 5 days)   4 = regularly (6 to 7 days)

11. I sought out smells to relax (e.g., lotions, candles, smells of baked goods).*
    0 = never (0 days)   1 = rarely (1 day)   2 = sometimes (2 to 3 days)   3 = often (4 to 5 days)   4 = regularly (6 to 7 days)

12. I sought out tactile experiences to help me relax (e.g., petted an animal, cuddled a soft blanket, floated in a pool, put on comfortable clothes).*

 0 = never (0 days)   1 = rarely (1 day)   2 = sometimes (2 to 3 days)   3 = often (4 to 5 days)   4 = regularly (6 to 7 days)

13. I prioritized activities that help me relax.

 0 = never (0 days)   1 = rarely (1 day)   2 = sometimes (2 to 3 days)   3 = often (4 to 5 days)   4 = regularly (6 to 7 days)

Add up your responses for each of the 13 questions. This is your total raw score. Your total raw score for this section can range from 0 to 52.

Total raw score: _____

Next, divide your total raw score by 13 to get your subscale score. Your subscale score should be a number between 0 and 4.

> The scoring key at the end of this chapter will help you interpret your scores.

Subscale score: _____

Embodying Practice
Self-Compassion Assessment

Self-compassion is about being able to relate to yourself in a way that is loving and kind. When you practice self-compassion, you treat yourself with the same kindness that you would a close friend. According to self-compassion guru Kristin Neff, self-compassion consists of three facets: (1) being kind, loving, and gentle to yourself in times of difficulty or failure; (2) acknowledging that all humans struggle, fail, and suffer; and (3) mindfully observing your experiences without getting caught up in them.

Self-compassion is the antithesis of perfectionism. When you subscribe to the notion of perfectionism, you buy into the illusion that you can be perfect and get everything right, even your recovery. Moreover, when you struggle to achieve the unattainable goal of perfectionism, you assume that there is something wrong with you. It is this romanticized rigidity that gets in the way of recovery rather than supporting it. Self-compassion makes space for your humanness, messiness, complications, and setbacks.

This past week, how many days did you do the following?

1. I was able to notice, without judgment, when I was struggling (e.g., falling short of my goals, not completing as much as I'd like).*
   0 = never (0 days)   1 = rarely (1 day)   2 = sometimes (2 to 3 days)   3 = often (4 to 5 days)   4 = regularly (6 to 7 days)

2. I harshly judged my progress and effort.
   4 = never (0 days)   3 = rarely (1 day)   2 = sometimes (2 to 3 days)   1 = often (4 to 5 days)   0 = regularly (6 to 7 days)

3. I kindly acknowledged my own challenges and difficulties.*
   0 = never (0 days)   1 = rarely (1 day)   2 = sometimes (2 to 3 days)   3 = often (4 to 5 days)   4 = regularly (6 to 7 days)

4. I engaged in critical or harsh self-talk (e.g., *I'm a failure. Why do I even try?*).
   4 = never (0 days)   3 = rarely (1 day)   2 = sometimes (2 to 3 days)   1 = often (4 to 5 days)   0 = regularly (6 to 7 days)

5. I engaged in supportive and comforting self-talk (e.g., *My effort is valuable and meaningful*).*
   0 = never (0 days)   1 = rarely (1 day)   2 = sometimes (2 to 3 days)   3 = often (4 to 5 days)   4 = regularly (6 to 7 days)

6. I reminded myself that failure and challenge are part of the human experience.*
   0 = never (0 days)   1 = rarely (1 day)   2 = sometimes (2 to 3 days)   3 = often (4 to 5 days)   4 = regularly (6 to 7 days)

7. I gave myself permission to feel my feelings (e.g., allowed myself to cry).*
   0 = never (0 days)   1 = rarely (1 day)   2 = sometimes (2 to 3 days)   3 = often (4 to 5 days)   4 = regularly (6 to 7 days)

Add up your responses for each of the 7 questions. This is your total raw score. Your total raw score for this section can range from 0 to 28.

Total raw score: _____

Next, divide your total raw score by 7 to get your subscale score. Your subscale score should be a number between 0 and 4.

Subscale score: _____

> The scoring key at the end of this chapter will help you interpret your scores.

Embodying Practice
Supportive Relationships Assessment

Supportive relationships can facilitate your healing journey and contribute to your well-being. A supportive relationship is reciprocal and loving and one in which you can set boundaries without reprisal. When you spend time with someone who truly cares about you and treats you with respect, your body feels at ease, you can laugh freely, and you do not feel self-conscious. The interaction feels genuine as opposed to contrived. You feel free to make mistakes and can talk openly about who you are without fear of rejection or criticism. In this manner, your relationships can support your well-being or become an obstacle to your mental and physical health, as well as to your recovery.

This past week, how many days did you do the following?

1. I spent time with people who support, encourage, and believe in me.*
   0 = never (0 days)   1 = rarely (1 day)   2 = sometimes (2 to 3 days)   3 = often (4 to 5 days)   4 = regularly (6 to 7 days)

2. I scheduled time in my week to be with people who are special to me.
   0 = never (0 days)   1 = rarely (1 day)   2 = sometimes (2 to 3 days)   3 = often (4 to 5 days)   4 = regularly (6 to 7 days)

3. I felt supported by the people in my life.*
   0 = never (0 days)   1 = rarely (1 day)   2 = sometimes (2 to 3 days)   3 = often (4 to 5 days)   4 = regularly (6 to 7 days)

4. I felt confident that the people in my life would respect my choice if I said no.*
   0 = never (0 days)   1 = rarely (1 day)   2 = sometimes (2 to 3 days)   3 = often (4 to 5 days)   4 = regularly (6 to 7 days)

5. I stood up for myself in relationships when I needed to.*
   0 = never (0 days)   1 = rarely (1 day)   2 = sometimes (2 to 3 days)   3 = often (4 to 5 days)   4 = regularly (6 to 7 days)

6. I made time for people who sustain and support me.
   0 = never (0 days)   1 = rarely (1 day)   2 = sometimes (2 to 3 days)   3 = often (4 to 5 days)   4 = regularly (6 to 7 days)

7. I felt that I had someone who would listen to me if I became upset (e.g., friend, counselor, group).*
   0 = never (0 days)   1 = rarely (1 day)   2 = sometimes (2 to 3 days)   3 = often (4 to 5 days)   4 = regularly (6 to 7 days)

Add up your responses for each of the 7 questions. This is your total raw score. Your total raw score for this section can range from 0 to 28.

Total raw score: _____

Next, divide your total raw score by 7 to get your subscale score. Your subscale score should be a number between 0 and 4.

> The scoring key at the end of this chapter will help you interpret your scores.

Subscale score: _____

Embodying Practice

Environmental Factors Assessment

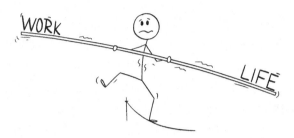

Environmental factors that affect your day-to-day life include your workspace, schedule, and overall life space. Although these factors are often overlooked when developing self-care, your physical environment can affect your well-being. The Chinese concept of feng shui is a great example of honoring the connection between your environment and well-being. In feng shui, the goal is to establish harmony between yourself and your environment. Just as it is in feng shui, well-being is supported when there is harmony and attunement between your inner and outer experiences. Thinking about your relationship with your environment and your schedule, consider what you might change to support your healing.

This past week, how many days did you do the following?

1. I maintained a manageable schedule.
    0 = never (0 days)   1 = rarely (1 day)   2 = sometimes (2 to 3 days)   3 = often (4 to 5 days)   4 = regularly (6 to 7 days)

2. I avoided taking on too many requests or demands.*
    0 = never (0 days)   1 = rarely (1 day)   2 = sometimes (2 to 3 days)   3 = often (4 to 5 days)   4 = regularly (6 to 7 days)

3. I maintained a comforting and pleasing living environment.*
    0 = never (0 days)   1 = rarely (1 day)   2 = sometimes (2 to 3 days)   3 = often (4 to 5 days)   4 = regularly (6 to 7 days)

4. I kept my work or school area organized to support my work or school tasks.*
    0 = never (0 days)   1 = rarely (1 day)   2 = sometimes (2 to 3 days)   3 = often (4 to 5 days)   4 = regularly (6 to 7 days)

5. I balanced other people's requests with what is important to me.*
    0 = never (0 days)   1 = rarely (1 day)   2 = sometimes (2 to 3 days)   3 = often (4 to 5 days)   4 = regularly (6 to 7 days)

6. I addressed any barriers to having a comfortable living environment (e.g., replaced light bulbs as needed, set the air at a comfortable temperature).
    0 = never (0 days)   1 = rarely (1 day)   2 = sometimes (2 to 3 days)   3 = often (4 to 5 days)   4 = regularly (6 to 7 days)

7. I made sure I wore suitable clothing for the weather (e.g., umbrella in the rain, boots in the snow, warm coat in winter).*
    0 = never (0 days)   1 = rarely (1 day)   2 = sometimes (2 to 3 days)   3 = often (4 to 5 days)   4 = regularly (6 to 7 days)

8. I took actions to make my everyday environment more pleasant (e.g., put a support on my chair, placed a meaningful photo on my desk).*

    0 = never (0 days)   1 = rarely (1 day)   2 = sometimes (2 to 3 days)   3 = often (4 to 5 days)   4 = regularly (6 to 7 days)

9. I took actions to make my work setting more enjoyable (e.g., planned fun Fridays, partnered with a coworker on an assignment).

    0 = never (0 days)   1 = rarely (1 day)   2 = sometimes (2 to 3 days)   3 = often (4 to 5 days)   4 = regularly (6 to 7 days)

Add up your responses for each of the 9 questions. This is your total raw score. Your total raw score for this section can range from 0 to 36.

Total raw score: _____

Next, divide your total raw score by 9 to get your subscale score. Your subscale score should be a number between 0 and 4.

The scoring key at the end of this chapter will help you interpret your scores.

Subscale score: _____

Spiritual Practice Assessment

Spirituality involves cultivating a relationship with something bigger than yourself. Some people find spirituality through their religion, community, or connection with nature. Regardless of its specific source, a spiritual practice can provide you with a mission and a sense of purpose. It helps you remember why you are doing what you do, why you matter, and why it is important to keep going even when things get hard. As you will explore more deeply in chapter 6, it can be very helpful to know your "why" when you are in the midst of difficult healing work.

This past week, how many days did you do the following?

1. I experienced meaning or a larger purpose in my work or school life.*
   0 = never (0 days)   1 = rarely (1 day)   2 = sometimes (2 to 3 days)   3 = often (4 to 5 days)   4 = regularly (6 to 7 days)

2. I experienced meaning or larger purpose in my personal life.*
   0 = never (0 days)   1 = rarely (1 day)   2 = sometimes (2 to 3 days)   3 = often (4 to 5 days)   4 = regularly (6 to 7 days)

3. I spent time in a spiritual place (e.g., church, meditation room, nature).
   0 = never (0 days)   1 = rarely (1 day)   2 = sometimes (2 to 3 days)   3 = often (4 to 5 days)   4 = regularly (6 to 7 days)

4. I read, watched, or listened to something inspirational (e.g., watched a video that gives me hope, read inspirational material, listened to spiritual music).
   0 = never (0 days)   1 = rarely (1 day)   2 = sometimes (2 to 3 days)   3 = often (4 to 5 days)   4 = regularly (6 to 7 days)

5. I spent time with others who share my spiritual worldview (e.g., church community, volunteer group).
   0 = never (0 days)   1 = rarely (1 day)   2 = sometimes (2 to 3 days)   3 = often (4 to 5 days)   4 = regularly (6 to 7 days)

6. I spent time doing something that I hope will make a positive difference in the world (e.g., volunteered at a soup kitchen, took time out for someone else).
   0 = never (0 days)   1 = rarely (1 day)   2 = sometimes (2 to 3 days)   3 = often (4 to 5 days)   4 = regularly (6 to 7 days)

Add up your responses for each of the 6 questions. This is your total raw score. Your total raw score for this section can range from 0 to 24.

Total raw score: _____

Next, divide your total raw score by 6 to get your subscale score. Your subscale score should be a number between 0 and 4.

Subscale score: _____

> The scoring key at the end of this chapter will help you interpret your scores.

—Embodying Practice—

Self-Awareness and Mindfulness Assessment

Being self-aware, also known as being mindful, is an essential and unique feature of being able to practice self-care in a thoughtful and attuned way. Jon Kabat-Zinn (1994), a pioneer in the field of mindfulness, defines mindfulness as the ability to pay attention right now, with intention and without judgment. Essentially, mindfulness is about turning your awareness to the present moment—to what is going on right here, right now—and being with the experience without trying to change it in any way.

Kabat-Zinn (2012) often explains that you should be practicing mindfulness "as if your life depends on it" (p. 17)—because it does. The benefits of mindfulness are far-reaching, as it not only supports mental clarity and cognitive functioning but also promotes better sleep, enhances mood, reduces stress, and supports immune system health. Mindfulness is serious business. Not only will cultivating mindfulness serve you well on your healing journey, but it can be a defining factor in creating the life you deserve.

This past week, how many days did you do the following?

1. I had a calm awareness of my thoughts.*
   0 = never (0 days)   1 = rarely (1 day)   2 = sometimes (2 to 3 days)   3 = often (4 to 5 days)   4 = regularly (6 to 7 days)

2. I had a calm awareness of my feelings.*
   0 = never (0 days)   1 = rarely (1 day)   2 = sometimes (2 to 3 days)   3 = often (4 to 5 days)   4 = regularly (6 to 7 days)

3. I had a calm awareness of my body.*
   0 = never (0 days)   1 = rarely (1 day)   2 = sometimes (2 to 3 days)   3 = often (4 to 5 days)   4 = regularly (6 to 7 days)

4. I carefully selected which thoughts and feelings I used to guide my actions.*
   0 = never (0 days)   1 = rarely (1 day)   2 = sometimes (2 to 3 days)   3 = often (4 to 5 days)   4 = regularly (6 to 7 days)

5. I meditated in some form (e.g., sitting meditation, walking meditation, prayer).
   0 = never (0 days)   1 = rarely (1 day)   2 = sometimes (2 to 3 days)   3 = often (4 to 5 days)   4 = regularly (6 to 7 days)

6. I practiced mindful eating (e.g., paid attention to the taste and texture of the food, ate without distraction).*
   0 = never (0 days)   1 = rarely (1 day)   2 = sometimes (2 to 3 days)   3 = often (4 to 5 days)   4 = regularly (6 to 7 days)

7. I practiced yoga or another mind-body practice (e.g., taekwondo, tai chi).
   0 = never (0 days)   1 = rarely (1 day)   2 = sometimes (2 to 3 days)   3 = often (4 to 5 days)   4 = regularly (6 to 7 days)

8. I tracked my self-care practices (e.g., journaling, used an app, kept a calendar).
   0 = never (0 days)   1 = rarely (1 day)   2 = sometimes (2 to 3 days)   3 = often (4 to 5 days)   4 = regularly (6 to 7 days)

9. I scheduled a meditation or mindful practice for the day (e.g., yoga, walking meditation, prayer).

   0 = never (0 days)   1 = rarely (1 day)   2 = sometimes (2 to 3 days)   3 = often (4 to 5 days)   4 = regularly (6 to 7 days)

10. I took time to acknowledge the things for which I am grateful.

   0 = never (0 days)   1 = rarely (1 day)   2 = sometimes (2 to 3 days)   3 = often (4 to 5 days)   4 = regularly (6 to 7 days)

Add up your responses for each of the 10 questions. This is your total raw score. Your total raw score for this section can range from 0 to 40.

Total raw score: _____

Next, divide your total raw score by 10 to get your subscale score. Your subscale score should be a number between 0 and 4.

> The scoring key at the end of this chapter will help you interpret your scores.

Subscale score: _____

General Maintenance Self-Care Assessment

There are three final questions critical to the development of your mindful self-care practice that address variety, planning, and exploration. Mindful self-care is powerful when it gives your body something it can count on, when it is planned, and when it takes uncertainty out of the question *Will I take care of or hurt myself today?* For your body, routinely engaging in self-care allows you to turn off protection mode and turn on connection mode. You give your body a sense of safety and support with each mindful self-care act you engage in and plan.

This past week, how many days did you do the following?

1. I engaged in a variety of self-care strategies (e.g., mindfulness, supportive relationships, exercise, nutrition, spirituality).
    0 = never (0 days)   1 = rarely (1 day)   2 = sometimes (2 to 3 days)   3 = often (4 to 5 days)   4 = regularly (6 to 7 days)

2. I planned my self-care practices.
    0 = never (0 days)   1 = rarely (1 day)   2 = sometimes (2 to 3 days)   3 = often (4 to 5 days)   4 = regularly (6 to 7 days)

3. I explored new ways to bring self-care into my life.
    0 = never (0 days)   1 = rarely (1 day)   2 = sometimes (2 to 3 days)   3 = often (4 to 5 days)   4 = regularly (6 to 7 days)

For these general questions, there is no need to sum or average your score. These questions are merely intended to help you get a more global understanding of how you actively plan for and consider new ways to engage in self-care. In the next section, you will learn how to set goals that help you bring more self-care into your life.

PAUSE

(**P** - Pause, **A** - Assess → **USE** your resources and supports)

☐ **Pause**, check in, and acknowledge how you are feeling. This is a chance to be kind to yourself. The pace of your work is very important. Press your feet into the earth and take four gentle breaths.

☐ **Assess** by asking yourself, *Is this a good place for a break?* If the answer is *yes* or *I don't know*, then fold over the corner of the page and take a break. This workbook is here for you for as long as it takes and for as many breaks as you need.

☐ **USE** your resources. Take a rest. Connect to your trusted friends. Contact your therapist. Practice your favorite well-being strategies. Get back to work when YOU are ready.

Need-to-Know: Developing Your Mindful Self-Care Plan

Now it is time to collect your scores and develop your self-care plan. The following steps will help you review your current levels of self-care, assess areas in which you can take action, and develop a reasonable plan. Consider subscale scores of 1 or 2 to be actionable, meaning these are areas where you need to take some action. However, many people with subscale scores of 2 or 3 still like to explore how they can diversify or strengthen their self-care in each area.

Over the past five years, my research team has collected data from thousands of participants and developed these general guidelines for interpretation. The goal is not to be perfect but to have a large variety of mindful self-care actions that you engage in on a regular basis.

Subscale Score Range	Score	Take Action?
0 to 1.5	Low	Yes
1.6 to 2.5	Moderate	Yes
2.6 to 4.0	High	Optional

Step 1: Get your scores all in one place. Flip back through your responses to each of the mindful self-care assessments, and write your score for each of the subscales. Then indicate whether your score indicates that you need to take action in that area to enhance your self-care routine.

Domain	Subscale Score	Take Action?
Nutrition and Hydration	Score: _____	Yes or No
Exercise	Score: _____	Yes or No
Rest	Score: _____	Yes or No

Domain	Subscale Score	Take Action?
Physical and Medical Care	Score: _____	Yes or No
Self-Soothing	Score: _____	Yes or No
Self-Compassion	Score: _____	Yes or No
Supportive Relationships	Score: _____	Yes or No
Environmental Factors	Score: _____	Yes or No
Spiritual Practice	Score: _____	Yes or No
Self-Awareness and Mindfulness	Score: _____	Yes or No

Step 2: Acknowledge your strengths. These are the domains where you have the highest averages. For example, perhaps you notice that you have mostly 0s, 1s, and 2s across several of the subscales, but you have a 3 or 4 in the area of supportive relationships. Write the names of your strengths in mindful self-care here.

_____

_____

_____

Step 3: Name your areas for growth. These are the domains where your average score is below 3. If you have no scores under 3, list your lowest scores here.

_____

_____

_____

Step 4: Circle one or two domains of mindful self-care that you want to target first.

Step 5: Within each domain, review specific areas that you can target for growth. Are there items that look like a good place to start? It can be helpful to look back over your responses to specific items. Choose one or two items from each domain and rework them into concrete goals. For example, if you are targeting Self-Awareness and Mindfulness and you circled a 1 for the question "I meditated in some form (e.g., sitting meditation, walking meditation, prayer)," you could reword it as the following goal: "Each day I will complete a guided meditation for five minutes before work or school."

_____

_____

_____

Step 6: For some of your goals, you might need to spell out specific details to increase your chances of success. For example, if your goal is to meditate each morning, your plans might include looking for a meditation app and downloading it. (Insight Timer is great option that has a lot of free content. I am even on there!) You might also make it a priority to create, or spruce up, your sanctuary spot for your practice. Or if your plan is to do yoga a few times a week, your plans might include checking out studio schedules and pricing, then going with a friend. Identify at least three goals that need accompanying plans:

Goal #1 (with plans)

_____

_____

_____

Goal #2 (with plans)

_____

_____

_____

Goal #3 (with plans)

_____

_____

_____

Now you are ready to dive into your mindful self-care practice. You only need to try. There is no need for daily perfection or 100 percent success. Just get out there and try. I was working with a yoga student, Jessalyn, who was struggling to meditate as a daily practice. After setting extraordinarily high goals, like meditating for 20 minutes a day, she crashed and burned after three days. She then began with a more moderate goal of meditating for 2 minutes three times a week—specifically on days when she had space in her morning routine to pause and sit for a moment. Her practice grew from there because she allowed it to be small enough to feel accessible and good. Consider that this is not a chore to prove that you are good enough; it is fuel for your life force, your well-being, and your happiness.

Mindful self-care is a foundational practice that will serve you well in life beyond simply allowing you to process your trauma. It is a lifelong practice that will support you in healing and also in flourishing. I encourage you to revisit this chapter periodically and to retake the self-care assessment to see how you are doing over time. If you would like an electric version of the assessment, you can find one at www.catherinecookcottone.com. Don't put self-care off until you feel better. Know that it *is* the pathway to feeling better. If it feels too big, start small like Jessalyn—doing just one small thing a day—and remember that you are worth the effort.

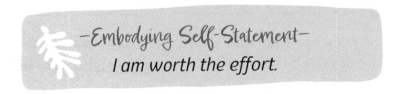

—Embodying Self-Statement—
I am worth the effort.

Chapter 5

Developing Your Resources

If you have experienced trauma, you may unconsciously hold your body in a very tense, constricted manner. In this state, your body is always on the edge of the window of tolerance, ready to move into a state of fight, flight, freeze, or shutdown. Even though the trauma is over, your body is overfunctioning as your *inner protector*. It is trying to shield you from future harm by arming up with a shield of muscular tension you can use whenever the need arises.

You might not realize how hard your body is working to protect you unless you use your sense of interoception to mindfully check in with yourself. In doing so, you may notice a constant clenching of your jaw, a chronic furrowing of your brow, or a sustained elevation of your shoulders and tightness through your neck. Maybe your legs are always engaged as you wrap one around one another in a tense hold. Maybe your feet are always gripping the floor instead of softening while sitting. Maybe your hands always maintain a tight grip on the steering wheel while driving. As your protector, your body is functioning as if it is chronically faced with a threat, ready to advance into fight or flight at any moment.

It is important to know that your body is not wrong for doing this. As your body's partner and friend, you want to make sure your body knows this too. Resist the urge to vilify your body for trying so hard to protect you. Your body is like a good friend; it was right there when you got hurt, and it is working very hard to make sure you do not get hurt again.

When your body is in protection mode, simply directing it to stop can feel threatening and result in the exact opposite. This is the time and place to offer gentle encouragement and to move at the speed of trust. Instead of trying to force your body out of protection mode, it is important to learn how to *pendulate*: to alternate between focusing on the memories, feelings, and sensations associated with the trauma and focusing on your resources of safety in the present moment. This process, which is used within the field of somatic experiencing, is based on your body's natural ability to recover from trauma (Grabbe & Miller-Karas, 2018; Levine, 2010b). With pendulation, you can create a shift where you start seeing your body not just as a battlefield of discomfort and pain but also as a growing reservoir of strength and calm. This happens over time.

Pendulation

Connecting with painful and traumatic experiences of the past

↕

Connecting to your inner and outer resources in the present

In this chapter, you will explore neutral, calming, and nurturing places to which you can pendulate. In particular, I will guide you through a systematic relaxation process, help you develop inner and outer resources, and then help you practice accessing these resources to create a deep reservoir of strength and calm. The goal is to invite your body to trust you and the world again, but that is a big ask. So it is important to be kind, to be patient, and to practice.

—Embodying Practice—
Letter to Your Inner Protector

In the box below, write a short letter to your body as your inner protector. You can acknowledge the work that this inner protector has done, express your gratitude, and give it permission to take a break. You might tell your inner protector that you are doing a lot of work to learn how to take care of yourself and to process what has happened to you. Let it know that you will be working to develop resources and skills so that it won't have to work so hard. You might also tell your protector that it needs to set aside its defense system from time to time so you can work with your memories, sensations, feelings, and thoughts. Remind your protector that you are going to work very hard to stay within your window of tolerance and keep this work manageable. Feel free to add anything else to this letter, but remember to be loving and kind.

Dear Inner Protector,

Love,
Me

—Embodying Practice—
Progressive Muscle Relaxation

Progressive muscle relaxation is a practice that helps you notice any tension you are holding in your body and then guides you through a gentle practice of releasing it. You can do this practice after a difficult therapy session, whenever you feel tense, to assess if you are holding tension, or when trying to fall asleep. If you'd like, it can be helpful to create a recording of this practice on your phone so you can relax and listen to your own voice taking you through the steps. This can also help develop your calm and supportive inner voice.

To begin, find a place where you feel safe and won't be interrupted. You can either lie down or sit in a chair. If you are feeling very unsafe, orient yourself near a wall and face the entrance to the room. Scan the room, and only when you are ready, soften or close your eyes. Allow your breath to move naturally in and out as you briefly scan your whole body from your head to your toes. In a gentle and curious manner, you might ask yourself, *Am I holding tension or stress?* as you scan your body. Breathe gently, allowing the question to orient you toward your body and any tension you may have.

Now, bring your awareness to your feet. Curl your toes and contract the muscles in your feet, scrunching them up as if you can make them smaller than they are. Hold this for 1, 2, 3, 4, 5 . . . then release your feet, letting go of any tension. Breathe here for three to five breath cycles, inhaling and exhaling. With each exhale, release a little more tension in your feet. Maybe you even think to yourself, *It's okay to let go.*

Next, engage your ankles by flexing your feet. Let your calves engage too, tensing everything from your knees down. If your toes want to join in, let them. Keep breathing while you engage your ankles, calves, and shins. Hold this tension for 1, 2, 3, 4, 5 . . . then release your ankles, calves, and shins, letting the tension go. Breathe here for three to five deep breath cycles, inhaling and exhaling. Notice the difference between holding tension and letting go. With every exhale, see if you can let go a little more. There is no pressure to let go. You can simply give your body permission to let go if it would like.

Now, engage your entire legs, from your feet through your glutes, drawing your muscles toward your bones. Keep breathing and tensing your legs and hips. Hold this tension for 1, 2, 3, 4, 5 . . . then release your legs and hips, letting the tension go. Breathe here for three to five deep breath cycles, inhaling and exhaling. Notice the difference between holding tension and letting go. With every exhale, see if you can let go a little more. You might offer your legs permission to let go, saying softly to yourself, *It's okay to let go.*

Bring your awareness to your core. Engage the muscles in your belly and back into a whole-core contraction. It's okay if your legs, shoulders, and even jaw also engage. But your focus is on your core. Draw everything into the center of yourself. Hold this tension for 1, 2, 3, 4, 5 . . . then release your core. Soften your body and breathe. Take five breath cycles here, letting each inhale lift your belly and each exhale lower your belly. Pause here and notice the difference between tension and letting go.

Next, bring your awareness to your shoulders, arms, and hands. Scrunch your shoulders up to your ears, clench your hands into fists, and engage your biceps by bending your elbows and upper arms toward your body. Keep breathing as you squeeze your hands, arms, and shoulders. Hold this tension for 1, 2, 3, 4, 5 . . . then release your shoulders, arms, and hands. Take five breath cycles here, letting your arms and hands rest on the floor or on your thighs, and allowing your shoulders to soften and move away from your ears.

Last, scrunch your face into itself. Close your eyes really tight, furrow your forehead, squeeze your jaw shut, purse your lips, and scrunch your cheeks. Keep breathing as you hold this tension for 1, 2, 3, 4, 5 . . . then release as you soften your jaw, mouth, eyes, cheeks, and forehead. Take 10 deep breath cycles, noticing how your body feels now. On every exhale, think of the word *release*.

When you are finished, you may want to journal about what you noticed. Did you notice any tension in certain areas of the body? Was it easier or more difficult to tense versus release in certain areas? Were there areas in which it was difficult to feel at all? What about the practice felt most helpful? How do you feel after practicing the first time, a few times, many times?

—Embodying Self-Statement—
I can connect to my body to relax and release.

Need-to-Know: Developing Your Inner Resources

An inner resource is anything within yourself that helps you feel empowered and in control of your life. You can think of it as a "place of refuge" that exists within you, supporting you as you traverse the pathway to healing (Miller, 2015, p. 53).

The next set of practices will walk you through the steps of creating your own personalized inner resource. This process includes remembering or imagining a safe place, developing a real or imagined protector, cultivating a felt sense of safety in your body, and identifying additional external resources (e.g., a ring, bracelet, or stone you carry with you) that will serve as material reminders of your inner resources.

Once you develop this inner resource, I will guide you through a yoga nidra practice intended to deepen your connection with this resource. This will prepare you for the final practice, pendulation, in which you practice using your inner resource to move back and forth between difficult memories, sensations, feelings, and thoughts as they show up.

By developing this place of refuge, you'll find that you can increasingly relax your body and seek comfort within yourself. When you realize that your comfort zone is accessible from the inside, this represents a powerful shift in your healing. It means when you are stressed or overwhelmed, you know you can ground, breathe, and turn inward for further sources of comfort.

—Embodying Self-Statement—
I have within me an inner resource of strength and calm.

Embodying Practice
Developing Your Inner Resources

Your Inner Refuge

Begin by imagining a place where you feel completely safe and content. It can be anywhere you want, real or imagined. This will be your inner refuge—a place you can call to mind whenever you need. Let go of any rigid expectations you have for this place. Let it be whatever you need it to be. Consider using your sense of interoception (inside listening), exteroception (outside listening), and neuroception (safety/danger listening) to help develop what you need in your inner refuge.

Where would you like your inner refuge to be? Is it far away or nearby? Is it inside or outside? Is it at the ocean, on a mountain, in a valley, or simply in a spot in your house? Would you like certain objects there? A certain blanket, meditation bench, garden, small waterfall, certain type of tree, swing? You can have anything you'd like or need here.

Use your senses to imagine what you would experience here. What sights do you see? Do you notice the stars, moon, sun, water, snow, or rain? Or is your place inside, with walls made of stone or wooden logs? What sounds do you notice? Do you hear the waves of the ocean, birds singing, a gentle melody playing in the background, or a loved one's voice? What does it smell like there? Do you sense the scent of lavender, fresh air, chamomile, or honey? What do you feel through your skin? Do you notice the wind, stillness, coolness, or warmth?

Describe your inner refuge here. Take your time as you bring detail into your image. You can use words, draw, or do both—whichever feels right for you.

Your Protector

Now create a protector who protects you and this inner refuge. With a protector out there, your body can release tension, soften defenses, and breathe more easily. I imagine mine as a great blue heron that flies overhead as I am meditating. She is strong and fierce and can see for miles as she circles my house.

Your protector can be anything real or imagined. If your inner refuge is a place in the mountains, perhaps your protector is a courageous bear or the mountains themselves. Perhaps it is a giant powerful crystal that keeps away all threatening things. Maybe it is a protective and powerful dragon. Maybe it is someone from your past who watches over you. Maybe it is an angel or the God of your understanding. What is it about your protector that helps you feel safe? Is it strong, big, wise, and comforting?

Describe your protector here. You can use words, draw, or do both—whichever feels right for you.

Your Body

Now use your sense of interoception to notice what you feel in your body when you imagine going to your inner refuge and being kept safe by your protector. Are there any sensations that arise? A warm glow from the inside? A stillness? A warmth, buzzing, or radiating feeling around your heart? Do you notice a release of tension as your body begins to feel safe enough to let go?

Now bring your awareness to your emotions. What does it feel like to be in this space? Do you feel comforted, loving, compassionate, grateful, neutral, or even a little scared considering the possibility of feeling okay? All feelings are welcome and can be held here. Perhaps you feel like you can let your anger free or feel safe enough to let love in. It is also okay to not know what you feel or to feel nothing.

Finally, use your sense of neuroception to tap into the safety or danger you feel as you imagine being in this place with your protector. Do you feel a little safer, happier, or at ease? Or is this sense of security more like a small seed that might grow into something? Consider, too, whether you feel clear, grounded, open, well, flowing, stable, steady, or still.

Describe the sensations and feelings you notice when you think of your safe place and protector, making sure to note where they are in your body. You can use words, draw, or do both—whichever feels right for you.

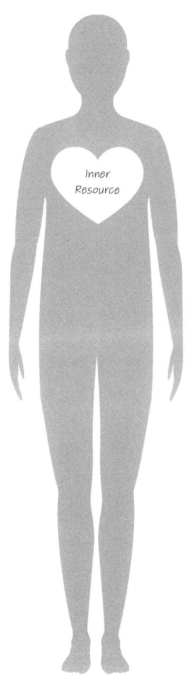

Inner Resource

Your Symbol

Next, develop a simple symbol that can bring your protector and inner refuge to mind. This symbol is an additional resource that can serve as a sort of access point, or a gateway.

If your inner refuge is a beach and your protector is a seagull, maybe your symbol is a jar of sand. If your inner refuge is in the mountains and your protector is a bear, perhaps your symbol is the shape of a mountain, tree, or bear paw print. If your safe place is your room and God is keeping you safe, maybe your symbol is the mantra "I am protected and loved."

My symbol is the lotus flower. It reminds me of the saying "No mud, no lotus." The lotus flower grows from the muddy bottom of the pond, toward the light. This reminds me of my resilience and my resources that have gotten me this far.

What might symbolize your journey, protector, and inner refuge for you? You can use words, draw, or do both—whichever feels right for you.

Your Talisman

A talisman is an object you can wear or keep with you. Like your symbol, it reminds you of your inner resources when you feel triggered, tired, or lost. In this way, it can also serve as an additional grounding tool.

Almost anything will work as a talisman. For people working on their sobriety, their 30-day or 1-year chip from Alcoholics Anonymous can be a powerful talisman. Others like to wear a specific bracelet, perhaps with something engraved, to remind them of their resources. I had a friend who wore a string around his wrist, a practice he learned in India. I have a bracelet with my grounding mantra etched on its surface. I have also worked with patients who got a tattoo of their protector on their wrist or bought a special crystal to wear as a pendant. It works best if it is something you can easily have with you all of the time.

Describe what you think you might use as your talisman here.

[Empty response box]

PAUSE

(**P** - Pause, **A** - Assess → **USE** your resources and supports)

☐ <u>P</u>ause, check in, and acknowledge how you are feeling. This is a chance to be kind to yourself. The pace of your work is very important. Press your feet into the earth and take four gentle breaths.

☐ <u>A</u>ssess by asking yourself, *Is this a good place for a break?* If the answer is *yes* or *I don't know*, then fold over the corner of the page and take a break. This workbook is here for you for as long as it takes and for as many breaks as you need.

☐ <u>USE</u> your resources. Take a rest. Connect to your trusted friends. Contact your therapist. Practice your favorite well-being strategies. Get back to work when YOU are ready.

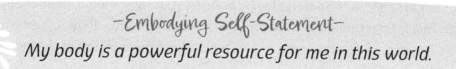

–Embodying Self-Statement–
My body is a powerful resource for me in this world.

—Embodying Practice—
Yoga Nidra

For this exercise, you will be practicing yoga nidra, which is also known as the yoga of sleep (Dinsmore-Tuli, 2021). This deeply relaxing meditative technique will allow you to connect to your inner resources, deepen your sense of self, and facilitate open awareness. Before you get started, take some time to consider the right place to practice. Find a comfortable and secure place you can retreat to for about 30 minutes without being disturbed.

Then create an intention for your practice. It can be something like *I practice so I know how to find my inner resources when I need them, My body is a powerful resource for me in this world*, or *I am open to peaceful, calm awareness*. It can be whatever you'd like. Keep it in mind, as there will be sections of the practice in which you will be asked to recall it. You may also want to bring your talisman with you, if it is a material object. Perhaps consider placing it next to you or wearing it as you practice.

When you're ready, lie on your back, with your palms facing up and your feet wide, orienting yourself so that you can see the door if you feel you need to. Use any props or supports you need to feel comfortable. Then gently soften or close your eyes.

Resolution and Permission

Take a moment here to reflect on your intention. Say it to yourself three times, pausing to breathe between each repetition. Next, give yourself permission to pause or stop this practice as needed. Be open to allowing calm awareness.

If you notice any difficulties or challenges arise as you continue with this practice, consider staying with it, as this will help you get practice staying in the growth zone. Allow your body to pendulate between being in the growth zone and in the comfort zone. However, if at any time you'd like to pause or stop, do so. Your sense of safety, agency, and empowerment comes first. If you notice any physical discomfort, first sit with it and see if it passes. If you'd like, pause and make an adjustment.

Body Scan

Now you are going to do a body scan, which is a practice of welcoming and loving yourself. This practice will involve briefly attending to various parts of your body. Simply allow your mind to follow my words, bringing your awareness to the body part being named. There is no need to move that part of your body, just bring your awareness to it. This will take some degree of alertness. See if you can find a balance between following the body scan and relaxing.

To begin, bring your awareness to your right side, noticing your right thumb, pointer finger, middle finger, ring finger, pinky finger, palm, back of your hand, wrist, forearm, elbow, upper arm, shoulder, underarm, waist, hip, thigh, knee, lower leg, ankle, heel, sole of the foot, top of the foot, big toe, second toe, third toe, fourth toe, baby toe.

Now, bring your awareness to your left side, noticing your left thumb, pointer finger, middle finger, ring finger, pinky finger, palm, back of your hand, wrist, forearm, elbow, upper arm, shoulder, underarm, waist, hip, thigh, knee, lower leg, ankle, heel, sole of the left foot, top of the left foot, big toe, second toe, third toe, fourth toe, baby toe.

Next, bring your awareness to the back of your body. Notice your right shoulder blade, left shoulder blade, right hips and glutes, left hips and glutes, your entire spine, and back.

Then, bring your awareness to the front of your body and then to the very top of your head. Notice your right temple, left temple, right eyebrow, left eyebrow, the place between your two eyebrows, right eyelid, left eyelid, right cheek, left cheek, right nostril, left nostril, upper lip, lower lip, chin, throat, right side of your chest, left side of your chest, the center of your chest, and over your heart. Notice your navel, belly, pelvis, and pelvic floor. Notice your entire right leg, then left leg, and become aware of both of your legs.

Now, notice your whole body and its connection to the floor, the earth below you. You are awake and aware, noticing your entire body resting, calm, relaxed, and softening with each breath. Bring to mind your whole body resting safely and relaxed on the earth. There is the possibility of open awareness in allowing any sensations that arise.

Pairs of Opposites

Now you are going to practice pairs of opposites. Your body, feelings, and experiences often have two sides. These opposites can both be held at the same time. Begin paying attention to your breath. Take a deep breath in, pausing your breath at the top of the inhalation and bringing awareness to the left side of your body. Then release and exhale, welcoming sensations through the left side of your body. Once more, bring your awareness to your breath, and at the top of the inhalation, pause and bring your awareness to the right side of your body. Then as you exhale, notice sensations through the right side of your body.

On your next breath, inhale as if you are breathing up the length of the left side of your body. Moving to the right side, exhale as if you could breathe down the length of the right side of your body. Then switching, inhale right side and exhale left. And back to inhale left and exhale right. Inhale right, exhale left. Then repeat one more time.

Breathe. When you are ready, take a pause in your breathing at the top of the next inhalation. Notice your entire body—all the parts at the same time—and then exhale, allowing your breath to return to its natural breathing pattern. Breathe here for several breaths, considering the words *welcoming* and *loving-kindness*.

Connection with Breath and Body

Now, bring focus back to your breath. On your next inhale, breathe in for a count of 1, 2, 3, 4 . . . then hold for 1, 2, 3, 4, 5 . . . and exhale for 1, 2, 3, 4, 5, 6. Repeat this four times.

Breathe in for a count of 1, 2, 3, 4 . . . hold for 1, 2, 3, 4, 5 . . . and exhale 1, 2, 3, 4, 5, 6.
Breathe in for a count of 1, 2, 3, 4 . . . hold for 1, 2, 3, 4, 5 . . . and exhale 1, 2, 3, 4, 5, 6.
Breathe in for a count of 1, 2, 3, 4 . . . hold for 1, 2, 3, 4, 5 . . . and exhale 1, 2, 3, 4, 5, 6.
Breathe in for a count of 1, 2, 3, 4 . . . hold for 1, 2, 3, 4, 5 . . . and exhale 1, 2, 3, 4, 5, 6.

Then return to your regular breathing pattern and settle into your body. Notice where your body connects to the earth below you. Consider that the earth is a steady, supportive foundation for your body. You can settle here. Notice the back of your head resting on the earth below you. Notice your feet, legs, back, shoulders, hips, hands, and arms. Remember, you can settle here.

Visualization of Your Inner Resources

It's time to bring your inner resources to mind. Give yourself permission to feel the safety of your refuge and your protector. Give yourself permission to feel safe and openly aware. If you have your talisman near you, you might want to hold it in one hand. Then begin by bringing your protector to mind. What does your protector look like? How does it sound? How does it move? How does it feel for your protector to be here? Breathe here, considering the word *protected*.

Now, bring to mind your inner refuge. Recall where it is and all of its elements, including any sights, sounds, textures, or scents from this place. Notice in your body where you feel these sensory experiences, and if it feels okay, invite these sensations in. How does it feel to imagine your inner refuge? Breathe here and consider the word *refuge*.

Then, connect back to the sensation of the earth below you. Recall that the earth is a steady, supportive foundation for your body. You can settle here. Again, notice the back of your head on the earth below you. Notice your feet, legs, back, shoulders, hips, hands, and arms. You are well supported here. Open awareness is possible.

Take a final moment to recall your inner refuge and your protector, including the feelings associated with them, and the sense of calm and peace that resides in your body. Consider that your body can be a resource, a growing reservoir of peace and calm.

Resolution

As you get ready to end your practice, take a moment to reflect on your intention. Say it to yourself three times, pausing to breathe between each repetition.

Now, imagine yourself going about your daily life, noticing any changing sensations, emotions, and thoughts as they arise and pass throughout your day. At the same time, bring to mind the steady calmness and centeredness that is also present within you, as symbolized by your inner resources. Bring awareness to your whole body, considering that your body can experience both your day-to-day experiences and the calm foundation of your inner resources.

Reentry

Your body has the capacity to relax, to open, to soften. As you breathe, know that each moment you spend with your inner resources is helping you create a reservoir of relaxation and calm that can resource you whenever you are stressed, triggered, or simply wanting to relax. This feeling is yours and yours uniquely to draw upon whenever you need it.

It is time to slowly come back to this moment. Take your time to slowly transition to an alert and awakened state. Sense your body and the room around you. Maybe you'd like to wiggle your fingers and toes or turn your ankles and wrists. Place your feet on the floor, bend your knees if it feels good, and slowly rock your knees from side to side. Gently open your eyes as you feel ready. Reorient to where you are.

Before ending your practice, take a moment to offer gratitude to yourself for taking the time to open yourself up to a sense of welcoming, loving-kindness, safety, protection, or support during this practice. If you'd like, take time to journal about your experience.

Embodying Practice
Pendulation

This pendulation practice is a wonderful resource for managing difficult memories, sensations, emotions, or reactions as they show up. The next time these difficult experiences arise, follow these steps.

Pause and find your breath. Sit or lie down in a way that feels grounded and well supported. Then bring your awareness to your body and notice where you feel the difficult memories, sensations, emotions, or reactions the strongest. Notice the intensity, size, and boundaries of this location in your body. Where does it end? Where are its edges? Then breathe gently and intentionally—breathing in for 1, 2, 3, 4 . . . and out for 1, 2, 3, 4, 5—as you notice this area of your body. Spend about four breath cycles here.

Now, scan your body and find a spot that feels neutral. It might be a toe, your hands, or the crown of your head. If you don't think you have a neutral spot, consider the area right outside of your body, whether it's one inch around your body, six inches around your body, a foot around your body, or two feet around your body. Notice where you begin to feel a neutral space. Bring your awareness to this neutral space, wherever it is. Breathe here for about four breath cycles— breathing in for 1, 2, 3, 4 . . . and out for 1, 2, 3, 4, 5.

Next, move back to the place where you felt the difficult memories, sensations, emotions, or reactions the strongest. Breathe here for about four breath cycles, breathing in for 1, 2, 3, 4 . . . and out for 1, 2, 3, 4, 5. Then pendulate back to your neutral space. Breathe here for about four breath cycles, breathing in for 1, 2, 3, 4 . . . and out for 1, 2, 3, 4, 5. Do this a few times, pendulating from one spot to the other.

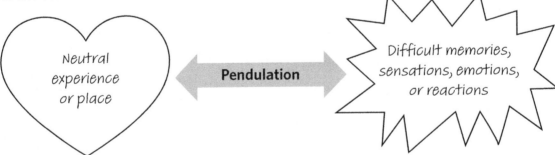

Last, bring your awareness to the place in your body where you felt these memories, sensations, emotions, or reactions most strongly and *simultaneously* hold an awareness of the neutral place in your body. Breathe while you hold this dual awareness of both places for about four breath cycles, breathing in 1, 2, 3, 4 . . . and out 1, 2, 3, 4, 5.

In your journal or in the space below, write what you noticed during this practice. You can describe the place where you felt memories, sensations, emotions, or reactions the strongest; describe your neutral place; reflect on the process of pendulating itself; or describe what it was like to hold both places within your awareness.

With your resources established, you are ready to move on to the next chapter, which reviews the steadying power of your sense of meaning or purpose. However, know that things can change over time. A resource that works for you now may not work in the future, so revisit this chapter to reinforce your inner resources or rework them as needed.

Chapter 6

The Steadying Power of Your Embodied "Why"

—Embodying Self-Statement—
My life has meaning.

What is your embodied "why"? Your answer lies in your sense of purpose. You may have known its mission since you were six years old. It's something you may have wondered about for half of your life. Your embodied "why" can be one clear thing or it can be many things. Either way, it is the driver behind your passion and creativity. It keeps you going when it feels like you can't. It is how you answer questions like *Why am I here? What is my purpose?* and *What is my reason for being?* Some people call this your heartfelt mission (Miller, 2015). Others may refer to it as dharma, or the fulfillment of your purpose. Either way, your "why" is what stirs your heart and is most certainly something bigger than you and your own self-interest.

This chapter will take you through the process of exploring your "why"—your reason for being. This process begins with thinking a bit about how you might clarify your "why." First, you will complete some work to clarify your values and explore how you find meaning. Next, you will imagine yourself being filled with meaning five years in the future. This will be done using a vision board and free writing. Finally, you will clarify your reason for being and develop a mission statement. There are several activities and a lot to process in this chapter. I encourage you to take on one (or part of one) activity at a time and then practice what you learn until it feels internalized.

Need-to-Know: Finding Meaning

The ability to find meaning in life is an important factor in developing resilience, which reflects your capacity to overcome hardship and persevere in the face of difficulty. In fact, research has found that when you have a greater understanding of your meaning in life, it can provide a buffering effect in the face of traumatic events and facilitate adaptive coping (Fisher, 2021), making it a critical aspect of trauma recovery.

In addition to being protective in the face of trauma, your "why" also contributes to a part of recovery that I like to call *mindful grit* (Cook-Cottone, 2020). Whereas the term *grit* reflects your ability to set goals and persist, mindful grit is about remembering why you set goals in the first place and why you should persist with love and self-compassion. Your embodied "why" is the driving power behind your mindful grit. Tapping into your mindful grit will be important in the next chapter, where you will begin to directly be with and work with your sensations and feelings. As part of this process, you may begin to move outside of your comfort zone and into the growth zone. You will be cycling through periods of great effort and great rest. Sometimes it will be difficult. It is during those most difficult times when it will be especially helpful for you to remember why you should keep going—what all this work is for.

Human beings are inherently meaning driven. This is why some of you reading this book might already know exactly what your "why" is. For you it is crystal clear, and you might wonder why this chapter is in this book at all. (Note: I still think this chapter is worth a go, no matter how sure you are of your mission and purpose.) However, some of you might be unfamiliar with your "why," have forgotten your "why," or have encountered trauma that seems to have stripped any notion of a "why" away. For you, this chapter is a step toward living the question: *What is my "why"?*

What does it mean to "live" a question? It means that you might not know the answer right now and that it's okay to spend some time, maybe a lot of time, wondering. As the Austrian poet Rainer Maria Rilke (2012) eloquently wrote to his mentee in *Letters to a Young Poet*, "Live the questions now. Perhaps you will then gradually, without noticing it, live along some distant day into the answer" (p. 24). Therefore, I encourage you to read through the chapter, and as it feels right for you, engage in the practices and see what comes up. There is no pressure to know what your "why" is right now, or to even have a "why." Consider simply allowing space for the possibility of one.

Getting to Your "Why"

As I've discussed, your "why" gives you an experience of meaning and purpose in life. It can be the simple notion of loving your children, being devoted to art, loving plants and trees, or dedicating your life to spirituality. No matter what it is, your reason for being informs your daily and ongoing actions. Sometimes your "why" manifests through broad connections to something outside of yourself, like a love of gardening, deep connected friendships, or your church. It can also be seen in more specific actions.

For example, you might translate your love of plants and trees into opening a co-op that creates access to plant care and ownership. You might express your love of animals by dedicating yourself to a horse-rescue mission and cleaning horse stalls. You might demonstrate your fascination with cooking by taking culinary classes and making meals for friends and family. Or maybe your passion for women's rights leads you to organize protests and help create sample legislation with a team. The process set forth in this chapter will help you explore your "why" and help you refine a holistic reason for being and develop a mission-driven plan for experiencing and actualizing your "why."

—Embodying Self-Statement—
My embodiment gives form to my values and dreams.

—Embodying Practice—
Exploring Your Values

Very simply, your values are what matter to you. They are what your heart cares about. In an embodied way, you feel them in your gut and your chest. They cause shifts in your breathing and heart rate, and in their presence, you become more alert and oriented.

Think about what matters to you. Then read through the list of values below and circle the ones with which you feel the most alignment. If you have more than 10 circled, go back and see if you can narrow it down to the 10 most important to you.

Achievement	Freedom	Physical challenge
Acknowledgment	Friendship	Pleasure
Adventure	Fun	Poise
Affluence	Generosity	Popularity
Agency	Gratitude	Recognition
Autonomy	Growth	Reliability
Balance	Happiness	Religion
Beauty	Healing	Resourcefulness
Belonging	Health	Respect
Benevolence	Helping	Responsibility
Boldness	Honesty	Risk
Challenge	Humor	Safety
Citizenship	Improvement	Security
Community	Independence	Self-determination
Compassion	Influence	Self-expression
Competency	Inner harmony	Self-respect
Competition	Integrity	Service to others
Connection	Inquiry	Social equity
Conservation	Justice	Spirituality

Creating	Kindness	Sportsmanship
Curiosity	Knowledge	Stability
Dedication	Leadership	Status
Determination	Learning	Strength
Devotion	Love	Success
Discipline	Loyalty	Teamwork
Education	Meaningful work	Thoughtfulness
Equality	Mindfulness	Trustworthiness
Equanimity	Nonviolence	Truth
Fairness	Optimism	Understanding
Faith	Patience	Validation
Fame	Peace	Vision
Family	Personal character	Wealth
Financial security	Personal development	Wisdom
		Other: _____

Now, rank your top 10 values and write them below. Put a star by your top 3. This is a good place to start.

1. _____

2. _____

3. _____

4. _____

5. _____

6. _____

7. _____

8. _____

9. _____

10. _____

LOVE
FAMILY
CONSERVATION
(taking care of the Earth)

Values and Deeper Meaning Meditation*

Meaning is what makes your values important to you. The following meditation will help you with this exploration. Before you get started, make sure you are mindful of your top three values. You will be recalling them during the meditation while noticing the body sensations and feelings that arise when thinking about what these values bring to your life. As with the other meditations, you might create a recording of this practice on your phone or have someone you care about record it for you.

To begin, find a supportive chair in a private and quiet space and get into a comfortable seated position. Be sure your feet are grounded on the floor and your sitting bones are connected to your chair. From grounded feet and a connected seat, extend through your spine, reaching through the crown of your head, keeping your chin neutral. If you'd like, soften your gaze or close your eyes.

Then, bring your awareness to your breath, noticing each inhale and exhale. Breathe here for several breaths. If you notice that your mind is wandering, simply label each thought as a thought, then return your focus to your breath. To support your focus, you might also label your inhalations and exhalations as you breathe, silently repeating *breathing in* and *breathing out* to yourself. Breathe here for five to seven breath cycles, in and out. Allow your body and mind to settle.

Now, gently take your hands place them over your heart. Bring your awareness to your hands and your heart. You may notice your heart beating. You may notice your breath. Rest your awareness here, pausing to notice your heartbeat and your breath. Consider that this is the place that might stir when you think about a heartfelt reason for being.

Now, keep your hands at your heart or rest them on your lap, then scan your body from your toes to your fingers to the crown of your head. Notice any tension, sensations, or emotions that arise. Notice your breath, your heartbeat, and any sense of lightness, heaviness, contraction, or expansion. There is nothing to do. Simply notice.

Now, bring to mind your top three values in order of importance. Say them to yourself here: *My first value is . . . , My second value is . . . ,* and *My third value is . . .*

Now, specifically bring to mind your third value. Think of this value and perhaps whisper the name of the value. As you think of this value, do you notice any shifts in your body? Do you notice a change in where you are feeling any tension, sensations, or emotions? Any change in your breath or your heartbeat? Do you notice any lightness, heaviness, contraction, or expansion? Allow for whatever you notice to be present just as it is. You might feel decreases or increases in sensation. You might feel substantial shifts and changes. Whatever you notice, allow it to be. Breathe here for five to seven breath cycles, simply noticing what is present.

Now, bring to mind your second value. Think of this value and perhaps whisper the name of the value. As you think of this value, do you notice any shifts in your body? Do you notice a change in where

---

* Adapted from Cook-Cottone (2020).

you are feeling any tension, sensations, or emotions? Any change in your breath or your heartbeat? Do you notice any lightness, heaviness, contraction, or expansion? Allow for whatever you notice to be present just as it is. You might feel decreases or increases in sensation. You might feel substantial shifts and changes. Whatever you notice, allow it to be. Breathe here for five to seven breath cycles, simply noticing what is present.

Finally, bring to mind your first value. This is your top value. Think of this value and perhaps whisper the name of the value. As you think of this value, do you notice any shifts in your body? Do you notice a change in where you are feeling any tension, sensations, or emotions? Any change in your breath or your heartbeat? Do you notice any lightness, heaviness, contraction, or expansion? Allow for whatever you notice to be present just as it is. You might feel decreases or increases in sensation. You might feel substantial shifts and changes. Whatever you notice, allow it to be. Breathe here for five to seven breath cycles, simply noticing what is present.

To end this practice, bring your awareness back to your breath. Take several breaths here to connect back with the present moment. When you are ready, gradually open your eyes and slowly bring your awareness back to the room, finding one thing upon which to anchor your awareness. As you are ready, slowly broaden your awareness to the whole room and to this moment. Thank you for practicing.

Values and Deeper Meaning Free Writing*

Now you are ready for your next, longer free-writing activity, which will also help you explore your values more deeply. This practice will take 10 minutes, so if you can't do it right now, jot down a few notes from your meditation that you can reference later. You can either write in the space provided or in your journal. If you choose to write in this workbook, you might want to have extra paper handy in case you need extra space.

The idea here is to let your thoughts flow. As you write, explain why each value is significant to you and why it might be significant to the world. Begin with your third value, then your second value, and then your top value. The goal is to keep writing on the topic, about the topic, or about the process of writing about the topic for 10 minutes. There is no perfect or right way to do this. Work toward allowing what *is*, while letting go of trying to get it right or not get it wrong. You might ask yourself, *How might my heart answer this question if my mind were quiet?*

As you write, breathe. If you are not sure what to write, you can write, "I am not sure what to write." You can also draw. The key is not to let your pen or pencil leave the paper for 10 minutes. Keep going, allowing what comes to flow. When you are ready, start a timer and write.

* Adapted from Cook-Cottone (2020).

When you are done, read over your free writing. In the space below, summarize why your top three values are meaningful to you, important to you, and important to the world. Describe this using three to five sentences *at most* for each.

My first value is meaningful because . . .

My second value is meaningful because . . .

My third value is meaningful because . . .

PAUSE

(**P** - Pause, **A** - Assess ➝ **USE** your resources and supports)

☐ **P**ause, check in, and acknowledge how you are feeling. This is a chance to be kind to yourself. The pace of your work is very important. Press your feet into the earth and take four gentle breaths.

☐ **A**ssess by asking yourself, *Is this a good place for a break?* If the answer is *yes* or *I don't know*, then fold over the corner of the page and take a break. This workbook is here for you for as long as it takes and for as many breaks as you need.

☐ **USE** your resources. Take a rest. Connect to your trusted friends. Contact your therapist. Practice your favorite well-being strategies. Get back to work when YOU are ready.

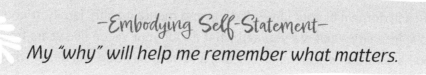

—Embodying Self-Statement—
My "why" will help me remember what matters.

Embodying Practice
Envisioning Your Future

A vision board is a multipurpose, flexible, and creative tool that allows you to express yourself through art. Since there are no real rules or ways to get things right or wrong, vision boards are accessible, fun, and easy to create. They are an embodied way of exploring questions related to your reason for being. They are holistic and can tap into imagination and creative, nonlinear thinking by promoting self-reflection without relying on verbal expression. Perhaps your vision board offers the space and creative freedom to include wishes or dreams that might be below your conscious awareness.

In his book, *The Biology of Desire*, Marc Lewis (2016) explains how neural pathways are more easily encoded into our brains when a set of actions or behaviors are meaningful to us. That means when you know your "why" and can link it to your recovery work, neural changes may come just a bit more easily. Right now, your brain is likely chronically exhibiting patterns of a traumatized brain, in which you have strong (and likely preferred) neural pathways that actively reinforce protection mode. To shift out of protection mode, it's important to engage your ventral vagal system, where you can be playful and creative. This is what a vision board allows you to do. Given its free and creative format, the vision board process can help you understand what matters to you without further activating your protective systems. Use of markers, paints, and images can activate the playful and creative side of you while allowing your protective side to take a break and let you explore.

Here are the materials you should consider when getting ready: a large piece of paper or a poster board (or a size that feels right for you); scissors, markers, crayons, colored pencils, or paints; magazines, photos, and other print media; scrapbook or colored paper; stencils and other scrapbooking materials; and anything else you think would be fun and inspiring. You will also need a glue stick or glue gun if you plan to adhere paper and objects to your vision board. You can also just use your pencil and a blank sheet of paper. Your vision board can be exactly what you want it to be—simple, complex, colorful, black and white, layered, or flat. It can be anything.

Find a table and a comfortable chair in a place where you feel you can do your deepest, most focused work. This might be at a coffee shop with your headphones on, playing your favorite music. It might also be your dinner table with a candle lit and your dog by your side. You will want to feel as comfortable as possible and well supported so your whole brain can dive into creativity.

When you're ready, sit back, maybe close your eyes, and ask the question *If I lived my life in accordance with my values, meaning, and heartfelt reason for being, what would my life look like in five years?* If that feels too specific, try asking, *If I listened to my heart, if I were safe, and if there were no limits, what would my life look like in five years?* Take some time to visualize your answers and jot down your ideas in your journal.

Now think about each domain of your life—physical and mental health, family, friendships, work, play, service, and spirituality—and ask yourself what about your vision five years from now is evidence that you have followed your values, heart, and purpose. Can you detail where you are, who

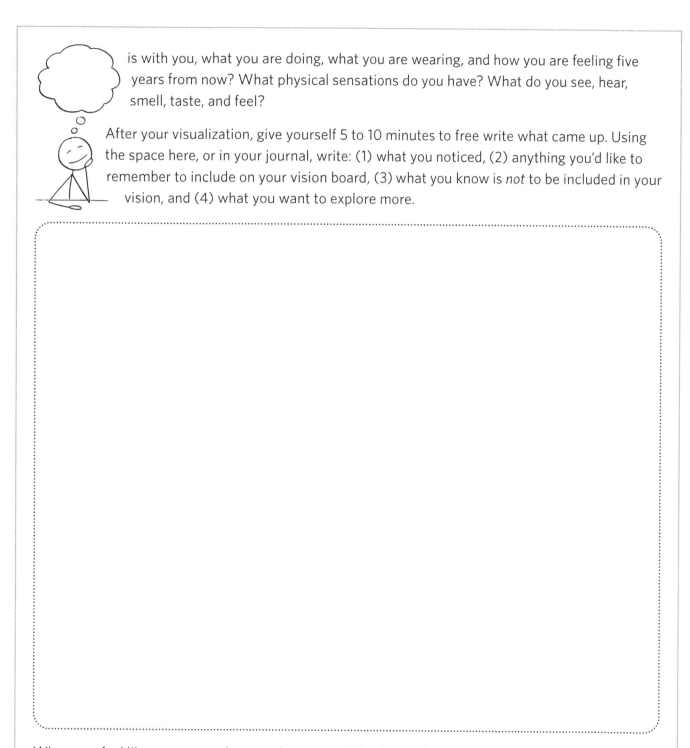

is with you, what you are doing, what you are wearing, and how you are feeling five years from now? What physical sensations do you have? What do you see, hear, smell, taste, and feel?

After your visualization, give yourself 5 to 10 minutes to free write what came up. Using the space here, or in your journal, write: (1) what you noticed, (2) anything you'd like to remember to include on your vision board, (3) what you know is *not* to be included in your vision, and (4) what you want to explore more.

When you feel like you are ready to work on your vision board, let whatever comes flow. Let go of the need for this to look any certain way. Give your protective self a little break. If the thought *What would this person or that person think?* comes to mind, simply notice it and maybe label it as "others' concerns." Then, let it go and get back to your imagination, creativity, and inspiration.

If it feels like something is holding you back from your flow, maybe offer your brain and body this prompt: *It's okay to let go. You don't need to worry about everything. Take a break. I am working on my vision board right now.* Be sure not to force anything, and know that you do not need to do this in one sitting. You can "live" the question for a while and come back to your vision board later, working on it for 10, 15, or 30 minutes at a time. Remember, all of this occurs on your terms.

Once you are done, describe what you experienced while creating your vision board in the space below. Did anything interesting come up? What was easy? What was challenging? What do you think was related to your heartfelt reason for being?

If you are working with a therapist, consider taking your vision board and accompanying notes (maybe even this workbook) to your next session and share what you created. You might also share your vision board with a safe friend or loved one. As humans, we each have a fundamental need to be seen and heard. Let your creation and your heartfelt future vision be seen and heard. As I write this, I wish I could see your vision board. You may even tag me on social media if you'd like (@catherine_cook_cottone). I would love to see your vision boards and creations.

Your vision board can and will evolve and change. Maybe even as you go through this chapter. You can update your vision board or even make a new one. I have my first vision board in my closet on the wall. I recall making it more than 10 years ago. I did not use any glue or scrapbooking supplies— just felt pens, beautiful new ones. I still love it. I love it because it represents possibility, even if some things I captured turned out a bit differently. It is part of how I engage in the practice of loving all versions of myself, even the version who was (and still is) trying with all of her heart to get it right. This workbook is all about opening up to the possibility that your reactions, patterns, and even ideas of how things might be in the future are all welcome here. Over time and with practice, you will create new ways of being that you might not even know how to hope for yet. So, yes, your vision board absolutely *will* change because that is exactly what healing is all about.

Clarifying Your Heartfelt Reason for Being

Your reason for being represents what you love. It is the core of your passions. It is a broad, heartfelt understanding that includes your values, meaning, and vision (Cook-Cottone, 2020). Your heartfelt reason for being is associated with devotion to experiences that bring joy and a sense of accomplishment. It moves and excites you to fully experience life. When you are connected to your heartfelt reason for being, you are compelled to be in action and share it with others. Having a sense of purpose is a universal need. In Sweden and the Netherlands, for example, citizens report that a sense of purpose is their primary reason for working. In Japan, the word *ikigai* describes the fulfillment of personal dreams and purpose.

The process of clarifying your heartfelt reason for being begins with the broad and general and moves to the more specific. As I mentioned earlier, some will feel at home in the holistic, broad, and general experience of their reason for being, while others prefer to be more formal and specific.

Kara, a previous patient, is a great example of someone who experienced her heartfelt reason for being in a very broad way. She had an inclination for art and poetry and worked as a social worker with a holistic understanding of her patients. Kara's vision board was filled with colors, images, and just one capitalized word: LOVE. Her trauma symptoms, she discovered, moved her away from love and the people she loved. Kara saw a future in which she embodied love. Her reason for being was to find and experience love. There was no need beyond doing her recovery work to set goals related to her heartfelt reasons for being. She knew as she healed, love would turn her in the right direction and let her know just what to do. For people like Kara, focusing on reasons for being, as a foundation, might be the extent of this work.

Another patient, Mark, lost his sister Sarah to a drunk driver when he was 15. When things got tough and he felt like he might want to quit trying, he thought about how Sarah didn't even get a chance to try. Mark planned to finish his undergraduate work and go into law. Although his legal interest wasn't directly related to Sarah's death, they used to watch legal shows together on TV and had joked they would be brilliant attorneys together one day. So when I asked his reason for being, Mark's answer was one word: Sarah.

You can, and probably do, have many reasons for being. But you might not have been aware of them. Here is how you find them. Reasons for being have a bit of heart, passion, and joy in them. Your reason for being probably started out pretty simple and grew up with you. As you and your world changed, so did your reason for being. For example, when you were little, your reason for being probably centered around being loved and cared for. In your school years, it was probably informed by your interests.

I can give you an example from my own life. Despite growing up to be a psychologist and researcher, in grade school I loved animals (I still do). Back then, my reason for being was to explore and be with nature. I spent long summer days trying to find tadpoles and crayfish in California water canals with my best friend. One glorious day, we swam in a pool with buckets of frogs we had captured. At the end of this day, we each had a frog-related rash and got into huge trouble with our moms. In case you are worried, the frogs were okay. That said, in that pool with my friend and the frogs, I was completely and utterly happy.

As an adult, your reason for being might be lived through your vocation (e.g., *I am here to be a teacher, researcher, and mentor*). It can be a set of actions (e.g., *I am an explorer, a world traveler, and a seeker of relationships across the world*). It can be community anchored (e.g., *I am here to seek social justice for myself, my neighbors, my ancestors, and the future of our children*). It can be serious or filled with joy (e.g., *I seek to make people laugh at themselves and with themselves, as a way to manage the pain and challenge of living*). It can be about creating beauty and art (e.g., *I am here to give voice to the beautiful unfolding of nature through my paintings*). It can be about work and honor (e.g., *I am here to document the lives of those who were lost in war*). It can be very focused and specific (e.g., *I am here to support the horse rescue in my town*) or broad and general (e.g., *I am here to be a good friend*). In our adult lives, a well-lived reason for being might fulfill its purpose and evolve (e.g., *I was here to raise my children with love. I am here, now, to support my children as they find their way in the world*).

For those of us who have been through trauma, reasons for being associated with joyful and meaningful moments can seem privileged and out of reach. There is no doubt that trauma can steal joy and any sense of meaning and purpose in life. You might say to yourself, *My reason for being was to make sure I didn't get abused* or *My reason for being was to figure out ways to hopefully get fed each day*. Consider that those were *survival tactics* and not reasons for being. They can be easily confused because both are purposeful. There is a difference. Reasons for being come from your heart, while survival tactics are in reaction to trauma. Yes, trauma can get in the way of this process. It can close your heart, and it may have done so for you. It did with me, for a long time. And it is also true that finding a smidgen of joy, passion, and meaning—remembering your heart—can be extremely helpful in your healing. That is what we are seeking to do here.

That summer with the frogs, both my and my friend's dads were in Vietnam. My mom was struggling with tremendous anxiety with three children to care for on her own. Our closest family was 3,000 miles away, and we were watching death counts every night on the TV. Those frogs were a lifeline. My adventures with my friend gave us a focus, something to be excited about when we woke up, and access to the here and now despite the horrors our fathers were going through.

As you think about your heartfelt reason for being, it can be helpful to look both forward (with your vision board) and backward. First, look backward by starting with a younger version of yourself. What was present when you were able to open your heart? What did you love? Do you recall any grade school, middle school, and high school interests or passions? It's okay if you don't.

Next, read through the previous values exercises you completed, and take a good look at your vision board. Notice the common threads in what you see. Let go of the need to find the right answer and ask, *What is my reason for being?* It is okay if you need a break and want to "live" the question for a period of time. It's a big question.

In the space provided, write down what comes up for you when you think of your heartfelt reason for being. Write what you know so far, remembering that there are no right or wrong answers.

PAUSE

(**P** - Pause, **A** - Assess ➝ **USE** your resources and supports)

☐ **P**ause, check in, and acknowledge how you are feeling. This is a chance to be kind to yourself. The pace of your work is very important. Press your feet into the earth and take four gentle breaths.

☐ **A**ssess by asking yourself, *Is this a good place for a break?* If the answer is *yes* or *I don't know*, then fold over the corner of the page and take a break. This workbook is here for you for as long as it takes and for as many breaks as you need.

☐ **USE** your resources. Take a rest. Connect to your trusted friends. Contact your therapist. Practice your favorite well-being strategies. Get back to work when YOU are ready.

—Embodying Practice—
Developing a Personal Sense of Mission

The word *mission* refers to a vocation, a calling, or an important assignment to be carried out for a purpose. Developing a personal sense of mission means translating your heartfelt reason for being into some sort of action. This is not for everyone. Some people find that this drives their healing, while others feel like it mandates them to do something. For some people, this level of detail is not helpful and does not align with how they see the world. Read through these next sections, and if they do not align with you right now, you can simply skip them. This will likely be true for those of you like Kara, who experience their heartfelt reason for being in a very holistic way. If so, it is okay for you to stop right now and move to chapter 7.

But if it does feel right for you, create a broad and general mission statement. Here are a few examples:

- I will value love over everything at home, work, and play.
- Nothing is more important than my integrity, and I will live by my truth each day.
- I am committed to social justice for myself and all people.
- My joy is bound to my service, and I will serve each day.
- I love horses and will work at the rescue center every chance I get.
- Family is all that matters.
- Balance is my ethic as I seek to increase understanding through research, love my family, and find joy in my own leisure time.

As you can see, these statements are general and value driven, and most speak to some sort of action. There is no standard form or required element that you must include.

Write your ideas for a general sense of mission here.

Mission Statement Visualization

With your general sense of mission underway, you might be ready to work on a personal mission statement. Your mission statement gives you a sense of direction and is intended to work like an internal compass. The magnetic fields it responds to are your values, your reason for being, and your personal sense of mission.

To do this practice, find a comfortable seat in a room or location where you feel safe and will have some time alone. You can either read through the questions in each step and then close your eyes and complete that aspect of the visualization, or you can make a recording of the script to play back for yourself. There are no right or wrong answers to the questions here. You might not know the answers to some of the questions, in which case you can just say, *I am open to wondering about that.* You might be unable to provide specific answers and instead give more general thoughts. That's okay too. The process of asking each question, looking forward, and considering possibilities can be healing in itself. If this feels scary to do all at once, do one part at a time and then take a break and come back to the next step as you're ready.

To begin, imagine that it is five years from now. Anything could be true. There are no limits. If it is helpful, think about your vision board, your values, and their meaning. Imagine that you are able to see forward five years and dial in the focus, seeing clearly what is there. How do you feel? Remember, anything is possible, so invite in the feelings that you hope for, that you want to be present in five years (maybe sooner). Take a moment, seeing yourself in five years, imagining how your body might feel, and breathe.

As you are there—your five-year, future self feeling your feelings—you might ask yourself, *What got me here?* Have you **accomplished** something? Maybe you have moved through some healing. Maybe you have been in therapy. Maybe you have worked out a new way to relate to your trauma. Maybe you have done something aligned with your heartfelt reason for being. What work have you done to get here? Take a moment, seeing yourself in five years, having done difficult and meaningful work. See yourself with a sense of accomplishment and breathe.

Still imagining your future self, look around. Where are you? What is the **location**? Is the answer very broad, such as in Europe, Africa, or Asia; at the beach; or in the mountains? Or do you see yourself someplace very specific, like home, or working with a certain company or living in a specific type of house? Is it a warm, mild, or cold location? Is it a city, suburban, or rural environment? Remember that for each part of this visualization, it is okay to be very general and unsure. Take a moment, seeing yourself in five years, asking, *Where might I be?* and breathe.

Now, bringing to mind your future self, what **strengths** helped you get here, and what **skills** have you practiced and developed? Consider the strengths and natural talents that you've had your whole life. Maybe you are creative, organized, or good with people. How have these strengths supported your journey? What new skills might you have used to accomplish these goals? What have you developed in yourself? Creativity, mathematical reasoning, writing, maybe even knowledge of carpentry, music, or yoga? Take a moment, seeing yourself in five years, to notice the strengths you have brought forth and the skills or dispositions you have developed. See yourself with your well-developed skills and breathe.

Next, thinking of your future self, what are you like? What kind of person are you? How do you behave? What are the **character** traits that you have developed? Truthfulness, reliability, trustworthiness, sobriety? Take a moment here and really see how you'd like to be in five years.

Last, consider your **priorities**. It is said that Gandhi's mission statement included a commitment to truth and an additional value statement in which he said, "And in resisting untruth, I shall put up with all suffering." With this statement, he prioritizes truth relative to suffering. What are your priorities? Think about your values and which ones come first. Is it family over career? Love over competition? Healing over perfectionism? Well-being over meeting everyone else's needs? This might be about letting something go so something better can happen.

Take a few moments to reflect on your future self with all of your accomplishments, in your chosen location, with all of your skills and strengths, your character, and a solid sense of priorities. If there are some areas you'd like to wonder about more, notice that. When you are ready, slowly open your eyes and orient your gaze toward something in the room. And then slowly broaden your gaze, taking in the room you're in.

Then work to develop a mission statement using each of the components from your visualization:

Accomplishments	What do you want to do and accomplish?
Location	Where do you want to be?
Skills and strengths	What personal skills and strengths will you use?
Character	How do you want to behave?
Priorities	Which values come first?

Using this frame, see what sections you feel ready to fill in to develop your mission statement.

I will _____ (accomplishments)

in _____ (describe the setting or location),

using _____ (list strengths and skills)

and integrating _____ (list character traits),

prioritizing _____ (values) over _____ (values/challenges).

The content of the mission statement will ultimately look something like these:

"I will become a poet in New York City and give voice to women's issues in my community, using my ease with words, music, and my writing skills and integrating my commitment to causes and my passion, persistence, and love, prioritizing truth over compromise in all poems."

"I will graduate from college feeling healed and less reactive to my traumatic past, using my love of learning and my newly developed coping skills to manage my symptoms and integrating my commitment to my well-being and healthy friendships, prioritizing my healing over giving into drama and mental-illness shaming."

"I will be an artist sharing the pain and challenge of my trauma to the world, using my sculpting skills and integrating my passion for creativity and my need to share my experience, prioritizing truth over hiding."

"I will volunteer at the horse rescue up the road, using my strong body, riding skills, and love of horses and integrating my commitment to stop the senseless killing of horses, prioritizing caretaking over letting someone else do the work."

—Embodying Practice—
A Letter of Encouragement to Future You

After reviewing your work in this chapter, write a short letter to a future version of you who has experienced a setback in recovery or who has encountered additional life challenges that were difficult to handle. Tell your future self the following:

- You see their struggle.

- You believe in their ability to heal and grow.

- You remember their meaning and purpose and that trying matters.

- They are worth the effort.

- They have tools and support.

Dear Future Me,

This letter is for you when you are having a difficult time . . .

Love,
Me

Think of your work in this chapter as your working draft. In the big picture, it is truly just that. Life moves you and changes you, and so does what you are working for. Having a sense of your "why," however, can serve you as you go forward into the next section of this book to face your trauma. This chapter is here for you (as are all the other previous chapters), supporting you like a big, old, comfortable chair you can fall into with your favorite blanket. It represents your comfort zone and includes content you can pendulate back to when things get difficult. Come back here anytime you need. This chapter's arms are open.

Part 2

Embodying
Your Life

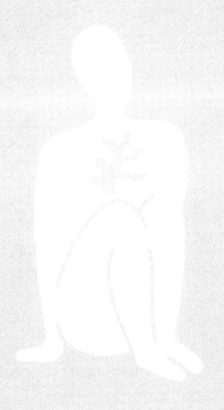

Chapter 7

Connecting to Your Sensing Body

-Embodying Self-Statement-
My body senses internal and external experiences.

This chapter provides you with opportunities to build deeper and healthier connections with the sensing self. After exposure to trauma, connecting with your sensing self can feel simultaneously fulfilling and overwhelming. This layer of self is your sensual connection to the world as you see, listen, taste, smell, and feel. It is also your connection to your inner experience of self as you notice interoceptive cues, such as sensations of hunger or fullness, the contraction of longing, and the expansion and warmth of love.

Sensations can be intense and are deeply meaningful. Your sensations help keep you safe and are at the core of the perpetuation of trauma-based symptoms. The sensing self is hardwired to the instinctual and protective parts of your nervous system. For thousands and thousands of years, the ability to react quickly to threatening stimuli has kept humans alive. In his work with somatic experiencing, Peter Levine frequently reminds his students that it is body sensations, even more so than intense emotions, that are the key to trauma recovery. Often, when a person avoids their feelings, they are in fact avoiding the bodily sensations integral to feelings.

While teaching workshops, I have had first responders, humanitarian workers, and veterans question the wisdom of unlearning their automatic reactions. They understandably assert there may be some automatic judgments and reactions we should keep in place. I agree. In cases of true danger, we want and need our nervous systems to immediately let us know if we are not safe. Therefore, know that the healing practices I provide here will *not* dull or silence your body's natural drive to keep you safe. Rather, they will help you integrate your automatic reactions with the parts of your nervous system wired for connection, reflection, and purpose. When you are well integrated (and not disconnected or dissociated), you can trust your body to let you know if you are unsafe and to react effectively to keep you safe. As you work on these embodiment skills, you reduce unnecessary reactivity as you become increasingly adept at accurately assessing your safety.

Learning to effectively partner with your body as you experience sensations will support your well-being in several additional ways. First, you will have better access to the sensations associated with your self-care (e.g., hunger, thirst, fatigue), letting you respond in turn (e.g., grabbing a blanket when you are cold). Second, connecting to and experiencing sensations will help you better experience and work with emotions, such as the heavy sensations associated with grief. Third, learning to be with and work with sensations will support your sense of agency and self-regulation.

Viktor Frankl (1946), a Holocaust survivor and famous existential scholar, wrote *Man's Search for Meaning*. This book is about his experience in concentration camps and the loss of much of his family during World War II. It is also a book about his theory of love and life. Upon first hearing, I loved his oft-cited quote:

> Between stimulus and response there is a space.
> In that space lies your power to choose your response.
> In that response lies your growth and your freedom.

As it turns out, this quote doesn't actually exist in any of his published writings. I spent years looking for it with our university librarian. We believe it is more of a summary of about a page and a half from his 1946 book. Nonetheless, I believe at the heart of finding what lies in the space between stimulus and response is having the skills and the courage to experience, as a felt sense, the way the sensations of life and your memories move through your body and affect your thoughts and actions. It is not easy work.

—Embodying Self-Statement—
I can work to create the space I need to find my growth and my freedom.

—Embodying Practice—
Core Breathing

Before you get started learning about sensations and your body, take a moment to connect with your breath with this core breathing practice. Core breathing can help you connect to your center, stabilize your abdominal muscles, strengthen your diaphragm (the muscle that helps you breathe), and comfort your nervous system. Robin Rothenberg (2020), a breathwork specialist, notes that it can also help support your overall health and well-being. Her practice for core breathing is described here.

To begin, find a seated position in a chair, in which you feel grounded and well supported. Move toward the edge of your chair so you can feel your sitting bones resting against the seat. Place a hand on your chest and another on your belly just under your ribs. Press your feet into the floor and your sitting bones into the chair, and extend through your spine. Draw your chin in, extending through your neck. Soften your shoulders and jaw. On the next inhale, allow your belly and rib cage to expand with the breath.

As you gently exhale, engage your belly muscles, from your pelvic bone to your navel to your lower rib cage. Create the feeling that you are hugging your spine from all directions as you draw all of your core muscles inward. Hold the contraction for about two to four seconds after you have completed your exhale. Then slowly release the contraction from the top down as you inhale.

As you practice, remain aware of your state of arousal. Keep your breath gentle and soft. Because you are recruiting your core muscles, your body might automatically begin to move into a higher state of arousal. Work to engage your core while remaining alert, relaxed, and engaged. If at any point you notice that the muscles in your neck, jaw, or shoulders are tensing, soften and relax your breath even more to release them.

Repeat this breath cycle 5 to 10 times and then allow yourself to resume your natural, relaxed breathing pattern. You can add this breathwork to your resource repository if you'd like.

Need-to-Know: What Happens When You Sense Something?

If you look at it from a distance, your sensations are just information sent to your brain about what is happening inside and outside of your body. For example, as you were completing the **Core Breathing** practice, you were aware of the internal working of your abdominal muscles and the movement of your breath. You were aware of the sensations of your chest and belly moving, which you could glean based on the internal cues within your body and the feelings from your hands.

Sensations are a pathway to your central nervous system, which comprises the brain and spinal cord. Because they are part of what is called the sensorimotor system, sensations can be quickly translated into action urges and actions. Your sensing and motor systems have established patterns of working together that reflect natural reflexes you are born with, like blinking when your eyes are irritated or coughing when your throat tickles. There are also established patterns that are related to pleasure and reward, such as smelling apple pie and having the accompanying urge to eat it. There are patterns that developed in response to trauma or threat as well, including the experience of your entire body tensing when you hear a siren. Very importantly, patterns also develop as a result of what you repeatedly do or practice, such as when you ground your feet and connect to your breath when you hear those same sirens. Shifting your patterns begins with your relationships with your sensations.

Building on what you already know about interoception (inside sensing), exteroception (outside sensing), and neuroception (safety/danger sensing), let's break down even further what happens when you sense something. While the process I describe here may appear to comprise discrete moments leading into one another, you often experience them as if they are happening all at once. How you experience these sensations depends on your level of awareness at the time, your body's state when the sensation is experienced, and the history of your nervous system (e.g., your trauma).

To begin, know that your trauma history affects your detection systems (interoception, exteroception, and neuroception). As you can see in the following figure, what happens within your detection systems affects your response and ultimately your relationship with the sensation and its source.

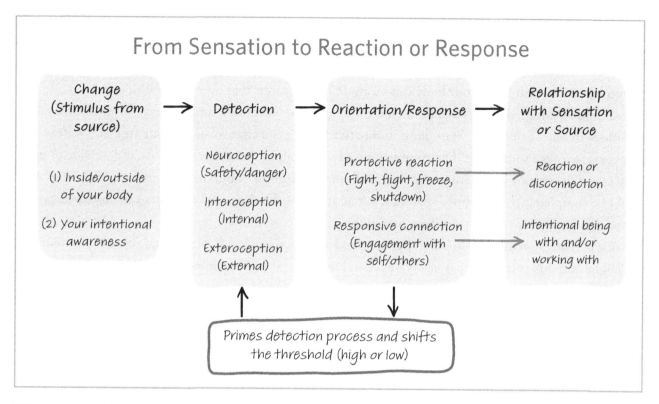

What's more, the process builds upon itself. First, in protection mode, your detection system goes on high alert. This is called having a *low threshold for detection*, meaning that it does not take much for protection mode to activate. Your detection system is focused on perceived threats or reminders of past threats (Ogden & Fisher, 2016). Without rest, you can remain in a state of chronic activation, causing you to see the world as threatening and leading you to become increasingly exhausted. This can lead to a state of being overwhelmed and shutdown.

Second, when you are overwhelmed and shutdown, your detection system dials down or turns off, making it difficult for you to notice much of anything at all (Ogden & Fisher, 2016). This is called having a *high threshold for detection*. When you are shutdown, it takes a lot for your detection system to be activated.

Through this work, you will develop your ability to notice your sensations. Then you will learn methods for being with and working with each aspect of experiencing your sensations so that more connected, intentional responses are possible. Over time, you will feel more skilled and confident moving through the world, and your activation threshold will be more functional—not too low and not too high.

—*Embodying Self-Statement*—
My body speaks to me through sensations, and I can listen.

Need-to-Know: Something Changes and You Become Aware

As you learned in chapter 1, your body can be aware of sensations that occur both inside and outside of your body through the processes of interoception and exteroception. You can become aware of these sensations in one of two ways: Your body automatically notices a change, or you intentionally shift your awareness to notice something. The combination of information coming from inside and outside of your body is so vast that it would actually be too much information for you to notice and process at once. You would be completely overwhelmed if you took it all in, all of the time. To keep things manageable, your nervous system automatically prioritizes sensations related to your safety and well-being. The best way for your nervous system to do this is to be very good at detecting changes inside and outside your body while ignoring things that remain steady or consistent. Let's take a deeper look at this process, starting with changes and awareness *inside* your body.

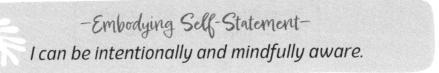

—Embodying Self-Statement—
I can be intentionally and mindfully aware.

Changes and Awareness Inside of Your Body

When you automatically notice a sensation in your body, it is typically related to homeostasis, (e.g., thirst, hunger, fatigue, comfort), something that is physically wrong (e.g., illness, disease, injury), or a shift in states due to feeling safe or unsafe. For example, when you wear shoes, your body doesn't constantly tell you, *Hey, you have shoes on your feet* unless your foot swells or a blister starts to form. When something is wrong, you get an automatic message that something has changed: *Hey, pay attention! Something is wrong with your foot!*

Through interoception, you may automatically notice that you are hungry because you feel a rumble in your stomach, an overall lack of energy, and a feeling of irritability. You also automatically feel your emotions in your body, which can give rise to sensations like the sinking feeling in your stomach associated with disappointment or the feeling of tension in your jaw, shoulders, and arms associated with anger. If you are suddenly frightened, you will automatically experience the sensations of the stress response (e.g., pounding heart, muscle tension) as your body prepares for fight, flight, freeze, or shutdown. In the same way, if you are feeling safe, your body will automatically experience the sensations associated with safety, like the sense of relaxation in your muscles and a warm feeling around your heart.

Another way to notice sensations inside your body is by practicing intentional, mindful awareness. For example, when you are frightened and notice a clenching around your heart and a tensing of your hips, jaw, and shoulders, you might bring intentional, mindful awareness to your breath. You may also find a part of your body, like a hand, that is not feeling distress.

To center and calm yourself, you can use the **Pendulation** practice from chapter 5 to pendulate from the clenching feeling around your heart to the neutral experience of your hand. You can also use several of the other tools you have already learned to help you with an intentional connection to your sense of interoception: **Grounded Breath and Centering** (chapter 1), **Positive Embodiment Body Scan** (chapter 1), **Awareness of Neuroceptive Cues** (chapter 1), **Self-Awareness Scale** (chapter 3), **Progressive Muscle Relaxation** (chapter 5), and **Yoga Nidra** (chapter 5). In this chapter, you will learn even more.

—Embodying Practice—
Exploring Your Interoceptive Awareness

Take a moment here to explore your interoceptive awareness. After trauma, many people report difficulty turning toward feelings or noticing sensations inside of their bodies. Some people report becoming overwhelmed or triggered by the sensations in their bodies. What is your relationship with your feelings in your body? According to Dr. Wolf Mehling and his colleagues (2018), there are several aspects of interoceptive awareness to consider. In the area below, there are several guiding prompts to help you explore your interoceptive awareness.

1. **Noticing:** Describe your awareness of uncomfortable, comfortable, and neutral body sensations.

_____

_____

_____

_____

2. **Connecting:** In what ways are you able or unable to connect to the wide variety of sensations that arise in your body? Do you dial in, notice the sensations, and stay with them for a while? Or do you distract, ignore, or disconnect from them?

_____

_____

_____

_____

3. **Managing difficult or painful sensations:** Describe how you handle difficult or painful sensations in your body. Do you ignore, distract, react, worry, push through, become upset, or shut down?

_____

_____

_____

_____

4. **Listening:** Describe the ways you take time to listen to your body to learn more about the state of your body, its needs and wants, or your emotions.

_____

_____

_____

_____

5. **Trusting:** When and if you listen to your body, can you trust it to guide and support you? Describe what it feels like to trust or not trust your body.

_____

_____

_____

_____

6. **Going forward:** As you look over your responses to the previous five questions, what do you hope for when it comes to your relationship with your body and its sensations?

_____

_____

_____

_____

Honeybee Breath

Arielle Schwartz (2022), an expert on the use of yoga for trauma recovery, shares the honeybee breath as a way to connect to the inner sensations and experiences of your body. By using your vocal cords to hum or chant, this practice can be a relatively quick way to shift your orientation inward and induce a calming response.

Begin by finding a comfortable seated position in which you can feel grounded and well supported. When you are ready, inhale through your nose, and then as you exhale, begin to hum. Choose a tone and volume that feel right for you. As you continue breathing and humming on the exhales, scan your body, beginning at your head and ears, then moving to your throat, hands, arms, chest, belly, and legs. Notice the parts of your body that do and do not vibrate with the tone.

Now, orient your awareness to your heart. Notice any sensation of vibrations near or around your heart. How does your heart feel? You can change the tone if you'd like by humming in short or long segments. You can hum a song you know or shift to singing a song. Schwartz suggests that you might play some music and hum along.

If you'd like, bring your hands to cover your ears, with your palms facing inward and your fingers facing behind you. The heels and the palms of your hands will be over your ears and your thumbs and fingers will rest on the back of your head and your neck. This hand placement can help you orient toward the inward experience of the sounds.

When you are ready, take a pause from your humming or sound making to breathe gently. Notice the resonance in your body from this practice. If it feels right, take a moment and record what you notice in your journal. You might even add this practice to your resource repository.

Changes and Awareness Outside of Your Body

Now that we have explored how to detect changes inside your body, let's shift to discussing changes and awareness *outside* of your body. Pat Ogden, the creator of sensorimotor psychotherapy, refers to this ability to automatically notice things on the outside of your body as orienting (Ogden & Fisher, 2016). The orienting response is considered a reflex, meaning that you don't think about it; it just happens. As humans, we are hardwired to orient toward changes in our environment, especially those that are pertinent to safety and well-being. As I have discussed throughout this book, trauma-related hypervigilance creates a state within which your orienting response is heightened and may detect threat or danger when there is none. According to Ogden, after cumulative and ongoing trauma or difficult experiences, your body and its orienting system can sometimes become inflexible and overly focused on things perceived as potentially threatening, disconcerting, or problematic. When all you see is potential threat, it can begin to feel like there is nothing positive in your life or the world.

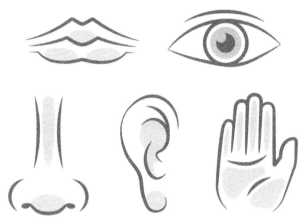

When orienting, you prioritize any sensations detected through your five senses—sight, hearing, smell, taste, and touch—which are a direct link to the present moment and external reality (Rothschild, 2017). Using your intentional, mindful awareness to purposely attend toward many different sensations can help you expand the range of things you notice. Beyond threat, there's so much out there to see: the beautiful, the wonderful, the quietly elegant, the adorable, the silly, the striking, and the awe inspiring. When you notice the wide range of things your life has to offer, you gain a more balanced view of the world. For example, when you see the furrow in someone's brow and withdraw in response, you may miss that they are worried about you. When you focus on the couple fighting in the park, you may miss the roses, the daisies, the children playing in the sprinkler, or the spoken-word poet. Intentionally expanding how you orient can change your life experience.

Embodying Practice
Exploring Your Exteroceptive Awareness

Take a moment here to explore your exteroceptive awareness. After trauma, some people find that certain external sensations are triggering, frightening, and overwhelming, especially those that remind them of their trauma. What is your relationship with your externally sensing self? Here are some guiding prompts to help you explore your exteroceptive awareness.

1. **Noticing:** Describe your awareness of uncomfortable, comfortable, and neutral sensations detected through your five senses (sight, hearing, smell, touch, and taste). What do you tend to focus on? What do you tend to orient toward?

   _____

   _____

   _____

   _____

2. **Connecting:** In what ways are you able or unable to connect to your five senses? Do you dial in, notice what your senses are telling you, and stay with that information for a while? Or do you distract, ignore, try to drown out, or withdraw from the information your senses are giving you? Which sense do you connect with the most? The least?

   _____

   _____

   _____

   _____

3. **Managing difficult or painful sensations:** Thinking of your five senses, describe how you handle difficult or painful external sensations. Do you ignore, distract, react, worry, push through, shut down, withdraw, or become upset?

   _____

   _____

   _____

   _____

4. **Listening:** Describe the ways you take time to tune into your five senses. They all are telling you about the world. Do you *listen* to them differently? Which one do you listen to the most? The least?

_____

_____

_____

_____

5. **Trusting:** When and if you listen to your five senses, do you use them to guide and support you? Describe what it feels like to trust or not trust your five senses. Which one do you trust the most? The least?

_____

_____

_____

_____

6. **Going forward:** As you look over your responses to the previous five questions, what do you hope for when it comes to your relationship with your five senses?

_____

_____

_____

_____

Interoception and Exteroception Inquiry

Looking over your answers to the interoception and exteroception awareness practices, what do you notice when you compare each section? Are you, or have you been, able to connect more to your sense of interoception or exteroception? Which is easier? Free write what comes up when you look at your responses and consider what you might want going forward.

Need-to-Know: Neuroception

As you learned in chapter 1, neuroception is the process by which your nervous system automatically takes in new stimuli and assesses if something is safe or unsafe (Dana, 2020; Porges, 2018). Following trauma, when your nervous system is in protection mode and you are on high alert, you may overreact to things that are actually safe, meaning that you have a neuroception of danger when there is none.

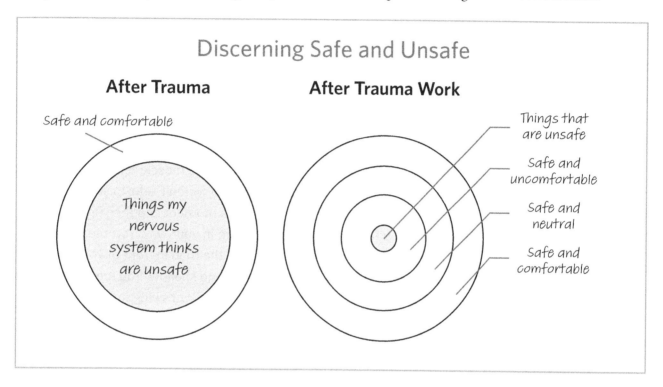

Neuroception can affect how open you are to a broad range of sensations. As you move from a state of connection to protection, your ability to openly and accurately see your environment shifts. To get a sense of how this process might show up in day-to-day functioning, read through the next visualization practice, inspired by Peter Levine (2010a).

—Embodying Practice—
Visualization of State Activation and Sensations

Imagine you are on your way to work. You are calm and listening to a comforting song. You can hear the high frequency of the flutes, the deep bass, and the violins weaving through the midrange. You see the other cars and notice a Volkswagen Beetle, trucks, vans, and motorcycles. You notice the colorful shops along the way—colors of cream, yellow, blue, and brick. You have the window rolled down and can smell delicious bagels baking nearby. You lift your coffee to your lips and smell the bold, full aroma and then taste your favorite creamer. You are in a connection state and can easily experience a wide range of sensations and their qualities.

Suddenly, you realize that you left the teakettle on the stove with the burner on high. You remember there wasn't much water in the kettle to begin with, and you are in danger of causing a fire. Your body immediately moves into fight-or-flight mode. These sensations—the muscle tension, racing heart, and feeling of panic—remind you of a time in the past when you weren't safe. In some ways, it feels like the past is happening right now. You become flustered for a moment and then unskillfully turn your car around to go back home. You think the other drivers are in your way. You see them as blocking you and thwarting your journey home. You see nothing but the road in front of you as your attention narrows, your heart beats, and your breath becomes rapid and shallow. You are sweating. When you get home, you are not even sure you remember driving there. You swing open the door and dart to the kitchen. Sure enough, the teakettle is burning up. Nevertheless, you got there in time.

Relieved, you take a deep breath. Your heart rate slows. You put the teakettle in the sink so it can cool down safely. You begin to move out of protective mode and back into connection mode. You notice your watch and realize you will be late for work. You message your boss, and all is okay. You are calmer, yet not all the way calm. You have a shaky feeling about your reckless trip home, your memories of your past feel so present, and your body shudders. You notice your range of awareness is still constricted.

As you turn to leave, you realize you left the front door open. Did the cat get out? Your cat is an inside cat and will be in danger outside. You rev up into a state of panic again. You do not have far to go this time. You slam the front door shut, then you run through the house calling the cat's name. This quickly escalates to screaming the cat's name. You can barely breathe. Twice you think you see the cat, only to realize that it was a pillow and then a shirt tossed on a chair. You realize that you aren't even seeing things as they are. You get a hold of yourself. You stop.

You realize you need to center and ground yourself. You press your feet into the floor beneath you and begin to breathe gently and slowly. You say, *I am right here, right now.* You place a hand on your heart, and as you breathe, you begin to slow your breath further. You lift your gaze and notice five things you can see: the lamp, the table, the picture of you and your family, the couch, and that darn pillow you thought was the cat. You then begin to focus on four things you can hear: the hum of the refrigerator, the wind on the windowpanes, your own breath as it begins to slow even more, and—wait!—you pause and hear the cat walking down the stairs. You pick her up and notice three things you can feel: her soft fur, the buzzing sensation of her purring, and the warmth of her body as you hold her. You then notice two things you can smell: yes, the cat, and the lingering burning smell from the teapot. Last, you think of one thing you know to be true. You think to yourself, *It is 100 percent true that I do better when I center and ground myself, even when something stressful is happening.*

As you think back through this visualization, notice how when your nervous system was activated, it constricted your ability to notice any sensations beyond what was determined an urgent need. The more activated and narrower your perspective became, the more likely you were to see things that were not even there. The fact that this high activation was also paired with the recall of past trauma was even more dysregulating.

This sort of roller coaster of state activation is not an uncommon thing for a nervous system. As Peter Levine (2010a) notes, we all move through states of activation and reaction all of the time. It is our ability to notice and to self-regulate that makes all of the difference. Noticing, centering, and grounding gives you access to the full range of your sensations, helps you correctly assess safety, and allows you to discern what is in the here and now and what is the past. In this story, the senses played a central role in both activation and deactivation. While your senses were narrowed and even lost to some degree as your activation grew, it was also your senses that helped bring you back to a state of centered calm and connectedness.

—Embodying Practice—
Shake It Off

This practice is inspired by Manuela Mischke-Reeds (2018), a somatic psychotherapy specialist. According to Mischke-Reeds, shaking is a natural response the body has in response to being in a state of fight, flight, freeze, or shutdown. It is believed to be a way that the body can return to balance. If you notice that you feel shaky, upset, jittery, or trembly after any of the activating practices, consider using this tool to help you reconnect to the experience of the body and partner with your body as it grounds and settles. The key is to gently allow the shaking to occur while at the same time maintaining connection to your body and the ground that is supporting you. You are not demanding the shakiness go away. The intention is to allow it to be there and settle as you are experiencing a comforting movement.

From a standing position, scan your body and notice any shakiness. Where do you feel shaky feelings right now? What is the shakiness like? What is its rhythm? Its quality?

Now orient your awareness toward the ground and allow the ground to hold and support you. Notice the sensations of the ground below you, supporting you.

Then return your awareness to the shaking sensations in your body. As you naturally and gently inhale, offer support to that area of the body that is shaking. As you gently exhale, let the shaky feeling settle and move toward your feet and the ground. Repeat this as many times as you'd like.

Pressing into your feet, encourage a gentle rocking back and forth, back and forth. This motion tends to calm the body and can further comfort the shaky feelings. As you rock, slowly move your awareness from the rocking sensations to the shaking feeling, taking a few breaths as you orient toward each area. The goal is for you to collect and integrate your shakiness into the rocking movement of the body.

Allow your breath to synchronize with the rocking of your body, inhaling on forward movements and exhaling on backward movements as you focus on the rhythm and motions.

Keep your awareness on your body, the sensations of rocking, and the ground below you. If you notice you are struggling to stay present and grounded, pause and reconnect to your surroundings, your body, and the ground below you. Begin again and continue rocking and breathing for two to five minutes as needed.

Slowly soften the rocking and pause. Take a moment to move your body. What sensations do you notice? Where are they? What parts of your body feel open, calm, and grounded? Do you feel more balanced?

Use this practice whenever you feel shakiness. You can add it to your resource repository if you'd like.

Chapter 8

Advanced Practices for Being with and Working with Sensations

As you increase your capacity to embody your life, it is important to develop a skill set for being with and working with sensations. Your relationship with each step in the sensation-experiencing process can propel you toward a state of responsivity and receptivity (connection mode) and away from a state of trauma-based overreaction, dissociation, or shutdown (protection mode). If you are mindfully aware and filled with intention, you are better able to notice what is happening inside and outside of your body, explore any sensations that arise, correctly assess your safety, and intentionally and meaningfully experience your life.

Your work here is to reduce protective reaction when it is not needed. Through intentional, mindful awareness of your sensations, you will create balance in your nervous system, empowering the parts of your nervous system over which you have voluntary control (e.g., the intentional movement of your muscles) and helping to regulate your autonomic nervous system. Your practice will reduce your automatic tendency to move into protection mode and strengthen your ability intentionally to be with and work with your sensations and experiences.

In this chapter, you will explore techniques for being with and working with sensations as they present in your day-to-day life. As you learn how to be with and work with these sensations, keep the following core guidance in mind:

- The goal is to engage in practices that help develop and maintain your interoceptive and exteroceptive skills.

- Work toward being with sensations, noticing their qualities.

- Consider that being with a sensation may be enough.

- Work toward being with sensations that are associated with moving into protection mode by engaging in practices that help you feel centered, grounded, and connected to your experience.

- Work toward being with sensations that are associated with a nurturing or self-caring response, such as eating when hungry, getting a sweater when cold, resting when tired, getting support when overwhelmed, and going to the doctor when sick.

Need-to-Know: What Should You Do if This Work Brings Up Trauma Memories?

First and foremost, remember that you can take a break or stop at any time. The goal is to get adept at being with day-to-day sensations. You are not trying to push for trauma memories to come up or to shut them down when they do. As you practice being with your sensations, simply notice if any memories come up. If, or when, they do come up, it can be helpful to make a note of them on **Your List of Distressing and Traumatic Experiences** (chapter 14). You can work with them later if you'd like. It can feel good to simply put them in a holding place, such as that offered by the following container and holding tree practices. You can also talk to your therapist or a trusted friend about any patterns you are noticing or any memories that arise.

—Embodying Self-Statement—
I don't need to hold everything all of the time.

—Embodying Practice—
Creating a Container

A container is any object, real or imagined, that can be used to hold anything distressing that you don't feel has been processed or don't feel ready to work with. Your container can be used when you need to wrap up a session or take a break from your work.

Your container is something you can bring to mind and easily find. It is strong enough to hold all of the upsetting and distressing stuff, including bodily sensations, smells, sounds, images, memories, worries, and thoughts. It can be anything you'd like, including a giant metal safe, a wooden box, a book, or a computer drive. Describe or draw your safe container here:

Once you have selected your container, bring each layer of the distress you'd like to place within it to mind. In the following order, place each layer in your container: body sensations, smells, sounds, images, memories, worries, and thoughts.

Once you have placed each item in the container, close the lid. You might want to add additional security measures, like additional locks. Then you can imagine where you'd like to place the container. Maybe in the middle of the ocean on an island or in a vault. Place it anywhere you'd like.

Embodying Practice
The Holding Tree

The holding tree was created to hold your distress, memories, and worries for you, for as long as you need it to. No less. No longer. There is no distress or challenge it cannot hold. In fact, it is said that no matter how overwhelming the distress, or how big the challenge, the work of holding inspires the tree to grow stronger and thrive.

To try out this holding tree practice, find a place where you can focus and relax, then find a comfortable position for your body. Slowly soften your eyes and allow your breath to move gently in and out. Do this for a few moments, allowing your mind to settle.

Now imagine that just past a meadow, in the midst of a beautiful, thriving forest, grows a powerful tree. You can see it as you arrive at the meadow, rooted into the crest of a small hill. Its roots are vast and weave down into the earth, where they are nourished and hydrated. Its trunk is wide, strong, and grand. The bark is thick and protective. The tree stands as tall as the mountain lines behind it. Its branches reach up to the sky, their leaves unfolding toward the sun. Somehow, as you look at the tree, it feels like a promise that everything will be okay. This is the holding tree.

Imagine that you are standing near the holding tree. Bring to mind any *thoughts*, *memories*, or *images* that you'd like the tree to hold for you. Imagine you can hold these thoughts, memories, and images in a small bundle, wrapped carefully in cloth to help hold each one in place. As you are ready, reach up and hand the bundle to the tree. As you do, its branches reach down while leaves carefully fold around your bundle. Slowly, the bundle is drawn into the tree to be well held until you need or want it back.

Now, bring to mind any *emotions*, *worries*, or *distress* you might be experiencing. Wrap these into a bundle using a soft cloth and tie them with twine. Hold this bundle up to the tree, allowing it to draw them in and keep them safe and protected.

Next, scan your body for any remaining *sensations*, *stressors*, or *tension* that you'd like the holding tree to care for. Imagine yourself wrapping them into a bundle with a soft cloth and twine. Then pass these, too, to the holding tree.

Know that you can go to the holding tree, lift your arms, and ask for any of your bundles back anytime you'd like. The holding tree will slowly bring it down to you by lowering its branches, gently and slowly unfurling its protective leaves. You can lift your bundle from the opened leaves.

Pause here, place your hands at your heart, and breathe. If you'd like, send gratitude to the tree, thanking it for holding your distress and keeping each layer safe until you are ready or need to come back. If you'd like, when you think of your worries or distress, you can imagine offering the holding tree gentle rainwater, sun, and more gratitude for holding and caring for them. As you are ready, become even more aware of your breath and connection to the earth. Then take three gentle breaths and slowly open your eyes.

Embodying Practice

Distress Tolerance: Paced Breathing and Paired Muscle Relaxation

If any of these practices become somewhat distressing, it can be helpful to engage in distress tolerance skills, which allow your body to downregulate so you can stay in the moment and remain calm. Distress tolerance skills are a type of crisis survival tool that you can use when you feel very overwhelmed and reactive (Linehan, 1993). You can draw on these skills when you notice you are shifting out of your growth zone and toward the edge of your window of tolerance. Here you will learn about two distress tolerance skills: paced breathing and paired muscle relaxation.

To practice paced breathing, inhale through your nose for a slow count of two (breathing in 1, 2) . . . then hold your breath for three seconds (holding 1, 2, 3) . . . and exhale out of your mouth for a count of five (breathing out 1, 2, 3, 4, 5). Do this for four to six cycles. This exercise will lower your blood pressure, slow your heart rate, and increase your sense of control.

When you're ready, you can add paired muscle relaxation. As you breathe in, tense or contract your toes on both feet (breathing in 1, 2) . . . then hold your breath and your toes (holding 1, 2, 3) . . . and exhale as you release your toes (breathing out 1, 2, 3, 4, 5). Continue this pattern of engaging and releasing the muscles in your body, starting at your feet and moving to your calves, thighs, glutes, belly, shoulders, arms, hands, and face. This will help you and your body notice any held tension and release it.

For some people, sensing the body at all can feel retraumatizing. There are just too many painful memories activated by the sensations. For others, the body can continuously feel numb when trying to work with sensations. They have become disconnected from their body as a means of survival or coping. If you find yourself being overly reactive or feeling numb, I strongly encourage you to seek the support of a therapist to help you connect with your body and its sensations.

PAUSE

(**P** - Pause, **A** - Assess → **USE** your resources and supports)

☐ **P**ause, check in, and acknowledge how you are feeling. This is a chance to be kind to yourself. The pace of your work is very important. Press your feet into the earth and take four gentle breaths.

☐ **A**ssess by asking yourself, *Is this a good place for a break?* If the answer is *yes* or *I don't know*, then fold over the corner of the page and take a break. This workbook is here for you for as long as it takes and for as many breaks as you need.

☐ **USE** your resources. Take a rest. Connect to your trusted friends. Contact your therapist. Practice your favorite well-being strategies. Get back to work when YOU are ready.

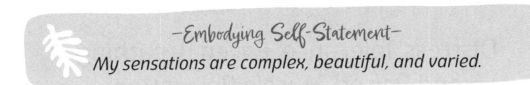

—Embodying Self-Statement—
My sensations are complex, beautiful, and varied.

Need-to-Know: Building Skills for Being with and Working with Sensations

This section will help you develop the skills you need to be with and work with sensations so you can fully experience sensations and their qualities. Often, we get so distracted by a lack of felt safety and our reaction patterns that we fail to notice what sensations actually feel like.

For example, when I first started doing yoga, I was in a class doing a plank pose, a position that looks like the top of a push-up. It is not an easy pose, and I was definitely starting to make judgments, such as *I am breathing too hard*, *My arms are hurting*, and *I don't like this pose*. Then the yoga teacher asked us to move our knees so they hovered just above the yoga mat. This made everything even worse! At that moment, I thought to myself, *What am I actually experiencing? What sensations am I having?* and *What are the qualities of these sensations?*

In response, I realized that my arms were actually fine. I could feel my hands pressing into my yoga mat and feel the warm texture of the mat under my fingertips. I could feel my arms and shoulders working, the muscles contracting and engaging as sweat formed on my skin. I could feel muscles contracting in my stomach, although it was not painful. I felt a burning sensation in my thighs that was uncomfortable but not terrible. I also noticed that these sensations shifted in response to small movements, such as when I pressed into my heels or drew my chest forward. Last, I felt my heart beating and my lungs breathing as I thought, *They are probably working to get oxygen to my muscles*. I oriented toward the yoga teacher's voice as she helped us track our breath and sent encouragement. When I focused on the qualities of the sensations, I realized that I was fine.

Sensations have all sorts of other somatic qualities that you can notice within your body. They include fundamental qualities (e.g., size and shape), secondary qualities (e.g., motion, organization, pain), as well as the qualities more closely associated with the body states they are eliciting.

Being with sensations—just noticing all of their qualities, movements, and associated action urges—can be very powerful. I have a phrase I share with my patients quite frequently, which is "Sometimes being with is enough." Consider that, in many cases, there is nothing to do beyond simply noticing each of the sensational qualities you are experiencing.

For example, Gianna, a previous patient of mine, suddenly lost her dog, Sky, in a traffic accident. As she experienced grief, she noticed a sensation that felt like a heavy, large weight on her chest, sometimes extending into her belly. It seemed to arrive in intense waves lasting 5 to 10 minutes. These waves were painful and accompanied by visceral memories of her dog. Gianna described the shape of the sensation as round and solid, yet somehow empty at the same time. When it moved through her body, she said it toppled her. Sometimes she had to find a chair or other form of support, as her knees felt weak. However, Gianna said she did not mind feeling this intense sensation, as it gave her a felt sense of her love for Sky and the powerful role she played in her life. She knew that feeling each sensation was an important part of integrating Sky's tragic death. Each sensation made it possible for Gianna to eventually move through the tragedy.

The next series of practices will help you be with and work with the various qualities associated with your sensations.

Table 8.1. Qualities of Sensations You Might Notice

Fundamental Qualities			
Size: tiny, small, medium, large, gigantic, all-encompassing, bloated, puffy	**Shape:** round, square, triangular, oval, octagonal, even, uneven, thick, thin, tall, short	**Solidity:** dense, firm, soft, squishy, formable, misty, ethereal, airy, bubbly, empty, flaccid	**Temperature:** boiling, scalding, scorching, hot, warm, balmy, cold, frozen, chilly, cool
Color: colorless, flushed, colorful, faded, bright, blue, gold	**Smell:** fruity, flowery, spicy, putrid, burned	**Taste:** spicy, mild, sweet, sour, salty, savory, bitter, tart, acidic	**Sound:** high, deep, rich, low, loud, quiet, pulsating, near, far
Humidity: clammy, fluid, dripping, damp, moist, sweaty, slimy, dry, soggy, soaked, dank, teeming	**Weight:** heavy, light, bulky, pressure, deadweight, lightweight, weightless, top heavy, unbalanced, leaden	**Sharpness:** stabbing, shooting, sharp, tingly, stinging, prickly, smooth, faint, penetrating	**Texture:** fuzzy, smooth, rough, goose bumps, itchy, prickly, tickly, gritty, lumpy, grainy, bristly, slimy, velvety
Secondary Sensation Qualities			
Pain: achy, burning, dull, electric, pins and needles, tingly, weak, strong, persistent, enduring, acute, throbbing, cramping, stabbing, sharp, shooting	**Stability:** static, changing, waving, pulsing, brief, enduring, steady, jerky, weak, strong, balanced, sturdy, firm, permanent, lasting	**Organization:** knotted, jumbly, tight, loose, ordered, concentrated, regular, irregular, systematic, unsystematic	**Motion:** still, fast, slow, blocked, expanding, contracting, radiating, drawing in, moving, churning, buzzy, constricted, fluttery, floaty, vibrating, pushing, pulling
Qualities Associated with Body States			
Intensity: mild, subtle, strong, severe, fierce, violent, extreme, energized, weak, strong, powerful, concentrated, acute, harsh, forceful, vigorous	**Breath:** congested, airy, smooth, choppy, constricted, suffocating, weak, strong, wheezy, gasping, gentle, short, extended	**Muscle state:** clenched, tense, relaxed, constricted, paralyzed, quivery, sore, stiff, tight, trembling, twitchy, weak, strong	**Conscious state:** dizzy, nauseous, numb, paralyzed, quaking, shivery, shuddering, trembling, floaty, wobbly

—Embodying Practice—
Describing a Sensation

The next time you are having a noteworthy sensation, pause and notice. Perhaps you feel a little triggered or the sensation is connected to a big feeling or trauma memory. Notice where in your body you feel the sensation most intensely. Look at the qualities listed in table 8.1, and describe what you feel and experience in the box below. Begin with the fundamental characteristics that align with what you are experiencing, such as the size, shape, solidity, color, smell, taste, and sound of this sensation. Next, explore its secondary qualities, including its organization, pain, and movement. Finally, notice the qualities associated with body states, including its intensity and how this affects your breath, muscles, and consciousness.

Fundamental qualities that I notice:

Secondary qualities that I notice:

Qualities associated with body states that I notice:

Overall reflections:

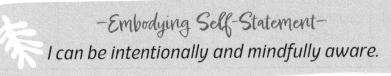

—Embodying Self-Statement—
I can be intentionally and mindfully aware.

—Embodying Practice—
Sensation Tracking: Being with Your Sensations

In this practice, you'll use a technique called sensation tracking to be with and notice the qualities of your sensations (Levine, 2010a). To prepare, you will need a pen or pencil as well as your journal, a blank piece of paper, or computer. Before you begin, review the qualities of sensations described in table 8.1, and make sure you set aside about 30 minutes to complete this practice. If at any point the practice feels overwhelming or overly triggering, stop and engage in a grounding and centering activity, reach out for support, and consider working with a therapist to continue your trauma work. Consider the feeling of overwhelm to be your body's way of asking for a break or more support.

To begin, go to your safe space and find a comfortable seated position. Make sure you feel grounded and well supported. Take a moment to breathe and scan your body for any discomfort or muscle tension. If you can, address the discomfort or tension by adding a pillow or adjusting your posture to provide more support. Make a mental note of where you noticed discomfort or tension. It can be helpful to know what is already there as you are looking for any new sensations. Take a few gentle breath cycles, with slightly extended exhales.

Now set the following intentions: *I can be intentionally and mindfully aware* and *There is nothing to fix*. Then bring to mind a memory of something mildly upsetting. For example, you might think of a time when you felt mildly disappointed or let down by someone close to you. Do not pick a big moment or a trauma memory; choose something smaller that will be easier to work with, like a friend canceling a night out at the last minute or it raining on a day you'd planned on spending outside. Bring this memory to mind.

As you do, scan your body for sensations. You do not need to label how you are feeling. Just scan your body for any arising tensions as you remember this upsetting moment. Then ask:

- **Location:** Where do you feel this sensation most intensely in your body?

- **Fundamental qualities:** What is this sensation like? What is its size, shape, solidity, temperature, sharpness, color, and so on?

- **Secondary qualities:** Do you notice sensations associated with pain? Does the sensation move or waver? If so, where does it move? In what ways does it waver? Does it expand or contract? How long does the sensation last before it moves or goes away? Does the sensation feel organized, jumbled, loose, or concentrated?

- **Qualities associated with body states:** How intense or strong is the sensation? How does it affect your breathing, muscle tension, and thinking?

- **Impulse to respond:** Does the sensation come with a drive to do something, an action urge? Is the urge directional in that it makes you want to push away, draw in, lift up, or press down? Does the urge make you want to run, fight, or withdraw? How strong is that impulse?

- **Difficulty and discomfort:** How difficult or uncomfortable is it to be with this sensation? How difficult is it to be with any action urges that are present? Which is more challenging: the sensation or the action urge?

- **Drive to fix or change:** Do you feel the need to fix or change what you are experiencing? If so, how strong is that drive? How difficult is it to not go with the drive?

There is no need to push for anything more than what you notice. Just be with what is there as you ask yourself these questions. If you'd like, you can place your hands on the spots where you notice any sensations. Allow yourself several minutes to experience any sensation that comes up. If a new sensation arises, go through the same series of questions with the new sensation. If yet another new sensation arises that interrupts your work, note the new sensation in your journal so that you can come back to it, then orient back to the second sensation. As you answer each question, just be with the answer. Once you feel that you are done or 15 minutes have passed (whichever comes first), document what you experienced. Jot down the location, qualities, impulse to respond, and level of discomfort associated with the sensation. You might say to yourself, *It is difficult to be with this sensation* or *This sensation is not easy to be with*. Last, note any drive to fix or change the sensation, and remind yourself that being with the sensation can be enough. There is nothing to fix.

By being with your sensations in this way, you are self-validating your experience as it is seen and heard by you. By being mindfully aware of each aspect of your sensations, you are further developing your capacity for reflection and self-compassion.

To continue with this practice, you can use any of the following prompts to track your sensations and be with them throughout a week. Remember a time this week when:

- You felt reactive.
- You were discouraged or had a setback.
- You had a loss.
- You were frustrated.
- You felt happy, calm, or at peace.

- You felt a sense of joy for someone you care about.
- You remembered something difficult.
- You were worried about something in the future.

→ PAUSE ←
(**P** - Pause, **A** - Assess → **USE** your resources and supports)

☐ **Pause**, check in, and acknowledge how you are feeling. This is a chance to be kind to yourself. The pace of your work is very important. Press your feet into the earth and take four gentle breaths.

☐ **Assess** by asking yourself, *Is this a good place for a break?* If the answer is *yes* or *I don't know*, then fold over the corner of the page and take a break. This workbook is here for you for as long as it takes and for as many breaks as you need.

☐ **USE** your resources. Take a rest. Connect to your trusted friends. Contact your therapist. Practice your favorite well-being strategies. Get back to work when YOU are ready.

—Embodying Practice—
Sensational Yoga Practice

To prepare for this practice, set aside 60 minutes in your practice space. You will need a yoga mat or blanket, a timer, your favorite soothing scent (e.g., infused in oil), a hand towel, and a bottle of flavored water or water infused with sliced fruit (strawberries, oranges, lemons, limes) to taste. You will also need a chime or singing bowl, or you can download a digital version on your phone. I recommend an app called Bowls HD Tibetan Singing Bowls by Oceanhouse Media. Have a pen or pencil and your journal on hand for processing your experience. Don't get stressed out about having the perfect set of materials. Find what works from the things you already have in your household.

Begin by finding a seated position on your yoga mat. Then follow the chart below, taking the posture or engaging the practice, breathing, then responding to the noticing cues in the right-hand column. Use table 8.1 to help you describe your sensations for each practice. You can say what you notice to yourself, say it aloud, or write it down in your journal.

You can take breaks and modify the practice as you'd like, or in response to any sensations that you notice. For example, if you are breathing very heavily, your heart is racing, and you feel like you need a break, you can pause, take a seated pose, and breathe. Take sips of your water until your body settles.

Although you are working with sensations, you might notice emotions and thoughts come up as well. Allow the thoughts or emotions to be there and label them—for example, *I am feeling . . .* or *I am thinking . . .* —then bring your focus back to your sensations.

Time	Practice	Pose	Guidance, Noticing, and Describing
2 min	Prep	None	Gather your mat, timer, water bottle, hand towel, scent, pen, singing bowl (or app), and journal. Silence your phone and start your timer.
2 min	Lotus (or seated) Pose		Press your hands together and your thumbs to your sternum and soften your body. What do you notice in your palms, your chest, the inside of your body, and your heart? Stay here for two minutes.
2 min	Forward Fold		Extend your legs forward, press down through your sitting bones, reach toward your feet, and extend your heart toward your toes. Notice the back of your legs. What sensations do you notice? Describe them. Soften your shoulders. What did you notice? Stay here for two minutes.
2 min	Tadasana (Standing Mountain Pose)		In a standing position, bring your hands to your heart center and press your thumbs to your sternum. Intentionally press your feet into your yoga mat. What do you notice about the yoga mat as your feet press into it? Press your hands together and then soften, releasing the tension. What do you notice in the muscles in your arms? Can you feel your heart beating? Describe the sensations you notice. Stay here for two minutes.

Time	Practice	Pose	Guidance, Noticing, and Describing
3 min	Crescent Lunge Both Sides		Step your left foot back so you are on the ball of your left foot, bring your right knee over your right ankle, lunge forward, and reach both hands toward the ceiling. This is an activating pose. What do you notice in your leg and arm muscles? What do you notice in your belly and chest? Has your breath shifted? Describe the sensations you notice, including any sensations that tell you things are shifting. After 90 seconds, change sides and hold for another 90 seconds on the other side.
2 min	Tadasana (Standing Mountain Pose)		Return to a standing position, bring your hands to your heart center, and press your thumbs to your sternum. Breathe in slowly for 1, 2, 3, 4 . . . and out for 1, 2, 3, 4, 5. Do this four times. Can you feel your heart beating? Your breath? What do you notice? Are things changing? Describe the sensations you notice. Stay here for two minutes.
2 min	Crescent Lunge Right		Step your left foot back into a crescent lunge again and lift your arms. Breathe here and notice the muscles in your legs and arms. See if you can describe the sensations you notice. You might also notice sensations in your belly and chest as you breathe and your heart beats. Stay here for two minutes.
1 min	Warrior II Right		With your right foot pressing down at the front of your mat, press back and down into your left foot, letting your back heel press into the mat, and angle your back foot toward the left side of your mat. Your front knee is bent so it aligns with your front ankle. Reach your right arm to the front of the room and your left arm to the back of the room. Engage your core and soften your shoulders, jaw, and eyes as you breathe gently. What new sensations do you notice in this pose? See if you can describe the sensations you notice. Stay here for one minute.
2 min	Crescent Lunge Left		Return to a standing position, then step your right foot back into a crescent lunge and lift your arms. Breathe here and notice the muscles in your legs and arms. See if you can describe the sensations you notice. You might also notice sensations in your belly and chest as you breathe and your heart beats. Stay here for two minutes.
1 min	Warrior II Left		With your left foot pressing down at the front of your mat, press back and down into your right foot, letting your back heel press into the mat, and angle your back foot toward the right side of your mat. Your front knee is bent so it aligns with your front ankle. Reach your left arm to the front of the room and your right arm to the back of the room. Engage your core and soften your shoulders, jaw, and eyes as you breathe gently. What new sensations do you notice in this pose? See if you can describe the sensations you notice. Stay here for one minute.
2 min	Drink		Return to tadasana (standing mountain pose) and pause. Open your bottle of water and pause to smell the scent coming from the bottle. Describe what you smell, noticing the qualities of the sensation, then take a sip. Describe the taste and temperature of the water. What does it feel like in your mouth? Can you feel it as it goes to your belly? What do you notice? Stay here for two minutes.

Time	Practice	Pose	Guidance, Noticing, and Describing
3 min	Dancer Pose Both Sides		Press your right foot into your mat and bend your left knee back so your heel moves toward your left sitting bone. Move your left hand back, and with your palm facing outward, catch your left ankle on the inside. Reach your right arm forward as a counterbalance. Stay here or gently press your foot into your left hand to extend the posture. What do you notice in this balancing pose? What sensations are present in your foot on the mat? Your foot in your hand? Are you steady? Wobbly? What sensations do you notice in your muscles, your breath, and your heart? After 90 seconds, change sides and hold for another 90 seconds on the other side.
3 min	Forward Fold		Return to a seated position on your mat and move into a forward fold by extending your legs in front of you, pressing your sitting bones in your mat, drawing your heart toward your toes, and reaching your hands forward. You can stay here the full three minutes, or after one minute, you can sit up, bend your left knee, draw your foot in, and place the sole of your left foot on your inner thigh. Reach toward your right foot, heart to toes. Breathing gently, hold for one minute and switch sides. What do you notice in your leg muscles? In what way is one side the same or different from the other? How do you know that? What sensations did you notice?
2 min	Drink		Come to a seated position and pause. Open your bottle of water and pause to smell the scent coming from the bottle. Describe what you smell, noticing the qualities of the sensation, then take a sip. Describe the taste and temperature of the water. What does it feel like in your mouth? Can you feel it as it goes to your belly? Do you notice anything that has changed from the first time? Describe what you notice. Stay here for two minutes.
10 min	Seated Pose		Come to a cross-legged seated pose. Soften or close your eyes. Bring your awareness to the sensation of sound. What do you hear? Consider listening for layers of sound. Can you hear anything from your body? Breath? The sound of small movements? What do you hear in the room? Outside of the room? Outside of the building? Notice sounds at each layer (8 min). Then, slowly orient your awareness back to you (2 min).
10 min	Singing Bowl		Bring your singing bowl or the singing bowl application to your mat right in front of you. Gently play the singing bowl. What sensations do you notice? Sounds? Vibrations? See if you can describe them. You can experiment with different bowls or put water in your singing bowl. What do you notice now? Stay here for 10 minutes.
5–10 min	Resting Pose		Place a drop of your favorite calming scented oil (or spray the infused water) on your hand towel. Lavender can be nice for this. Fold your towel so that it is the right size to cover your eyes. Lay on your back with your feet apart and place the towel over your eyes, scented side up. Place a hand on your belly and a hand over your heart. What sensations do you notice? Do a brief body scan, noticing your muscles, belly, chest, breath, and heart. Notice the sounds and the scent. After a few minutes, relax and let go of noticing. Just breathe and let your mind rest on your breath. Stay here for 5 to 10 minutes.

Once you are done with your practice, take a moment and free write in your journal about your experience. Describe the sensations you noticed and their qualities. Describe if you noticed judgment or even any cues of connection or protection. Describe any thoughts that came up and note whether it was easy or difficult to focus on and describe your sensations. Going forward, you can use this practice or vary the poses and the other sense stimuli for variety.

Embodying Practice
Beauty Seeking: Intentional Orienting

This practice is designed to help you balance your orienting response—which might be chronically oriented toward safety—with a broader experience of exteroceptive sensations. You can do this practice every day, everywhere if you'd like. You can also do it in discrete episodes throughout the day. For example, you might pause at work to do some beauty seeking every two hours. Or you might beauty seek on the way to work, at lunch, and on the way home. The goal is to engage your senses in the process of finding beauty in the world, expanding the experiences to which you orient.

Begin by stepping outside your home and taking a gentle breath in, then release an extended exhale. Press your feet into the earth and lift up through your spine. Take another gentle breath in and an extended exhale. You might say to yourself, *I can be intentionally and mindfully aware.*

From right here, use each of your senses with an orientation of beauty seeking. If at any point your mind wanders to critical thoughts or tries to detect threats around you, take a few gentle breaths and say to your brain, *Brain, we are beauty seeking right now* and orient yourself back to the process.

With your feet grounded and body breathing, take a moment to look all around you. Look side to side, to the area around your feet, and then over your head. Look in front of you and behind you. There is no need to settle quickly on one thing. If you notice something beautiful, let your eyes rest there. You might say, *With my eyes, I see . . .*

Now, soften or close your eyes and listen. Listen to the sounds closest to you. Slowly expand your listening to sounds within 20 feet of you. Then expand more to sounds that might come from something far away. If you hear something beautiful, you might say to yourself, *With my ears, I hear . . .*

Next, bring your awareness to your nose and your sense of smell. Take in a slow breath, breathing only through your nose. What do you notice? You might be able to smell scents that are with you, like the smell of the laundry detergent on your clothes or a lotion you rubbed on your skin earlier in the day. Broaden your awareness and seek out a beautiful smell from your environment. If you notice something beautiful, say to yourself, *With my nose, I smell . . .*

Bring your awareness to your skin. You might notice your clothing, the wind, the temperature, the warmth of the sun. Breathe gently and notice what you feel using your felt sense. If you notice something beautiful, you might say to yourself, *With my felt sense, I feel . . .*

Take as much time as you'd like noticing the beautiful things. Then begin your walk. Pause three or so times to take in what is around you and beauty seek using each of your senses. You do not need to find something beautiful in each area to get it right. Maybe you just notice one thing—a distant sound of a bird chirping or a blade of grass forging its way through concrete. You can close the practice when you arrive at home by mentally noting or journaling about the most beautiful thing you noticed.

Continue to use and develop these practices as you move forward to the chapters on feelings, cognitions, and relationships. Your sensations—and your ability to be with, relate to, and work with them—are central to embodiment. Without a working relationship with sensations, there is no foundation for working with feelings, truly understanding thoughts, or being effective and loving in relationships.

Chapter 9

Connecting to Your Feeling Body

—Embodying Self-Statement—
My body feels emotions.

Building on your sensation work, this chapter digs into the feeling, or emotional, aspect of the embodied self. Throughout this chapter, I will use the words *emotions* and *feelings* interchangeably. I like the word *emotion* because it is composed of *e* (which I like to think represents shifts in energy) and *motion* (which represents the action urges and tendencies that come with emotions). I also like the word *feeling* because it honors the close relationship between sensations and feelings. We feel emotions.

Need-to-Know: Befriending Your Emotions

Emotions are discrete experiences that arise and pass. They are not enduring, like a bad mood, feelings of depression, or free-floating anxiety. They are intentional in that they are about something (Ortony, 2022). Feelings function as reminders of what is important to us and our values. For things that matter to us, they help coordinate our behavior and physiological state. They give us insight into our intuition, our inner knowing. Feelings are a bridge between our sensing, thinking, and relational selves. In essence, feelings are messages. They tell us about how reactive we are, what we are drawn to, what we wish to avoid, how well we are caring for and connecting to our body and its needs, and how well we are caring for and connecting to others. Our emotions also communicate to others through emotion-driven facial expressions, posture, and tone of voice, which all influence how others respond to us.

Critically, emotions are different from facts, yet they are central to making decisions and navigating life. Marsha Linehan, the creator of dialectic behavioral therapy (DBT), believes that true wisdom comes from the integration of our emotional and cognitive experiences. She calls this state *wise mind* and asserts that you cannot be wise without your emotions (Linehan, 1993). Therefore, to embody wisdom, you must first befriend your emotional self.

Emotions are embodied in that we physically feel and experience them, and they motivate and prepare us for action (Mazza et al., 2016; Ogden & Fisher, 2016). For example, when we are sad, we feel heavyhearted, down, lost, downtrodden, or burdened. Sadness is often associated with reduced movement, a closed and somewhat protective posture, and withdrawal. With sadness, we might crawl under the blankets in bed and cry. In contrast, when we are happy, we might feel revved up, light as a feather, on cloud nine, on top of the world, or over the moon. Happiness is often associated with increased movement, an openhearted posture, and social engagement. When we are happy, we might laugh, dance, and socialize with friends.

Although it can be tempting to push away or distract yourself from uncomfortable emotions, there are substantial benefits to befriending *all* your emotions and their accompanying sensations, action urges, and thoughts. If you don't, your emotions and their associated activation patterns can get you into trouble. You might recall from chapter 2 that when you are highly emotional and activated, the feeling part of your brain (the limbic system) tends to act without sufficient input from the thinking part of your brain (the neocortex), leading you to feel hijacked by your emotions. This explains why you might hurt someone you love when you are upset, only to deeply regret it once you have calmed down. With practice, you can learn how to keep the thinking and feeling parts of your brain working together even when you are upset.

Importantly, if you have a history of trauma, it can sensitize you into reacting with trauma-based activation patterns. As a result, you might not realize you are experiencing an emotion until you are already in action—maybe saying something you don't mean in anger, withdrawing from a conversation in fear, or shutting down at a party. This can result in feelings of shame and accompanying thoughts like *Look at what I did again. I am a bad (or out-of-control, hurtful, bitter, harmful) person.* If this is your experience, know that there is no need for shame. Rather, there is a need for you to learn about and practice being with your emotions. However, deconstructing your trauma-based patterns of activation may be challenging, which is why I started this book by expanding your knowledge base, helping you cultivate mindful self-care practices, building your resources, and connecting to your "why." You will need these tools to feel your emotions in an embodied way.

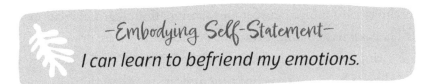

—Embodying Self-Statement—
I can learn to befriend my emotions.

Need-to-Know: Embodied Approaches to Feeling Your Emotions

In this chapter, you will be developing your capacity to experience and notice emotions as they arise. Noticing, which is an aspect of mindfulness, can be a very powerful tool for being with and working with emotional reactivity. When you engage in the practice of noticing, it activates the parts of your brain that help you be less reactive (your neocortex). In order to further develop your mindful noticing skills, you will learn about and practice being with and working with these various qualities and components of emotions.

The Qualities and Components of Emotions

While exploring these qualities and components of emotions, you may move outside of your window of tolerance, or your brain may detect danger and move directly into fight, flight, freeze, or shutdown mode. If this occurs, remember that all of the work you have done so far—developing your ability for mindful awareness, learning grounding and centering skills, and growing your resources—will help you develop the ability to be with and work with emotions. However, if you are moving out of your window of tolerance too frequently or this work begins to feel too overwhelming, pause, take a break, and connect with a therapist or other form of support.

Prompting Event

A prompting event is any event that initiates the experience of a feeling. Prompting events can be internal (like a thought, memory, or internal sensation) or external (like an upsetting email, a near-miss car accident, a hurtful text, an old song, or the experience of seeing a loved one). In order to start tracking the prompting events associated with your emotions, I encourage you to spend the next week or so bringing awareness to the internal or external experiences that seem to prompt or initiate a feeling. By considering the location, context, and associated body sensations associated with these events, you can start making changes to your trauma-based reaction patterns.

For example, a patient of mine, James, tracked his prompting events for three weeks. Most of his prompting events involved interacting with loved ones, especially his parents and his partner. He noticed that most prompting events occurred in the evenings and on the weekends. He also noticed that when he was hungry or tired, he tended to be more sensitive within his relationships, so he made intentional changes to his meal planning and made sure he wasn't skipping meals. He also began taking once-per-week rest days from his workout routine and began going to bed a half-hour earlier.

Another patient, Antonio, tracked his prompting events for two weeks. He noticed right away that Mondays were his worst day. He often isolated himself on the weekends by staying at home, and the transition back to interacting with others on Monday was exhausting for him. As a result, he noticed that many experiences became prompting events on this day that were not prompting events on Fridays. This awareness helped him make changes. For example, on Saturday afternoons, he began going to the gym to decrease his isolation. He also joined a biking group that trained on Mondays, Wednesdays, and Fridays. Although the group didn't talk much, being part of it decreased his isolation, and the exercise helped stabilize his nervous system before going to work. After he made these adjustments, he was able to focus on prompting events that were more closely related to his trauma than those associated with his weekend isolation and Monday transitions back to work.

You can use the log on the next page to track the prompting events for your emotions over the next week.

—Embodying Practice—

Exploring Prompting Event Patterns

Use this log to explore the prompting events for your feelings. For each prompting event, note the date it occurred, the day of the week, the time of day (e.g., morning, midday, afternoon, evening, middle of the night), the location and context (e.g., at work, alone, with others, after yoga class), and any associated body sensations (e.g., hungry, tired, hormonal, sick, hungover). If you feel you are able to identify the specific emotion associated with the prompting event, make note of that as well. At the end of the week, review your list and see if you notice any recurring patterns. Then use the questions below to explore possible patterns in these prompting events.

Date	Day of the Week	Time of Day	Prompting Event	Location and Context	Body Sensations	Emotion

Describe any patterns associated with the day of the week or the time of day. Are there more prompting events in the morning? Afternoon? Are there certain days of the week that seem to have more prompting events?

_____

_____

_____

Describe any patterns associated with location or context. Is there a certain place associated with more prompting events? Are there more prompting events when you are alone or with others? If others, whom?

_____

_____

_____

Are there certain body experiences that are associated with prompting events, such as being tired, hungry, physically exhausted, hormonal, or ill?

_____

_____

_____

Feelings as Sensations

In their groundbreaking study, Lauri Nummenmaa and his colleagues (2014) established a crucial connection between our feelings and sensations. In particular, they found that different emotions provoke discernible patterns of sensations in the body. For example, disgust is associated with increased sensations in the throat and abdomen, while happiness is associated with enhanced activation throughout the entire body. Depression is associated with deactivation in the arms, legs, and head region. Their findings are illustrated in the following body maps, which illustrate the activation level for varying emotions. They concluded that somatosensation (that is, sensations in the body) and embodiment play critical roles in emotion processing. This work, and the studies that have since followed, gave practitioners a pathway for working with patients on the embodiment of emotions.

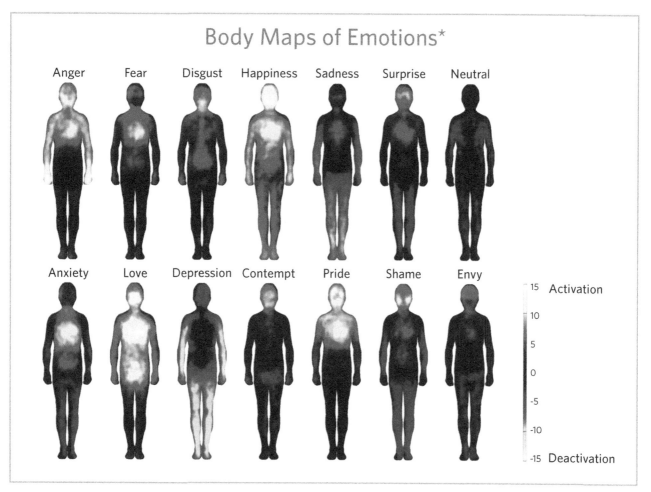

* From "Bodily Maps of Emotions," by L. Nummenmaa, E. Glerean, R. Hari, & J. K. Hietanen, 2014, *Proceedings of the National Academy of Sciences, 111,* p. 647. Reprinted with permission.

So many people get caught up in the story of their emotions that they don't even realize they are having body sensations in response to their feelings. Your work in the previous chapter, in which you learned how to connect to your sensations, will serve as a foundation for working with emotions in this chapter. Look over the body maps and get a sense of what others have noticed when they feel an emotion. In an informal way, begin to notice your body the next time you notice you are having a feeling. It's okay if your experience is different from the body maps above. They are just averages based on data collected to date. Each of us has our own way of feeling our emotions.

—Embodying Self-Statement—
My feelings are an important source of information.

—Embodying Practice—
Informal Tracking of Feeling Sensations

The next time you notice you are having a feeling and can take a few moments to be with it, grab your journal and head to a private location where you can write. As you notice the sensations that accompany your emotions, look back to table 8.1 (**Qualities of Sensations You Might Notice**) and use it to describe what you are noticing. Allow the feeling to just be and turn your awareness toward your body. See if you can let go of the need to label your emotion, judge it, or tell a story. Simply turn back to your body and notice the body sensations that accompany this emotion. As with other sensations, notice its qualities:

- **Location:** Where do you feel this feeling sensation most intensely in your body?

- **Fundamental qualities:** What is this feeling sensation like? What is its size, shape, solidity, temperature, sharpness, color, and so on?

- **Secondary qualities:** Do you notice sensations associated with pain? Does the feeling sensation move or waver? If so, where does it move? In what ways does it waver? How long does the sensation last before it moves or goes away? Does the sensation feel organized, jumbled, loose, or concentrated?

- **Qualities associated with body states:** How intense or strong is the sensation? How does it affect your breathing, muscle tension, and thinking?

- **Impulse to respond:** Does the feeling sensation come with a drive to do something, an action urge? Is the action urge directional in that it makes you want to push away, draw in, lift up, or press down? Does the urge make you want to run, fight, or withdraw? How strong is that impulse?

- **Activation:** What areas of your body feel activated, neutral, or deactivated? Look at the body maps of emotions.

- **Difficulty and discomfort:** How difficult or uncomfortable is it to be with this feeling sensation?

- **Drive to fix or change:** Do you feel the need to fix or change what you are experiencing? If so, how strong is that drive? How difficult is it to not go with the drive?

If it helps, you might want to draw what you notice instead of writing. You might also want to place your hand on the area where you feel the sensations or place your hands on either side of the area to give it a container. Like other sensations, know that these feeling sensations will arise and pass. Just gently breathe and notice each sensation as it appears.

Close the session by acknowledging the effort it took to be with your feeling sensations. Use your name when you do, for example: *[Your name], I am really proud of you for taking time to track your feeling sensations instead of reacting to or engaging with these symptoms. I know this wasn't easy for you. I love you.*

Naming Feelings

When you are able to notice and name your emotions, it activates the thinking part of your brain (the part of your brain associated with language) and brings balance and integration to the emotional part of the brain. This is a cornerstone of healing and self-regulation. It also helps you meet your own fundamental needs of being seen and heard. If you abandon your body, numb out, or distract yourself every time you have a feeling, you miss the chance to get to know yourself during the deepest and most salient moments of your life. You are valuable, and your life is worthy of knowing and honoring.

When you first notice the markers of an emotion, simply say to yourself, *I notice that I am having an emotion.* Then attempt to name the emotion by looking for its associated body experiences and activation patterns. The following table lists several basic emotions and accompanying body experiences you might notice. Use this table to support your exploration about what each feeling feels like for you. Once you have an idea about what feeling you might be experiencing, say to yourself, *I am feeling . . .* (name of emotion).

Table 9.1. Feelings and Associated Body Experiences

Feeling	Body Experiences	Activation Patterns
Love	Increased heart rate; rapid or paused breathing; warmth; a sense of radiating, whole-body activation; a feeling of safety; a sense of wanting or longing; a desire for closeness; excitement; energy; generosity; and activation of the heart area, core, face, arms, and feet	Activating
Happiness	Steady and slightly increased heart rate; steady belly breath; extended exhalation compared to inhalation; increased energy; feeling of being active; sense of fun or peace; feeling open and expansive; and activation of the full body, especially the heart area, face, and hands	Activating
Sadness	Decreased or slowed heart rate (unless very upset, then increased); slow and shallow breathing; breathlessness; heaviness all over (especially in the heart area); fatigue; emptiness; tears; deactivation of the arms and legs; and some activation around the heart, throat, and eyes	Generally deactivating
Anger	Increased heart and breath rate; extended inhalation compared to exhalation; muscle tension; churning in stomach; tight chest; substantial activation in the whole body (especially the upper body, hands, and arms); warmth and heat; sweating; pounding head; facial flushing; shaking; trembling; and urge for sudden expansion (explosiveness)	Activating
Fear	Increased heart rate; breathlessness or short shallow breaths with a longer inhalation compared to exhalation; clenched teeth; urge to vomit; waves of heat followed by coldness and clamminess; butterflies or a dropping feeling in the stomach; and tight hips, shoulders, and jaw	Activating

Feeling	Body Experiences	Activation Patterns
Guilt	Increased heart rate; shallow irregular breaths; a sense that it is difficult to breathe; clenched stomach; redness in the face; jitters; shakiness; slight activation around the heart and face area; and deactivation of the arms and legs	Both activating and deactivating
Shame	Increased or irregular heart rate and breath; heaviness or a sinking feeling in the pit of the stomach; a feeling of contracting in from the side of the body; redness in the cheeks; a sense of shutting down; activation around the heart and face; and deactivation in the arms and legs	Both activating and deactivating

Informed by Cook-Cottone (2020), Ogden & Fisher (2016), Mazza et al. (2016), and Rothenberg (2020)

As you work to name your feelings, slow down if at any point it feels overwhelming. You are worthy of patience and compassion. Go back to just noticing your heartbeat. Gently breathe and place your hands on your heart until you feel a sense of calm. If this is intense or is happening frequently, it is a signal that you might need more support. Consider connecting with your therapist or finding a therapist to work with.

However, if you would like to continue, below is an expanded list of feeling words that you can use as a reference. You can work through each one, using the following exercise to identify the body experiences and activation patterns with which it aligns.

Table 9.2. List of Feelings

Love	Happiness	Sadness	Anger	Fear	Guilt/Shame
Affection	Joy	Dismay	Contempt	Alarm	Regret
Adoration	Cheerfulness	Displeasure	Disgust	Anxiety	Remorse
Attraction	Amusement	Defeat	Revulsion	Fright	Contrition
Caring	Bliss	Dejection	Envy	Horror	Self-reproach
Compassion	Delight	Insecurity	Jealousy	Hysteria	Misgiving
Fondness	Ecstasy	Loneliness	Exasperation	Panic	Liability
Liking	Elation	Rejection	Frustration	Shock	Embarrassment
Tenderness	Gaiety	Despair	Aggravation	Terror	Anguish
Longing	Gladness	Gloom	Agitation	Dread	Disgrace
Desire	Glee	Melancholy	Annoyance	Apprehension	Dishonor
Kindness	Jolliness	Misery	Grumpiness	Distress	Humiliation
Warmth	Jubilation	Sorrow	Irrationality	Worry	Contempt
Appreciation	Contentment	Woe	Bitterness	Tenseness	Humility
Devotion	Pleasure	Agony	Fury	Uneasiness	Stigmatization
Reverence	Eagerness	Anguish	Hate	Jumpiness	Degradation
Admiration	Optimism	Hurt	Loathing	Trepidation	Scorn
Yearning	Pride	Suffering	Spite	Jitteriness	Culpability
Craving	Triumph	Unhappiness	Vengefulness	Consternation	Repentance
Lusting	Thrill	Hopelessness	Torment	Concern	Responsibility
Passion	Excitement	Grief	Wrath	Timidity	Abasement

Embodying Practice
Feeling Exploration

To complete this practice, write down a prompting event that caused you to experience the markers of an emotion. Allow yourself to be with the emotion, noticing the feeling sensations, body experiences, and activation patterns associated with it. Then use pencils, pens, felt pens, or colored pencils to draw or write about what you noticed in your body. When you're done, use this information to put a name to the emotion you are experiencing.

Date: _____

The prompting event was: _____.
(a few words to label the event)

What I noticed was (include feeling sensations and shifts in activation patterns):

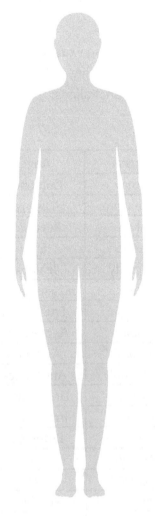

I am feeling: _____
(name of the emotion)

—Embodying Practice—
Feeling, Sensing, and Naming an Emotion

This meditation practice is designed to support your ability to be with and explore both a pleasurable emotion and a difficult emotion. When choosing an experience associated with a difficult emotion, select something that is only mildly difficult. Your goal is to practice being with and experiencing your emotions somatically. If you choose a very difficult or a traumatic experience, it can be too challenging to effectively practice and gain skills. As you gain competency over time, you can work your way up to more difficult emotions.

To begin, find a quiet space and set about 45 minutes that you can devote to this practice. You will need your journal and a writing tool. You can read this meditation or record it so you can listen to it while you breathe and relax.

Pleasurable Feeling

First, bring to mind a recent experience when you noticed that you were feeling a pleasurable emotion. Maybe you felt happy, at peace, joyful, proud, accomplished, or content. Think about the experience and who was there, where you were, what was happening, and even what you were wearing. Pause and write down a brief title for the experience, or say it to yourself. When you have a good sense of the feeling you are experiencing, you can pause and say or write, *I am feeling* . . . This might happen now, or it might happen as you spend time with the feeling sensations.

Now, bring the experience to mind more deeply. Scroll in your mind to the moment you realized you were having this pleasurable feeling. Bring it to mind as if you were there now. What shifts do you notice in your level of activation? Do you feel activated, deactivated, or both? Where in your body do you notice this activation or deactivation? What other sensations do you notice related to your level of activation? Is your heart beating faster or slower? What is your breath like? Is it smooth and deep? Are there longer inhales or exhales? Does your breath vary or stop?

Next, do a body scan. Notice where you experience any associated feeling sensations most intensely and bring awareness to this area. Can you describe any particular feeling sensation? What is its size, shape, solidity, temperature, sharpness, and color? How intense, strong, or big is it? Does it move or waver? Where does it move? In what ways does it waver? How difficult or uncomfortable is it to be with this feeling sensation? Is it activating or deactivating? When you're done noticing all the qualities of this feeling sensation, see if you notice any other feeling sensations in other areas of the body. Go through each feeling sensation and notice its qualities. If you'd like, you can pause here and write or draw what you noticed.

Difficult Feeling

Now, in the same way, bring to mind a recent *mildly* difficult experience, one where you recall feeling a more challenging emotion. Maybe you felt frustrated, angry, worried, guilty, or regretful. Think about the experience and who was there, where you were, what was happening, and even what you were wearing. Pause and write down a brief title for the experience, or say it to yourself. When you have a good sense of the feeling you are experiencing, you can pause and say or write, *I am feeling . . .* This might happen now, or it might happen as you spend time with the feeling sensations.

Now, bring the experience to mind more deeply. Scroll in your mind to the moment you realized you were having this difficult feeling. Bring it to mind as if you were there now. What shifts do you notice in your level of activation? Do you feel activated, deactivated, or both? Where in your body do you notice this activation or deactivation? What other sensations do you notice related to your level of activation? Is your heart beating faster or slower? What is your breath like? Is it smooth and deep? Are there longer inhales or exhales? Does your breath vary or stop?

Next, do a body scan. Notice where you experience any associated feeling sensations most intensely and bring awareness to this area. Can you describe any particular feeling sensation? What is its size, shape, solidity, temperature, sharpness, and color? How intense, strong, or big is it? Does it move or waver? Where does it move? In what ways does it waver? How difficult or uncomfortable is it to be with this feeling sensation? Is it activating or deactivating? When you're done noticing all the qualities of this feeling sensation, see if you notice any other feeling sensations in other areas of the body. Go through each feeling sensation and notice its qualities. If you'd like, you can pause here and write or draw what you noticed.

To close, bring yourself back to the present moment. You are in your quiet space. You are doing difficult and important work, getting to know your feelings and befriending your body. Take a moment to acknowledge your work and your worthiness. Then take three gentle breaths. If you'd like, go back to your journal to document any additional observations.

PAUSE
(**P** - Pause, **A** - Assess ➝ **USE** your resources and supports)

☐ **Pause**, check in, and acknowledge how you are feeling. This is a chance to be kind to yourself. The pace of your work is very important. Press your feet into the earth and take four gentle breaths.

☐ **Assess** by asking yourself, *Is this a good place for a break?* If the answer is *yes* or *I don't know*, then fold over the corner of the page and take a break. This workbook is here for you for as long as it takes and for as many breaks as you need.

☐ **USE** your resources. Take a rest. Connect to your trusted friends. Contact your therapist. Practice your favorite well-being strategies. Get back to work when YOU are ready.

Level of Activation

In your work with the window of tolerance, you have learned what it means to notice your level of activation, or arousal. Your level of activation can help you know how important the prompting event is to you, or how close the prompting event is to your trauma memories. It can also reflect a lot of other things, including your current level of fatigue or exhaustion. This is why it is important to pause and use the Self-Awareness Scale from chapter 3 as you progress through this trauma work.

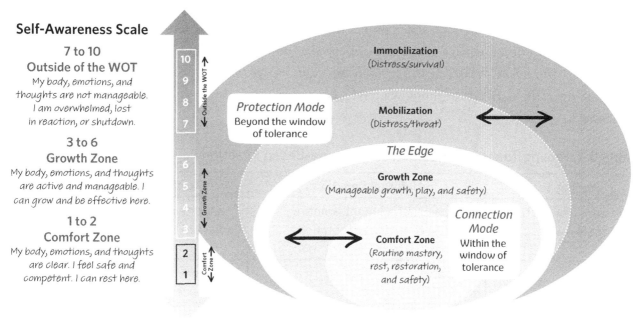

Your level of activation will evolve like an arc: beginning at your typical state, moving up into activation, and eventually moving back down to your typical state. As you learn how to feel your emotions in an embodied way, you will want to note where you are on the arc. For example: *I am activated at a 4 and increasing, I am activated at a 7 and peaking,* or *I am activated at a 6 and decreasing.* The direction you are headed is as informative as your number.

Remember that if at any point your activation level gets above a 6, it is important to pause. Once you are outside of your window of tolerance (score of 7–10), it can be difficult to make well-regulated and integrated decisions. In these moments, you don't want to reply to a hurtful email or text, give someone "a piece of your mind," or commit to a project because you are excited and feel happy.

Feeling Tones and Habitual Reactions

A feeling tone is your experience of something being pleasant and comfortable, neutral, or unpleasant and uncomfortable. A habitual reaction is the automatic process of reacting to the feeling tone with attachment or aversion (Cook-Cottone, 2020; Grabovac et al., 2011). For example, when someone has a pleasant or comfortable emotion, they might think, *This is wonderful. I like this feeling. I can't wait to do this again!* This primes them to do something to maintain the feeling or repeat what they believe is creating it (*attachment*). In contrast, when someone has an unpleasant or uncomfortable feeling, they might think, *This is bad. I don't like feeling this way. I am not doing this again*, which primes them to avoid or push away the feeling or what they believe is causing it (*aversion*). This automatic process happens every day, all day, to all of us.

For individuals who have been through trauma, this process is experienced through the lens of threat and protection, causing them to react with trauma-based reaction patterns. Trauma-based reaction patterns are more intense and linked to threat and safety rather than preference (Ogden & Fisher, 2016). For example, when a feeling is experienced as pleasant, a traumatized person might think, *This is good. I am safe. But if this stops, I am not okay*, which primes them to desperately cling to the experience or attempt to recreate it. In contrast, when a feeling is experienced as unpleasant, a traumatized person might react by thinking, *This is bad. I don't like feeling this way. I can't tolerate this. I am not okay*, which primes them to go into fight, flight, freeze, or shutdown mode. Neutral experiences can go either way, depending on the context.

Table 9.3. Feeling Tones and Habitual and Trauma-Based Reactions

Feeling Tone	Habitual Reaction	Trauma-Based Reaction
Pleasant, comfortable, desirable ➡	Approach, attachment, wanting, desire, receptivity, acceptance, openness	Desperate clinging, craving, addiction
Neutral ➡	Neutral	There may be no neutral; feelings are experienced as safe or unsafe
Unpleasant, uncomfortable, aversive ➡	Avoidance, aversion, refusal, repulsion, rejection	Escape, defend, fight, flight, freeze, shut down, numb with substances

Being aware of and noticing the feeling tone associated with your trauma-based reaction patterns will give you more space between the feeling and your response. It gives you a chance to pause, slow down, stop the automatic process, and do something more intentional that supports your well-being. This, in turn, enhances the connections between the thinking and feeling parts of your brain. The more these parts are integrated and working together, the more balanced and intentional your response can be.

For example, a patient of mine, Joey, had a complicated relationship with anger. Whenever he felt anger, it was extremely uncomfortable (feeling tone), and he would try to avoid the feeling (habitual reaction). He also found that whenever he became really activated by anger (6+ on the Self-Awareness Scale), he was at risk for being aggressive, violent, or shutting down (trauma-based reaction). Being aware of this process was Joey's first step in changing his automatic and harmful patterns of behavior.

Emotional Expression

The way we express our emotions plays an integral role in meeting our needs and informing our relationships. However, trauma can lead people to underexpress and overexpress their emotions. People who underexpress their emotions may silence themselves, not speak out for fear that others will lash out, smile to suppress tears, or brush off their experience (e.g., "I am fine" or "There is nothing wrong"). They may also exhibit overcontrolled body movements and modulate their voice in a way that looks and sounds stiff. Conversely, people who overexpress their emotions might yell at others when irritated, let others know what they are feeling (even when it is ineffective to do so), or roll their eyes in professional settings when they disagree with someone.

Clinically, I have observed that the underexpression of feelings is often followed by the overexpression of feelings. For example, Joey rarely expressed his anger, but when he did, it came out hurtful and raw. As a child, he grew up in a household where his parents fought constantly, often screaming at each other and sometimes striking out physically. When he was old enough, Joey joined the military and married his high school girlfriend. They had two children. When he returned from a difficult deployment, he struggled at home—often shutting down, isolating, and working hard to keep his emotions to himself (*underexpression*). This wasn't sustainable, so these periods of emotional suppression were often followed by emotional outbursts where Joey would lose his temper with his wife and children (*overexpression*). This was the reason he came to get help.

In order to effectively express your emotions, you must be able to experience a feeling, manage your accompanying activation level, and then share the experience of the feeling with someone else (e.g., a trusted friend, a loved one, a therapist) or in other meaningful ways (e.g., in a journal or through movement, art, music, poetry, activism). At the end of this chapter, you will explore ways to be with, express, and work with your emotions. Right now, I would like you to explore your relationship with several basic emotions, including the feeling tone, natural reactions, activation levels, and your tendency to over- and/or underexpress the emotion.

Noticing Habitual and Trauma-Based Reaction Patterns

This practice helps you explore your reaction to some of the more basic emotions. As you progress through this work, you might explore more variants of these emotions and add them to your table. It might also be helpful to check out the feelings and body experiences listed in table 9.1 to see if you notice any additional patterns. For example, are there certain types of sensations that you more readily allow? Are there certain sensations that you avoid?

In the table below, fill in the feeling tone, habitual or trauma-based reaction pattern, and activation level you experience for each emotion. In addition, note whether you tend to overexpress or underexpress that emotion.

Emotion	Feeling Tone	Habitual or Trauma-Based Reaction	Typical Activation Level (1–10)	Overexpression vs. Underexpression
Love				
Happiness				
Sadness				
Anger				
Fear				
Guilt				
Shame				

After filling out the table, what patterns do you notice? Is there anything you'd like to work on? A feeling you'd like to get better at being with? Conversely, what strengths do you notice?

_____

_____

_____

The next time you are having a big emotion, use the following script to help you organize your experience. This might give you space to make an effective choice that serves you, your context, and your relationship.

"I notice the feeling tone for this emotion is _____ and my reaction pattern

is _____. My activation level is a _____,

and I realize I tend to _____ (over- and/or under)express this emotion."

Action Urges

An action urge is anything you feel like doing or tend to do while having a particular emotional experience. Action urges can be experienced in two ways: (1) a readiness or tendency to accept, receive, and approach or (2) a readiness or tendency to defend, escape, avoid, or shut down (Ogden et al., 2006). Action urges extend from your habitual reactions to feeling tones, and they shift with activation levels. For example, when you are in your comfort or growth zone, you have a readiness to accept, receive, and approach. But whenever you get to the edge or outside of the window of tolerance, you experience a readiness to defend, escape, avoid, or shut down.

I have worked with many patients who mistake action urges for the feeling itself. For Joey, it played out like this. Once he was activated, his action urge was to yell at whoever was in the room—often his wife and the kids. Sometimes he felt his arms activate with anger and he felt like striking out. He responded to this urge by swiping dishes off the table, throwing plates or glassware against the wall, storming out the door, and driving to a bar. Joey initially thought these behaviors *were* his anger, but through our work together, he began to see that his action urges and accompanying tendencies were not the feelings themselves. Once he was able to be with his anger without getting so activated, he began learning more about the ways this feeling could help him. He learned that anger let him know when his needs and desires were not being met in his relationships. This was important because it was his relationship problems, and not his trauma history, that brought him to therapy.

Another patient of mine, Lala, had difficulties with action urges too. She had a strong history of numbing out her past sexual abuse with alcohol. Whenever she began to feel anything at all, she drank. This worked—until it didn't and Lala ended up in the emergency room with alcohol poisoning. The prompting event? Her boyfriend told her that he loved her. Although this is what she wanted, Lala was overwhelmed with feelings. She drank excessively that night because she did not have skills for being with her emotions. Learning about her emotions and developing the ability to be with big emotions was extremely helpful in Lala's work to get sober.

Action urges have a drive behind them. You feel compelled to do the thing that it feels like your body wants you to do. Once they are in play, it can be difficult to deny them. Imagine how difficult it would be for Joey to stop throwing a glass at the wall once it was in his hand, or for Lala to not drink once she had opened a bottle of wine. It helped both Joey and Lala to learn that action urges have an arc. That means that they arise, peak, and pass. Therefore, if you notice an action urge coming on, you don't need to act on it. You can ride it out and let it pass. The following meditation practice will help you practice this skill.

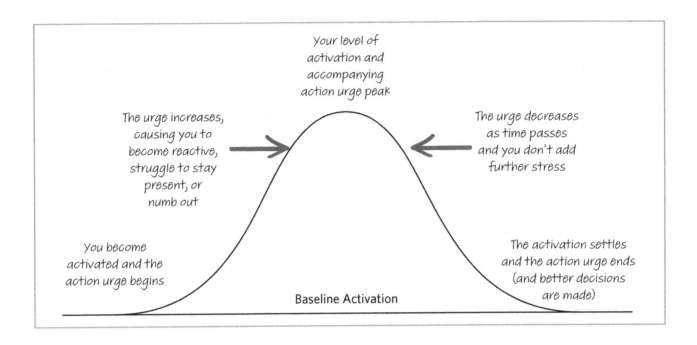

Your level of
activation and
accompanying
action urge peak

The urge increases,
causing you to
become reactive,
struggle to stay
present, or
numb out

The urge decreases
as time passes
and you don't add
further stress

You become
activated and the
action urge begins

The activation settles
and the action urge ends
(and better decisions
are made)

Baseline Activation

—Embodying Practice—
Riding the Wave of Arousal and Action Urge*

This meditation will help you practice riding the wave when you experience the urge to act out on a big emotion. You can either read through the script or make a recording of it to play back for yourself. Before you begin, make sure you have at least 10 minutes you can devote to the practice. Then find a seat in a comfortable chair that allows your feet to feel well supported on the ground. Make any adjustments as needed, then continue.

Now imagine the last time you felt activated by a feeling, and you had a relatively strong urge to do something about it. Maybe you received a hurtful email or text and you wanted to fire one right back. Or maybe you heard about something hurtful that someone did and you wanted to call them out. If you can, name the feeling you were experiencing in this moment and say to yourself, *I am feeling . . .*

Scan your body and locate the feeling sensations associated with this emotion. If you notice them in more than one spot, focus on the spot where you feel it the most. Then describe the qualities of this sensation, including its size, shape, solidity, temperature, sharpness, movement, color, and so on. As you describe this feeling sensation, notice your level of activation and whether you have any accompanying action urge. Describe this urge and what you'd like to do.

Then bring your awareness to your breath and notice as it moves in and out of your body. Allow your breath to be gentle and soft. Allow each exhale to last a bit longer than each inhale.

Turn back into your feeling sensations, activation level, and action urge. Imagine that they are all a part of a big wave. Just like a wave on the beach comes and goes, this wave will arise and pass. However, also like a wave at the beach, when you try to fight the ocean, it can crash down on you or exhaust you in the process. Therefore, rather than trying to fight this wave, imagine yourself riding it like a surfer gliding through the ocean. If you need more support for this visualization, find something stable and grounded you can touch, like the arm of a chair. Just as the surfer grabs onto the edge of the surfboard, it is okay to ground yourself and breathe.

Once your level of activation and accompanying action urge have peaked and subsided, you might want to use the Self-Awareness Scale to note how activated you were and how long this activation lasted before it peaked. These data points can help you the next time a wave comes your way.

—Embodying Self-Statement—
I feel so that I can heal.

* Informed by Juarascio et al. (2016) and Cook-Cottone (2020).

Feeling-Based Thoughts

When you experience strong emotions, you can have feeling-based thoughts that are driven by these emotions. Importantly, feeling-based thoughts are *not* an accurate read of the current moment and context. Rather, they reflect the emotion you are having, your activation level, and your action urge. When you are having a feeling-based thought, the feeling part of your brain is highly activated, and the thinking part of your brain is not contributing much at all. This is why after you have calmed down, your thoughts are more balanced and you can speak from a more integrated state of being.

Feeling-based thoughts have three general characteristics: They are global, stable, and certain. They are *global* in that these thoughts are broad and inclusive, such as *Everything is bad, All people are hurtful,* and *You can't trust anyone.* They are *stable* in that they assume an enduring and unchangeable future, such as *I will never be safe, People never change,* and *I will always be afraid.* Finally, they are *certain* in that everything feels absolute and you accept your emotions as facts. You basically tell yourself, *I feel it, so it must be true.* However, this type of emotional reasoning lacks factual context and is often short on logic because it lacks a careful and honest balancing of the probability of things.

When you are in a state of high emotionality, your thoughts have these global, stable, and certain characteristics. In contrast, when you are in a state of low emotionality, your thoughts tend to be more specific, variable, and uncertain in that they correctly and honestly assess probability. You realize nothing is really certain. The following table provides examples of high- and low-emotionality thoughts.

Table 9.4. High- and Low-Emotionality Thoughts

Emotion	High Emotionality: Global, Stable, and Certain	Low Emotionality: Specific, Variable, and Uncertain
Happiness	I am over the moon. Other people are amazing. The world is a loving place.	I am feeling happy right now. Other people can be really lovely. This world has many good people in it.
Sadness	I am devastated. Other people are soulless. The world is hopeless.	I am feeling so sad right now. Other people can be selfish at times. This world is a precarious place.
Anger	I am so frustrated. Other people are hurtful jerks. The world is unfair.	I feel angry right now. Other people can do hurtful things sometimes. The world is a complicated place.
Fear	I am not safe. Other people are dangerous. The world is unsafe.	I am feeling afraid right now. People can be scary when they are upset. At times, it can feel like the world is unsafe.
Guilt and shame	I am bad. Other people are bad. The world is a bad place.	I am feeling regretful. Other people make mistakes too. I am hopeful the world can be forgiving.

—Embodying Practice—
Exploring Your Feeling-Based Thoughts

The next time you are having a big feeling, grab your journal and write down any thoughts you are having. In your list, include thoughts that take the form of *I am . . .* , *Other people are . . .* , and *The world is . . .* statements. Do not go into a story about these thoughts. Keep it to a list of statements. Continue to write this list, without judgment or evaluation, until there are no feeling-based thoughts that you have not documented.

When you are done, choose a grounding or centering practice from your list of resources. Take at least 10 minutes to engage in this practice. If you are really upset, consider connecting to your inner refuge and calling in your protector.

Once you feel calmer, more grounded, and centered, go back to your list. Look at each thought with a sense of curiosity and see what you notice. Then ask yourself these questions:

- Are these statements global, stable, and certain? Do they look like high-emotionality statements?

- What was your activation level (1–10) as you wrote these statements? Were you outside of your window of tolerance?

- What did your body feel like when you were writing these statements? What feeling sensations and action urges were present?

Then, see if you can rewrite your statements using the following suggestions:

- **Add the word *feeling*:** Differentiate yourself from the feeling. For example, if you said, "I am furious," rewrite it to say, "I am feeling furious."

- **Add specificity:** Add specificity where your statements are global. Look for words like *everyone, everything, always, never, all of the time, every day*—anything that indicates all-or-nothing thinking. For example, if you said, "Everyone is hateful," you might reword it to say, "My father was drunk and angry. He is scary when he's like that." Or if you said, "I am always hurt by others," you could rework it to say, "I am feeling hurt that my friend did not include me today."

- **Add accurate probability:** Consider the probability that your statement is true 100 percent of the time. Very few things are true all of the time (e.g., gravity holds things to the earth and 2+2=4). Most things have varying levels of probability. If a statement has a strong sense of certainty, it is very likely that it is a high-emotionality statement. Watch for absolute words word like *never* and *always*.

- **Add self-compassion:** This is a very important step, as the goal is not to invalidate your highly emotional self. Offer yourself some loving-kindness in this moment by looking over your high-emotionality statements and recalling the sensations and activation you felt in your body at the time. Consider how stressful it was for you to feel so much and for it to affect your thoughts in this way. Then offer your highly emotional self some loving-kindness, and remember that you are not alone in this experience. We all have moments when our emotions run the show.

When you are done, write a bit about what you noticed while doing this exercise. What sensations, emotions, and thoughts did you notice before and after completing the centering and grounding practice? What was it like to rework your feeling-based thoughts? How did it feel to offer yourself some self-compassion?

Chapter 10

Advanced Practices for Being with and Working with Your Feelings

—Embodying Self-Statement—

I can build my capacity to be with and work with my emotions.

The capacity to be with and work with your emotions gives you choice. You are no longer stuck in a trauma-based reaction pattern. The more you practice, the more resilient you will become, and with increased resiliency comes stronger self-regulation and determination. You will be increasingly able to stay mindfully aware, noticing what is happening inside and outside of your body. You will be better able to stay connected to your intentions and embody intentional choice.

To facilitate your ability to be with and work with your emotions in this manner, this chapter offers more advanced feelings-based practices to support a deeper processing and understanding of your feelings. Some of these practices are yoga-based, movement exercises that are designed to help you be with and experience action urges within a low-cost context. A low-cost context means you can be with your feelings and accompanying action urges without substantial impact to yourself or others. For example, on the yoga mat, you can safely be with the experience of anger, with the action urge to fight, and with the movement of pushing someone away. You can explore all these feelings within the context of safety, privacy, and an opportunity to grow and learn.

—Embodying Practice—
Being with Difficult Emotions

This meditation practice can be helpful when you have experienced a challenging prompting event that has caused a difficult, yet manageable, emotion to arise. It will allow you to experience the emotion fully without acting on it.

Begin by sitting in a comfortable position, with your feet and sitting bones grounded, your core engaged, and your spine extended. If it feels right, soften your gaze or close your eyes. Then bring to mind the difficult situation or prompting event. Imagine it as if you were there in that moment. What are you wearing? Who is there? Are you inside or outside? Let the moment play out to the point where the difficult emotions become most intense.

Now, move your attention to the difficult emotion associated with the prompting event. Locate the emotion in your body. If it is helpful, do a simple body scan here by bringing your awareness to your feet, legs, hands, arms, torso, neck, and head. See if you can sense the area in your body where you feel the emotion most intensely. Bring your awareness to this place and pause to be with these feeling sensations.

Once you locate this place, see if you have a sense of how big the area is. Notice if there is an outer edge to where you are feeling the emotion. What is the experience of your body at the edge? Notice if your body is contracting around the feeling or trying to contain it in some way. Now see if you can soften yourself around the very edge of the area where you are feeling the emotion most intensely. You might offer, *I am here. I am being with my emotion. I am not asking it to go away. I am simply being with my emotion.* Your softening and your words are a form of physical compassion for you and your embodied emotion. Take time to pause here and be with the physical sensation of the emotion.

While you are sitting here being with your emotion, notice the qualities of this emotion. Is it hard, deep, tingly, clenched, tight, or painful? Is it big, small, warm, or cool? Does it radiate or contract? Is it still or moving? Is its size stable? Or does it get bigger or smaller? As you notice, remind yourself that you can continue to soften around its edges.

Remind your emotion that it has your permission to be there. Imagine breathing around the edge of the feeling, as a way of softly holding a physical space for this embodied emotion. There is nothing to fix or change, and everything to notice. Pause here and allow the experience of being with this emotion to simply be. If it feels right for you, place your hands on the spot where you are noticing the emotion. Be with that part of your body, with your hand resting on the spot. You can also slowly massage the spot in circles while you breathe. You might gently repeat to yourself, *I am here. I am here. I am here.*

Take a moment to acknowledge to yourself how hard it is to feel difficult emotions and to stay with them, softening and being with them. It is challenging for all humans to feel difficult emotions. We all struggle in this way sometimes. Offer loving-kindness to the emotion and to yourself. Offer yourself gratitude for engaging in this practice and for doing the work that it takes to grow. Thank yourself for remembering that you are worth the effort. As you are ready, bring your awareness to your breath, slowly open your eyes, and anchor your gaze on something in the room.

—Embodying Self-Statement—
Feeling difficult emotions is challenging and important to my growth.

Self-Soothing with Internal Somatic Resources

When intense, highly activating, or arousing emotions are present, you might want to pause and engage in self-soothing practices in which you access your internal somatic resources. These include any postures, movements, or actions that you take to help you feel calmer and less activated. The following are suggestions for self-soothing practices that you can incorporate into your routine so you can more effectively be with and work with difficult emotions. Check the ones that might work for you and add ideas of your own. It can also be helpful to keep a journal to record whenever you engage in a self-soothing practice, describe the context in which it was used, and the effects of the self-soothing practice.

☐ Hug yourself. You might also gently rock yourself, softly hum, or quietly sing a calming song.

☐ Find a cozy chair, couch, or bed where you can curl up into a ball; draw a blanket or sheet over you for comfort; and hold a pillow.

☐ Rub or self-massage your stress points (i.e., your temple, jaw, arms, shoulders).

☐ Rock your body side to side or front to back while sitting or standing.

☐ Cuddle under a heavy or weighted blanket.

☐ Place one or both hands on your heart.

☐ Do "butterfly taps" by crossing your arms over your chest and gently patting your upper arms with your hands.

☐ Offer yourself gentle stimulation by gently blowing air into your cupped hands or running your fingers gently up and down the insides and outsides of your arms.

☐ Give yourself a foot or hand massage with body butter or a soothing lotion.

☐ Touch your thumbs on each finger as you breathe in, finger 1, 2, 3, 4 . . . and then breathe out, finger 1, 2, 3, 4. You can use one or both hands.

☐ Spray your favorite scent on a towel and place the towel over your face (the unscented side on your skin) as you lie down.

☐ Practice self-holding by gently placing your hands on either side of your head (or one hand on your forehead and one on your heart, or one hand on your belly and the other on your heart).

☐ Move! Walk, shake, pace, run, or move your body in any way that feels good and allows energy to move through you.

☐ Stretch anywhere you feel tension, such as your neck, shoulders, back, glutes, legs.

☐ Settle your body into stillness and gently breathe.

☐ Create your own list of self-soothing practices that are helpful to you:

_____

_____

Having an Emotion over for Tea*

When you are experiencing an emotion and are not sure what your action urge is or even what the prompting event for the emotion is, this practice can be helpful. It can also be a good way to give your feeling self a voice. This can be especially healing if you have been raised or conditioned to suppress or silence feelings.

To begin, make sure you are in a comfortable and private space and you're feeling well supported in your seat. Orient toward your feet and sitting bones for a sense of groundedness. Extend through your spine and soften your shoulders, jaw, and eyes. Then bring to mind the feeling you would like to work with.

Imagine that you are in your house sitting at your kitchen table. Your emotion approaches, knocks on the door, and says, "Hello, it's me, _____ (anger, fear, love, etc.)."

You reply, "Hello, _____ (anger, fear, love, etc.). Please come in. Would you like some tea?"

Your emotion says, "Yes, I would like some tea," and you ask your emotion to take a seat at the kitchen table while you brew some tea.

Once you have made the tea, you bring two cups to the kitchen table, one for you and one for your emotion. Then you ask your emotion any questions you'd like, such as:

- "Why are you here?"

- "What do you want or need?"

- "Are you concerned with the past, future, or present moment?"

- "Are you feeling a sense of urgency or distress? Tell me about that."

- "Is there anything you'd like me to do?"

- "Have you consulted the thinking or intuitive self? What might it say?"

* Adapted from Cook-Cottone (2020).

Allow your emotion to answer each question fully. If you'd like, you can write the emotion's answers in your journal. Or, to better embody them, you can take the emotion's point of view and act out its answer.

As you finish your tea, ask your emotion if there is anything else it would like to say. Thank your emotion for using its voice and sharing its experience. As you walk your emotion to the door, assure it you will consider everything it has said very carefully.

Once your emotion has left, place a hand on your belly and a hand on your heart. Offer yourself comfort and acknowledgment for being with your emotion. As you are ready, bring your awareness back to your breath, body, feet, and sitting bones. Soften your shoulders and jaw. Slowly connect back to the here and now as you notice the space around you. Then close your practice with three gentle inhales and exhales. If you'd like, take a moment to write what you noticed in your journal. It can be helpful to date the entry and provide any context that might be helpful when you read over this in the future.

—Embodying Self-Statement—
*I can work to be open to the messages
my emotions are sending me.*

PAUSE

(P - Pause, **A** - Assess ➡ **USE** your resources and supports)

☐ **Pause**, check in, and acknowledge how you are feeling. This is a chance to be kind to yourself. The pace of your work is very important. Press your feet into the earth and take four gentle breaths.

☐ **Assess** by asking yourself, *Is this a good place for a break?* If the answer is *yes* or *I don't know*, then fold over the corner of the page and take a break. This workbook is here for you for as long as it takes and for as many breaks as you need.

☐ **USE** your resources. Take a rest. Connect to your trusted friends. Contact your therapist. Practice your favorite well-being strategies. Get back to work when YOU are ready.

Need-to-Know: Yoga-Based, Somatic Practices for Working with Emotions

When you are working with emotions, the goal is to integrate the experience of the emotion (including its associated feeling sensations and thoughts) while staying within the comfort and growth zones. In this way, you are mindfully aware of and connected to your emotional experience, while also staying connected to your intentions and capacity to choose your responses and actions carefully.

As you are feeling your feelings, you will need to explore what is the best way for you to be with and work with each one in the moment. Sometimes this means mobilizing your body and moving through the accompanying action urge. Other times this means working to balance your nervous system as you experience the emotion. And other times it means calming and deactivating your nervous system as you experience the emotion. What you need in the moment will depend on the state of your body (e.g., fight, flight, freeze, shutdown). For example, if you are feeling frozen, you will need practices that facilitate accessible movement to get you unstuck. If you are feeling overwhelmed and overactivated, you will need grounding practices that provide a sense of balance.

Here is where yoga-based somatic practices add tremendous value to working with emotions, as they are based on what you need in the current moment. Yoga provides you with the time and space to experience the way energy moves in your body. In its most basic form, energy moves in four directions—up, down, out, and in—which connect nicely with your action urges. One way to experience this association is by working with small simple movements in a seated position and notice what you feel energetically. You can also do this as you are having difficult feelings and notice how yoga may shift your bodily experience and emotional state.

In this section, I offer the following types of yoga-based practices: (1) accessible movement practices; (2) balancing, centering, and grounding practices; (3) mobilizing and activating practices; (4) softening and heart-opening practices; and (5) containing practices. These practices will give you a chance to experiment with matching movement and direction with what is needed as you are feeling an emotion. These practices are based on techniques from trauma-informed yoga (Spence, 2021), therapeutic yoga for trauma recovery (Schwartz, 2022), somatic experiencing (Levine, 2010b), dialectic behavioral therapy (Linehan, 1993), and sensorimotor psychotherapy (Ogden & Fisher, 2016). The following table can help you explore which practices might be right for you, depending on the state of your body.

Table 10.1 Matching Needs, Practices, and Directions

Body State	What Is Needed and Suggested Yoga Practices	Directions to Explore
Shutdown or freeze	What is needed: Gentle, small movements to get unstuck and slowly begin to mobilize the body Suggested yoga practices: • Accessible movement practices • Balancing, centering, and grounding practices • Softening and heart-opening practices • Containing practices	• Press down • Draw in • Lift up • Express out
Fight or flight	What is needed: Practices to settle your nervous system and return to within your window of tolerance Suggested yoga practices: • Balancing, centering, and grounding practices • Mobilizing and activating practices • Softening and heart-opening practices • Containing practices	• Connect down and turn in (to settle) • Lift up and express out (to express)
State of connection (growth and comfort zone)	What is needed: Movements that align with the action urge or that bring balance Suggested yoga practices: • Balancing, centering, and grounding practices • Mobilizing and activating practices • Softening and heart-opening practices • Containing practices	All directions: • Up (lift, rise, reach) • Down (ground, connect, press) • In (draw, turn, hug, pull) • Out (express, push, release)

As you work through these practices, take time after each session to review how the practice went for you. You might make notes about what sensations were most present in a particular pose or posture. It can be helpful to note the postures that were activating or overwhelming, as well as which ones you feel you should revisit. Use your journal to document what works for you and what does not. For any practices that you find particularly helpful, consider adding them to your resource repository and remember to add the context within which the practice was helpful.

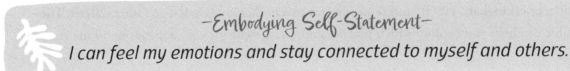

—Embodying Self-Statement—
I can feel my emotions and stay connected to myself and others.

—Embodying Practice—

Exploring Directions in Movement

Find a seated position in a safe and comfortable place where you can practice exploring different forms of movement. This can be in a chair or well supported on the floor. You will want to be able to move your belly, shoulders, and arms freely. Here you will be practicing four simple movements that involve your core, hands, and breath. Begin with your hands resting on your thighs.

Up: Press into your sitting bones, engage your belly, and extend through your spine. As you breathe in, lift your hands in front of you to shoulder height, your palms facing down with your elbows somewhat extended and slightly bent.

Out: Now, extend your wrists so your palms are facing forward and away from you. On your exhale, push your hands away extending fully through your elbows.

In: Then, turn your palms toward you, and slightly overlap your hands so there is a sense of holding. On your inhale, bend your elbows and draw your soft, inward-turning hands toward your heart.

Down: On your exhale, press your hands down, allowing your elbows to extend and your hands to separate and move down to the sides of your body.

Repeat this series of movements for several sets: inhaling up, exhaling out, inhaling in, and exhaling down. As you do this, notice what each direction feels like. Which direction feels most aligned with you? Which one is most uncomfortable? Do any make you feel agitated or upset? Do any make you feel a sense of calm or groundedness? There are no right or wrong answers, just notice. If you do this practice while you are feeling different emotions, see if you notice changes in how you experience the different directions.

191

Yoga: Accessible Movement Practices

If an emotion has you feeling immobilized and stuck, you want to work toward small and slow accessible movements that can get you moving without being too abrupt or overactivating. There are a few accessible movements offered here. Begin by practicing these. You can also look for slow flow or restorative yoga classes online or in your area. Keep a journal record of poses that are helpful in getting you moving. These can be helpful for feelings that are associated with deactivation, like sadness, depression, shame, and guilt. If you'd like to pair any of these movements with music, choose calm and gently uplifting or light music, like that which involves a harp, an acoustic guitar, or a flute.

For the practices offered here, you will need a yoga mat or blanket, a timer, and a chime or singing bowl (either a real one or a digital version you can download on your phone). Have a pen or pencil and your journal on hand for processing your experience.

Time	Practice	Pose	Guidance, Noticing, and Describing	Movement Direction
2 min	Prep	None	Gather your mat, timer, singing bowl (or app), pen, and journal. Silence your phone and start your timer.	None
5 min	Gentle Breaths		In a seated position, place one hand over your heart and one hand over your belly. Breathe gently into the hand on your belly. Count slowly with each breath, taking time to pause after each inhale and exhale: Breathe in 1, 2, 3 . . . pause . . . breathe out 1, 2, 3. Do this for several cycles, breathing in and out. Stay here for five minutes.	In and out
5 min	Arms and Breath		As you inhale, lift your arms up, and as you exhale, lower your arms. You can continue the slow, even pace: Breathe in 1, 2, 3 . . . pause . . . breathe out 1, 2, 3. Do this for several cycles, moving your arms up and down as you breathe in and out. You can also begin to add energy as you feel ready by increasing the muscle engagement in your core and arms slightly. Stay here for five minutes.	Up and down
2 min	Mountain Pose		Now come to a standing position. Notice your feet pressing into the floor, soften your knees, and engage your legs. Lift up through your core and extend through your spine. Draw your chin in slightly and reach through the crown of your head. Allow your shoulders, jaw, and eyes to be soft. Breathe here, continuing to count with each breath: Breathe in 1, 2, 3 . . . pause . . . breathe out 1, 2, 3. If you'd like, raise and lower your arms with your breath. Stay here for two minutes.	Down, in, and up

10 min	Walking Meditation		As you are ready, begin to slowly walk. Take a breath with each step, noticing each foot as it steps forward and connects with the ground below you. You can do this inside or outside, whichever feels most accessible. As you walk, you can move your awareness throughout your body, noticing your muscles and breath move as you walk. Continue for 10 minutes.	Down, in, up, and out
5 min	Singing Bowl		Using your singing bowl or app, close this gentle mobilization practice by humming with the sound of the singing bowl. Inhale and gently play the singing bowl. Begin to hum as it rings. As you need to, begin gently breathing until the sound settles and then repeat. Stay here for five minutes.	Out

—Embodying Self-Statement—

My emotions can move me, and I can move through my emotions.

Embodying Practice

Yoga: Balancing, Centering, and Grounding Practices

Balancing, centering, and grounding practices help restore the state of your nervous system when you are feeling overactivated or underactivated. Balancing practices focus on the center or midline of your body, which is helpful when you are feeling drawn outward, scattered, and off-center. Centering practices turn you inward toward your own experiences, heartbeat, and breath. Finally, grounding practices help you connect to the earth and help you feel rooted. Below are a few balancing, centering, and grounding practices that can help you work with emotions that take you off-balance, like anger, anxiety, fear, happiness, pride, and love. If you'd like to pair any of these movements with music, try restorative yoga playlists or slow, gentle drumming.

For the practices offered here, you will need a yoga mat or blanket, lotion, and a timer. Have a pen or pencil and your journal on hand for processing your experience.

Time	Practice	Pose	Guidance, Noticing, and Describing	Movement Direction
2 min	Prep	None	Gather your mat, timer, lotion, and journal. Silence your phone and start your timer.	None
2 min	Alternate Nostril Breathing (Balance)		In a seated pose, bring your right hand to your nose. With your thumb and ring finger extended, draw your second and third fingers toward your palm. Press your thumb on your right nostril, closing it. Using your left nostril, exhale, pause, and inhale. Pause and press your ring finger on your left nostril, closing it, releasing your thumb and right nostril. Through your right nostril, exhale, pause, and inhale. Alternate left to right exhaling, pausing, and inhaling on each side before you switch. Stay here for two minutes.	In and out
2 min	Cat and Cow (Balance)		Move to the floor, getting on your hands and knees. With each exhale, arch your spine and draw your belly in, dropping your head and tailbone like a cat. With each inhale, drop your belly, lift your head, and tilt your pelvis up like a cow. Continue aligning your movement and your breath, slowly moving your spine. Stay here for two minutes.	In, out, up, and down

2 min	Tree Pose (Balance)		From a standing position, press your left foot into the floor and bring the sole of your right foot to the inside of your left ankle, shin, or thigh. Press through the centerline of your left foot and draw your belly in and up. Breathe here with your hands at your heart center. If you feel balanced and well grounded, reach your hands toward the ceiling. Stay here for one minute, then switch sides for another minute. You can use a chair for support as needed.	Down, in, up, and out
2 min	Low Belly Holding (Centering)		In a standing position, place your hands on your low belly. Bring your awareness to your hands as they touch your belly at your center of gravity. Breathe gently. Stay here for two minutes.	Down and in
2 min	Heart Holding (Centering)		In a standing position, place one hand on your belly and one hand on your heart. Bring your awareness to your hands as they touch your belly and your heart. Breathe gently, noticing your heartbeat and your breaths. Stay here for two minutes.	Down and in
2 min	Mountain Pose (Grounding)		In a standing position, notice your feet pressing into the floor and imagine them deeply rooting into the earth below you. Then engage your legs, lift up through your core, and extend through your spine. Draw your chin in slightly and reach through the crown of your head. Allow your shoulders, jaw, and eyes to soften. Stay here for two minutes.	Down and in
2 min	Forward Fold (Grounding)		Return to a seated position on the floor and extend your legs out in front of you. Press your sitting bones into your mat and extend through your spine. Soften your knees and draw your heart toward your toes, your hands reaching forward. You can use your towel to help reach your toes or place your hands on the floor next to your legs. Breathe gently and notice the earth below you and the stretching sensations on your legs. Stay here for two minutes.	Down and in
4 min	Foot Massage (Grounding)		Close your practice with a foot massage, spending two minutes with each foot. Take your right foot into your hands and press your thumbs into the sole of your foot, massaging the area from your heel to your big toe. Then massage the area from your heel to your second toe, repeat through all the remaining toes. Then use your fingers to massage the top of your foot and ankle. Hold your foot with both hands and press gently before switching sides. Massage your left foot in the same way. Spend two minutes with each foot, using lotion if you'd like.	Down and in

Yoga: Mobilizing and Activating Practices

Mobilizing and activating practices increase energy, so they can be used to explore action urges, enhance feelings of empowerment, and add activation in general. Below are a few practices that can help you move through action urges associated with feelings like anger, fear, anxiety, frustration, happiness, and being overwhelmed. As you work through these practices, be mindful of your activation level and cycle in balancing, centering, and grounding practices as needed. If you feel shaking as your muscles activate, experiment with it. You might want to let the shaking run its course. However, you should not feel pain or activate yourself so much that you push yourself outside of your window of tolerance. If you notice either experience happening, take a break, connect with resources, self-soothe, and get some water.

If you'd like to pair any of these movements with music, consider your intention for engaging these practices. You might want music aligned with your action urges, whether that is something inspiring and powerful or something playful and energizing. Match the music with your intentions.

For the practices offered here, you will need a yoga mat or blanket and a timer. Have a pen or pencil and your journal on hand for processing your experience.

Time	Practice	Pose	Guidance, Noticing, and Describing	Movement Direction
2 min	Prep	None	Gather your mat, timer, and journal. Silence your phone and start your timer.	None
4 min	Shaking		From a standing position, press your feet into the floor and soften your knees. Begin by shaking your hands, letting your fingers move with the shaking. Then add your elbows to the shaking and, next, your shoulders. Then bring in your legs, followed by your whole body, allowing it to shake, jiggle, and bounce. If you feel yourself holding any tension, breathe and say to that body part, *It's okay to let go.* Include as little or as much shaking as feels good. Stay here for four minutes.	Up and out
2 to 5 min	Running in Place		From a standing position, run in place. As you run, extend your hands out to the side for balance. For more activation, lift your knees higher. For less activation, lift your knees less. Notice your breath and heartbeat. Pause as needed. Stay here for two to five minutes.	Up and out

8 min	Warrior I and II		From a standing position, begin with Warrior I by pressing your right foot into your mat and stepping your left foot back. Press your back heel into the mat with your foot angling toward the outer edge of your mat at about 45 degrees. Collect your energy at your belly and extend through your spine, reaching your hands up toward the ceiling with your biceps by your ears. Then move to Warrior II by rotating your back foot to a 90 degree angle to the left so your toes face the outside of the yoga mat, the front foot remaining planted. Reach your right arm to the front of the room, your left arm to the back of the room, and open your body to the long side of the mat as you look forward over your right fingers. Create a powerful connection to the earth, engage your muscles, and let warrior energy radiate out from your chest, fingers, and eyes. When you are ready, repeat Warrior I and Warrior II on the other side. Spend four minutes on each side.	Down, in, up, and out
4 min	Lunge		From a standing position, step your left foot back so you are on the ball of your left foot, bring your right knee over your right ankle, and lunge forward. Collect your energy at your belly and extend through your spine, reaching your hands toward the ceiling with your biceps by your ears. You can add activation by lowering, hovering, and then lifting your back knee: Lower 1, 2, 3, 4, 5 . . . hover 1, 2, 3, 4, 5 . . . and lift 1, 2, 3, 4, 5. Stay here for two minutes, and as you are ready, switch to the other side for another two minutes.	Down, in, up, and out
2 to 4 min	Chair Pose		From a standing position, sink your hips back, engage your belly, and reach your arms up. Breathe. If you want to add activation, lift your heels up and stand on the balls of your feet. Keep your breath steady, staying connected to your body. You can cycle through a few chair poses if you'd like, pausing between each one. Stay here for two to four minutes.	Down, in, up, and out
2 min	Dancer Pose		Press your right foot into your mat and bend your left knee back so your heel moves toward your left sitting bone. Move your left hand back, and with your palm facing outward, catch your left ankle on the inside. Reach your right arm forward as a counterbalance. Stay here or gently press into your left hand to extend the posture. After one minute, change sides and hold for another minute on the other side.	Down, in, up, and out
2 to 3 min	Whole-Body Breathing		From a standing position, inhale as you reach your arms up over your head. As you exhale, fold over and release your arms to the floor. Repeat this several times. You can experiment with the intensity of your inhales and exhales. Try thinking of taking in energy as you inhale and letting go as you exhale. Engage in the practice for two to three minutes.	Down, in, up, and out

Yoga: Softening and Heart-Opening Practices

Softening and heart-opening poses can be very challenging for those who have experienced trauma, as the body holds tension and curls the shoulders forward in a defensive and protective effort. Therefore, it is important that you do not force an opening process. Encourage yourself to gradually move toward softening and opening as you work through this book. Below are some practices that can get you started. These practices can be helpful in countering emotions that cause you to close up, such as anger, fear, sadness, anxiety, depression, guilt, and shame. If you'd like to pair any of these movements with music, find music that inspires you to open your heart and trust.

For the practices offered here, you will need a yoga mat or blanket and a timer. Have a pen or pencil and your journal on hand for processing your experience.

Time	Practice	Pose	Guidance, Noticing, and Describing	Movement Direction
2 min	Prep	None	Gather your mat, timer, and journal. Silence your phone and start your timer.	None
2 min	Shoulder Rolls		From a standing position, press your feet into the floor and soften your knees. Allow your arms to hang by your sides. Then begin moving your shoulders in large circles, drawing them up by your ears. Circle them back as your shoulder blades move toward each other, and draw them down as your shoulders press toward the floor. Then circle them forward, drawing the shoulders toward each other. Circle your shoulders several times and then change directions. Stay here for two minutes.	Down, in, up, and out
2 min	Swaying to Soothe		From a standing position, move your feet a little more than hip distance apart. Begin by swinging your arms from side to side, with one arm forward and the other arm around your back. Let your body move, swinging from side to side with your arms. As you sway side to side, you can let as much of your body join the movement as you'd like. Stay here for two minutes.	Down, up, and out
2 min	Hip Circles		With your feet a little more than hip distance apart and your hands on your hips, bend your knees and make big circles with your hips. Move forward, back, and side to side, changing directions after several cycles. Stay here for two minutes.	Down, up, and out

2 min	Standing Heart Openers		From a standing or seated position, inhale as you bend your elbows, move your arms back, draw your shoulder blades together, and open your chest. As you exhale, let your arms and your chest soften. Repeat these movements for several cycles, taking deep, gentle breaths. Stay here for two minutes.	Down, in, up, and out
2 min	Supine Twist		Lying on your back, draw your right knee in toward your chest, and then take it over to the left side. Let your left hand rest on your knee and extend your right hand out to the right. Look out over your right hand. Stay here for one minute, and when you are ready, switch to the other side for another minute.	Down, up, and out
2 to 5 min	Resting Pose with Open Heart		Lying on your back, extend your arms out to either side. For more heart opening, you can place one yoga block under your heart and one under your head, extending your arms to the floor. Stay here for two to five minutes.	Down, up, and out
5 to 10 min	Resting Pose with a Hand on Heart and Belly		Lie on your back and remove any blocks, then place one hand on your heart and one hand on your belly. Breathe gently. Stay here for 5 to 10 minutes.	Down and in

Yoga: Containing Practices

Your body is a container. It holds everything you experience, including your sensations, emotions, memories, plans, and thoughts. Containment practices help you sense the physical container of your body. They can help you feel like a baby swaddled up in a blanket. The practices offered here can be a good way to end any of the previous yoga practices or to remind yourself of your body and its boundaries. If you'd like to pair any of these movements with music, choose something that puts your nervous system at ease.

For the practices offered here, you will need a yoga mat or blanket and a timer. Have a pen or pencil and your journal on hand for processing your experience.

Time	Practice	Pose	Guidance, Noticing, and Describing	Movement Direction
2 min	Prep	None	Gather your mat, timer, and journal. Silence your phone and start your timer.	None
2 min	Hands at Heart		In a seated position, place one hand on your belly and one hand on your heart. Be mindfully aware of your body touching the floor, your skin in contact with your clothes and the air. Breathe and notice your heartbeat. Notice your breath move in and out of your body. You might say to yourself, *This is my body, my heartbeat, and my breath.* Stay here for two minutes.	Centered
4 min	Patting the Body		Still in a seated position, gently pat your feet with your hands as you say, *This is my foot. This is my other foot.* Then pat your ankles and say, *This is my ankle. This is my other ankle.* Continue to do this over your whole body, gently patting the area with your hands and stating, *This is my . . .* Use each hand to pat the other hand and shoulder. Do this all the way to the crown of your head and end by gently rubbing your hands in a circle over your heart. Say to yourself, *This is my heart.* Spend about four minutes with this practice.	Centered
2 min	Child's Pose		With the front of your body facing the yoga mat, bend your knees and your hips, and extend your sitting bones to the back of the mat. Let your chest and head relax toward the mat. Reach your hands toward the front of the mat, and relax your arms so your forearms and hands can rest on the mat. Bring your awareness to your heartbeat and breath. Stay here for two minutes.	Grounded
2 min	Crocodile Pose		Lying face down on your yoga mat, bend your elbows, stack your forearms one over the other, and then rest your forehead on your forearms. Bring your awareness to your heartbeat and breath. Stay here for two minutes.	Grounded

Chapter 11

Embodied Connection in Relationships

We are deeply connected beings (Bullock, 2016). As far back as historians can see, humans have lived in communities. We need each other to meet our most basic physiological needs, including the need for food, clothing, and shelter. Further, we need each other to meet our psychological need to be seen, to be heard, to be connected, and to belong. This means that our existence as embodied beings can only happen within the context of our webs of interconnectedness (Osher et al., 2020). We are our parents' and caregivers' children. Some of us are parents, friends, siblings, mentors, and mentees. We are neighbors and community members. We cocreate our cultures and our countries. You and I are, because *we* are.

Need-to-Know: Embodiment and Relationships

Relational work is about identifying, securing, cultivating, and nurturing relationships aligned with your healing and well-being (Cook-Cottone, 2020). You need relationships within which you can feel seen, heard, safe, supported, and empowered. However, your interconnections with others in your life are always changing, and as they change, you change (Osher et al., 2020). This can happen in a reactive and externally directed manner—for example, if you constantly adjust your behavior so that others are happy, feel too vulnerable to let anyone get close, or always follow the lead of others, for better or worse. It can also happen in a proactive and internally directed way as you decide how to shape these experiences and who you are going forward.

Either way, how you manage your interpersonal interactions can help you become an architect of your own interpersonal and social landscape (Cook-Cottone, 2020). As an embodied person with a sense of personal boundaries, you do not need to look outward to self-regulate. You do not need to have someone accept you to feel okay. You do not need to hope that another person is safe so that you are safe. Instead, you can self-regulate with an inward sense of agency and self-determination. You can choose friends and nurture relationships that align with your empowerment.

Many of my patients align with what some researchers call highly sensitive people or HSPs (Smith et al., 2019). Individuals who are HSPs tend to be sensitive to internal and external stimuli, have a strong neuroceptive focus on detecting threats, and are highly attuned to the moods, activations, and experiences of others. Although some people demonstrate this sensitivity across their lifespan, trauma (especially interpersonal trauma) can also lead you to protectively orient toward the behavior of others. In particular, if you have grown up around or within abusive relationships, you can develop a tendency to focus on other people's needs above your own. This means that you might get a sense that your partner is hungry before you notice that you are hungry. At a party, you might know who is fighting, who is stressed, who is on edge, and who is drinking too much before you notice if you want to be there or not. When you are other-oriented in this way, there is often a corresponding lack of attention to your own physiological, emotional, and cognitive needs.

I call this way of being an externalized orientation to the management of self (Cook-Cottone, 2020). This happens when you are so attuned to what others need and want that you have no sense of your own experience. This is a disembodied way of interacting with the world. Rather than sensing, feeling, or taking action from your internal experiences, you interact with your environment in accordance with the ever-changing, unpredictable, and often objectifying external world. Mary Pipher (1994) brilliantly called this way of being "empathy sick." Over time, your inner world functions around the demands of the external world. Your nervous system is always asking, *What do other people need or want?* and you believe *If they are okay, I will be okay.*

In order to create a more balanced way of being, your mindful awareness, intentions, and actions must come from a deep connection with yourself that is maintained within the context of your relationships. At no point should your interactions with others result in the abandonment of self or well-being. When you are living from an embodied experience of self, you are experiencing life as it unfolds in your world and simultaneously honoring your own needs, desires, and intentions. You are able to set boundaries and say no when something does not allow you to stay connected to who you are. In this way, your relationships are developed around a true sense of self and not an empathy-sick, abandoned version of yourself (Cook-Cottone, 2020). You can be truly loved because you are connected to, and express to the world, who you truly are.

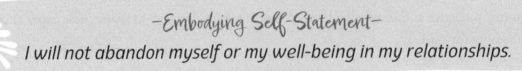

—Embodying Self-Statement—
I will not abandon myself or my well-being in my relationships.

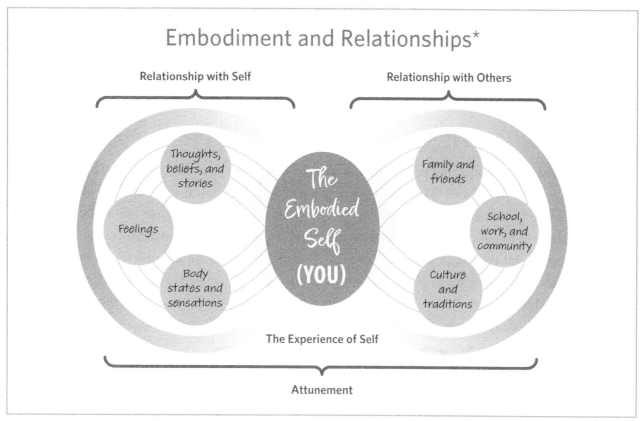

Embodiment and Relationships*

Relationship with Self

Relationship with Others

Thoughts, beliefs, and stories

Feelings

Body states and sensations

The Embodied Self (YOU)

Family and friends

School, work, and community

Culture and traditions

The Experience of Self

Attunement

* Informed by Cook-Cottone (2020).

Need-to-Know: The Development of an Embodied Self

The foundation of an embodied experience of self is the cultivation of attunement between self and others. Since infancy, our nervous systems develop within the context of the other nervous systems around us. If a person was lucky enough to have a responsive caregiver, they likely engaged in a "didactic dance of connection" (Dana, 2020, p. 9) in which their nervous system and the nervous systems of their caregivers created an experience of attunement as they coregulated at the autonomic level. To create this didactic dance, a caregiver does not need to be perfect, as no one is. What they *do* need to do is facilitate a reliable and recursive rhythm of connecting, falling out of connection, and returning to connection. This disconnection-reconnection rhythm creates the foundation of what the child's nervous system experiences as safety in connection (Dana, 2020).

These early and important connections create a child's core beliefs about themselves, others, and the world. They learn that a relationship can be a safe haven and secure base from which they can explore the world. These moments of being attuned to and cared for by another help create a foundation of beliefs, such as *I am worthy and my needs matter*, *Other people can be counted on and I am not alone*, and *The world is generally safe and kind*. However, many people do not experience this type of attunement and connection in infancy and early childhood. If this is your experience, it can set you up for even more vulnerability to the effects of trauma and make it even more important that you work to understand and function effectively within your relationships.

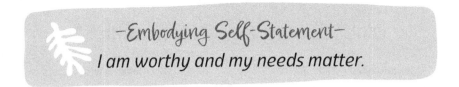

-Embodying Self-Statement-
I am worthy and my needs matter.

Need-to-Know: Embodiment of Self and Boundaries

The term *embodiment* implies that your body is a container in which you are embodied. This container of you has boundaries that signify where you end and the world begins. This means that your relationships are another aspect of your embodied being that you can become mindfully aware of and create sets of intentions for. You can determine and set boundaries for what you need and what you cannot or will not tolerate in your relationships. This idea of having boundaries would be much easier if we were just talking about physical boundaries, but in reality, there are several different types of boundaries: physiological, sensory, risk, time, physical, energetic, emotional, sexual, intellectual, professional, spiritual, and material.

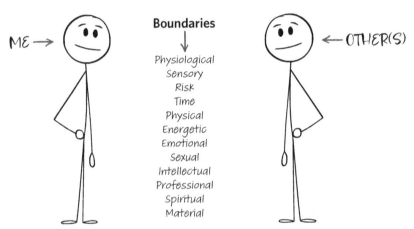

Unfortunately, those who have survived trauma, especially interpersonal trauma, are susceptible to engaging in relationships that are fraught with boundary violations, many of which are repeat violations that have occurred in the past (Ogden et al., 2006). In some cases, those who have experienced interpersonal trauma do not know what a boundary is or what a healthy boundary feels like.

For example, a patient named Soka had a history of sexual abuse in childhood and relational violence in later relationships. Due to her trauma history, she had no real sense of her own sensory, risk, physical, emotional, time, or sexual boundaries. She had learned to disconnect from herself, as the people in her life discounted her needs, preferences, and well-being. Boundaries were a big part of her recovery. She had to explore and cultivate her own list of nonnegotiable boundaries, especially with her mother. Given that Soka was never allowed to have nonnegotiable boundaries before, this realization was painful for Soka.

If this is your experience, part of your healing work will be to establish well-developed boundaries that reflect your rights and preferences (and that serve healthy connections within your relationships), as opposed to trauma-associated, protective boundaries that are often organized around safety and threat (Ogden et al., 2006). This chapter offers a few points of inquiry and practices that will help you do so.

—Embodying Practice—
Exploring Your Boundary Types

To learn about different types of boundaries, read through the examples in the following table and allow them some time to sink in. Maybe even keep them in mind for a week or two as you experience your day-to-day life and journal about what you notice.

Then, as you are ready, create a list of nonnegotiables for each type of boundary. These are the experiences you know are firm boundaries for you. Write a few notes about how you might know this nonnegotiable boundary has been crossed. Perhaps recall times when someone crossed (or tried to cross) this nonnegotiable boundary. How did you know it was happening? What did it feel like? Think about what your whole body felt like at the time, including any tension, activation, or body sensations.

Last, consider how past trauma may have impacted your ability to honor these boundaries in relationships with others, as well as in relationship with *yourself*. For example, if you are physically tired, do you rest? If you are overwhelmed, do you take a break? It can be very difficult to honor boundaries within yourself that others have ignored. It can also be difficult to know when your boundaries have been crossed by others when you regularly override or ignore them on your own.

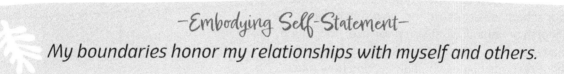

—Embodying Self-Statement—
My boundaries honor my relationships with myself and others.

Type of Boundaries	List of Nonnegotiables	Potential Impact of Trauma
Physiological: Related to your homeostatic balance and well-being, including what you eat and drink, your work and rest schedule, how much and how often you exercise, the physical demands of your job and obligations, the extent to which you are exposed to ranges of temperatures, how much distress you can tolerate and comfort you need, and how your life is supported or managed when you are ill or injured		
How do you know when this boundary is crossed? What do you notice? What does it feel like?		

Type of Boundaries	List of Nonnegotiables	Potential Impact of Trauma
Sensory: Related to how much sensory stimulation you can take in, including the level and types of noise, the intensity and types of smells, the smells and tastes of foods, the textures you experience, exposure to allergens or irritants, and sensations associated with cuddling and other forms of skin-to-skin contact		
How do you know when this boundary is crossed? What do you notice? What does it feel like?		
Risk: Related to the level of risk you experience, including levels of risk you expose yourself to at work, with your own body, when traveling, in your interactions with others, with finances, and in your daily life		
How do you know when this boundary is crossed? What do you notice? What does it feel like?		
Time: Related to how you spend your time, including how your schedule is constructed, how much your time is worth or valued, what you prioritize, how much time you reserve for yourself versus others, how many projects or responsibilities you handle, and how much control you have over your time		
How do you know when this boundary is crossed? What do you notice? What does it feel like?		
Physical: Related to your personal space, including the types and frequency of touch you are comfortable with, who can touch you (including animals), how you give and deny consent for touch, and your need for general privacy		
How do you know when this boundary is crossed? What do you notice? What does it feel like?		
Energetic: Related to how you use your energy, including how you allocate resources to yourself and others, the time and space you give yourself to recharge, the time you spend with people and projects that require or consume a lot of energy, and the time you spend with people and projects that help generate energy		

Type of Boundaries	List of Nonnegotiables	Potential Impact of Trauma
How do you know when this boundary is crossed? What do you notice? What does it feel like?		
Emotional: Related to how you express and experience feelings, including how much you believe others are responsible for your feelings, how much you believe you are responsible for others' feelings, how much validation you need for your feelings, and how much emotional energy you can manage		
How do you know when this boundary is crossed? What do you notice? What does it feel like?		
Sexual: Related to sexual intimacy and behavior, including limits to how people touch your body, the types of sexual activities you're comfortable with, access to and use of contraceptives, managing risk of sexually transmitted diseases, and consent		
How do you know when this boundary is crossed? What do you notice? What does it feel like?		
Intellectual: Related to your thoughts and ideas, including how your personal ideas are shared, how ownership of ideas is cited or acknowledged, how others respect your ideas, how you communicate ideas to others, and how disagreements are handled		
How do you know when this boundary is crossed? What do you notice? What does it feel like?		
Professional: Related to your professional ethics at work, including how you avoid dual relationships (e.g., being someone's teacher and friend), how you honor power structures and processes, the extent to which you do tasks outside of your job description, how you navigate social media behaviors, and the extent to which you are able to separate your home life from your work life		
How do you know when this boundary is crossed? What do you notice? What does it feel like?		

Type of Boundaries	List of Nonnegotiables	Potential Impact of Trauma
Spiritual: Related to how you practice your religious or spiritual beliefs, including your right to believe in what you want, worship as you'd like, and worship where you'd like		
How do you know when this boundary is crossed? What do you notice? What does it feel like?		
Material: Related to your possessions, home, and finances, including how you share your possessions, whom you share them with, how much you can afford to share, and what you are not willing to share		
How do you know when this boundary is crossed? What do you notice? What does it feel like?		

After completing this list of boundaries, what do you notice? Are there any patterns?

_____

_____

_____

Was it easy, neutral, or difficult to create a list of nonnegotiables? Why?

_____

_____

_____

In what ways do you think your boundaries may be associated with your trauma history?

_____

_____

_____

—Embodying Self-Statement—
Working on my boundaries is a form of tending to my energetic and creative self.

Embodying Practice
Physical and Energetic Boundaries Meditation

Consider doing this meditation when you feel like you have lost track of your physical and energetic boundaries, or when you feel like you have not been given enough space.

To begin, find a comfortable seated position in a safe and private location. Make sure you have a few feet on all sides of you so you have a sense of space. Sit with your feet and sitting bones grounded, engage your core, lift through your spine, and soften your shoulders, jaw, and eyes. Then orient your awareness to your breath and breathe three to five gentle breath cycles.

As you are ready, orient your awareness inside of you—to the space contained by the boundary of your skin. Consider your bones, your muscles, your cardiovascular system, your organs, and all the amazing parts of your body. You might send the beautiful inside of you a warm energy of loving-kindness. You might add some compassion for all the work your body does for you inside, like digesting food and helping you heal and recover. Consider that this energy—the energy that is you—is powerful.

Now, move your awareness to the space outside of your skin, perhaps two to four inches outside of your body. See if you can get a sense of that space and the energy that radiates from you. What would it be like if someone reached into that space? Even if your eyes were closed, do you think you might notice? What would you notice, sense, or feel? Consider that this space is still you. You can sense it, and it is filled with warmth and energy.

Now, extend your awareness to the space about 12 inches away from your body. You might sense it as a sphere or layer of energy around you. With your eyes closed or softened, see if you can get a sense of that space. Consider that this space is still energetically you. What if someone reached into this space. What would you notice or feel?

Then, become aware of an even larger space radiating about two feet around you, maybe a little more. Consider that this space is still energetically you or may be yours. For a moment, open your eyes and consider this space. Then reach out your arms, as they are probably just a little over two feet on each side. Reach your arms out wide, then overhead. Move them around to get a good sense of this energetic boundary around you. As you are ready, settle in and close or soften your eyes. What would it be like if someone reached into this space? What might you notice, sense, or feel? Consider that this is still energetically your space.

As you bring this meditation to a close, slowly bring your awareness in through the two-foot layer, the one-foot layer, and the two-to-four-inch layer. Bring your awareness to your skin and then all the way into your heart. Gently breathe, aware of your lungs and your heart as you breathe. If you'd like, place your hands on your heart and say, *This is my physical body*. With a sense of your energetic space, you might say, *This is my energetic space* and *I have boundaries*. If you'd like, take out your journal and note anything you noticed that you'd like to process further.

Note that you can informally continue the practice as you go through your day. Notice the effect others might have as they move in and out of your physical and energetic space. Consider that resting might mean having time when no one is in that space. Maybe you remember your boundaries.

Embodying Practice

Exploring Your Personal Boundaries

To explore your personal boundaries, look at the following figure with your embodied self in the center. Around you are different layers, or spaces, that make up your life: your body, your home, your neighborhood, and the large social community around you. You get to decide who has permission to come into each space and who does not. Reflect on the people in your life and record in the rings below who is allowed to be close to you and how close they can be. When filling in each ring, consider loved ones, family and extended family, friends, acquaintances, work colleagues, and social friends. Also consider where you'd like those who have hurt you to be and where they are typically. Note what each layer feels like and what it feels like for each person to be in that layer with you.

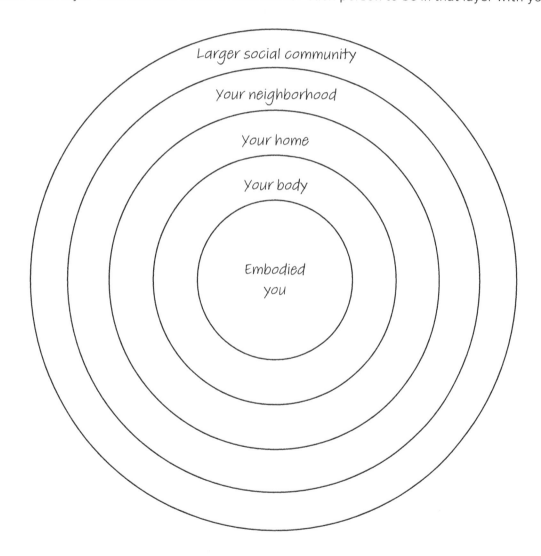

Your body: The people in this space may frequently connect to or touch your body with consent. With your knowledge and consent, they can go into your intimate spaces, such as your bathroom or bedroom. Your body feels relaxed when they are nearby. You have a strong trust for people permitted in this layer.

Your home: The people in this space are often part of your day-to-day life, such as your extended family or close friends who might stop by or stay for a visit. You feel good about having them in your home. These people tend not to move into your intimate spaces. Your body feels at ease when they are around. You trust them.

Your neighborhood: The people in this space are your friends and close acquaintances whom you see at work, the gym, your children's school, or your school. You see them often, recognize them, and know many of their names. They would not drop by your house and would never be in your intimate spaces. You are nonetheless familiar with them, and your nervous system feels generally at ease despite some of the typical guardedness that you might have in public places.

The larger social community: This space represents the larger community around you, including the stores you go to, the restaurants you eat at, and the social events you attend (e.g., football games, parties, festivals). You don't necessarily recognize people in this space or have a sense of familiarity with them. In these public settings, you feel the typical balance of ease and guardedness.

When you are done, use the space below to write or draw anything you noticed as you explored your personal boundaries.

PAUSE

(**P** - Pause, **A** - Assess ➝ **USE** your resources and supports)

☐ **P**ause, check in, and acknowledge how you are feeling. This is a chance to be kind to yourself. The pace of your work is very important. Press your feet into the earth and take four gentle breaths.

☐ **A**ssess by asking yourself, *Is this a good place for a break?* If the answer is *yes* or *I don't know*, then fold over the corner of the page and take a break. This workbook is here for you for as long as it takes and for as many breaks as you need.

☐ **USE** your resources. Take a rest. Connect to your trusted friends. Contact your therapist. Practice your favorite well-being strategies. Get back to work when YOU are ready.

Embodying Practice
Exploring Your Boundary Qualities

You can have boundaries that are characterized by an underbounded, overbounded, pendulum, or incomplete boundary style (Ogden & Fisher, 2016). Take some time to read through the various boundary styles described here. Then, over the next week or two, explore what your boundary style is like for each boundary area and record it in the following table. Some people notice a pattern or a dominant style across each boundary area. When you're finished, describe what a healthy boundary might look and feel like for you in each boundary area. For example, Soka discovered she had an unbounded style across nearly all of her boundaries. She also noticed that she had a healthy boundary style in relation to physiological and spiritual boundaries. For example, she always went to bed when she was tired, rarely used substances, worked out within healthy limits, stayed hydrated, and ate healthy food. She also loved yoga, which not only helped her explore her physical boundaries but was a mainstay in terms of supporting her spirituality.

Boundary Style	Boundary Area(s) Present
Underbounded: In this style, you have diffuse and lax boundaries. It is hard to discern what is me and you, mine and yours. In relationships, it may not feel acceptable or safe to set boundaries. You might have a difficult time saying no or fear rejection if you set a boundary. You may not have a sense of when you are too close to someone. You may also have difficulty differentiating your feelings, opinions, needs, and preferences from those of others. You may overempathize with others and prioritize their feelings. This style overemphasizes connection (perhaps unhealthy connection) over protection.	
Overbounded: In this style, your boundaries are rigid, inflexible, impenetrable, and solid. It is easier to say no than yes. You might feel like you have to put a wall between you and everyone else. You don't like to share personal information and do not want to hear it from others. You are protective of your space and don't like people too close. You don't ask for help, opinions, or thoughts from others. You are self-reliant, independent, and spend a lot of time alone. It is difficult for you to experience empathy or attunement with others, and other people might see you as emotionally vulnerable. This style overemphasizes protection over connection.	
Pendulum: In this style, you pendulate back and forth between being underbounded and overbounded. When you are underbounded, it feels overwhelming to be vulnerable and open with others, so you close down. When you are overbounded, you miss having connection and feel alone. You go back and forth from feeling too vulnerable to feeling too alone. This style shows conflict related to protection and connection, and the way you react is variable.	

Incomplete: In this style, your boundaries have holes or spots that vary from context to context. You might be overbounded at work and underbounded when you're dating or around authority figures. Perhaps you can easily say no to a spouse or someone with equal or less authority, but you are unable to say no to your own parents or other authority figures. Perhaps you can say no to strangers but not people who you are close to you. You may lose the ability to hold a healthy boundary when you are tired, sick, emotional, or activated. This style shows a lack of mindful awareness, intention, and purposeful action related to protection and connection systems.	
Healthy: In this style, your boundaries are generally consistent from context to context. You say yes and no based on your needs and plans, as well as consideration of your impact on others. Your boundaries are steady even when you are tired, sick, or emotionally activated. There is a mindful awareness and purposeful action related to your connection to yourself and others. When you are unclear on what is the right boundary to set in a novel or crisis situation, you kindly and assertively communicate with others involved to find a boundary that addresses the immediate needs of the situation while still maintaining space for your needs and the needs of others. Your boundaries leave others with a sense that you are trustworthy in that you carefully consider what you can and cannot do so that when you say yes, it is a dependable and honest yes.	

What did you notice? Do you tend toward protective or connection patterns? What do those patterns look and feel like? In which areas would you like to begin to explore setting healthy boundaries?

_____

_____

_____

_____

_____

_____

_____

_____

—Embodying Self-Statement—

Boundary work is a pathway to knowing what I want and need.

Embodying Practice
Creating a Boundary Work Journal

Boundary work is a lifelong process that changes as you change from a child to an adolescent, to emerging adult, to a partner, to maybe a parent, to a professional mentee (and then to a professional mentor), and perhaps one day to a wise elder. Throughout all these changes, your body is a valuable source of information about how you experience relationships and your boundaries in these relationships.

Therefore, as you continue with your boundary work, it can be helpful to dedicate a section in your journal to write about your body's experiences in relationships across time. Begin with an easier relationship, such as someone you know socially, and work your way up to the more intimate and difficult relationships. Be sure include:

- Your body experiences when you are near this person

- The internal and external sensations you notice when you are near this person

- The feelings you notice when you are near this person

- The action urges you have when you are near this person (i.e., what you would like to do), as well as what you did do in real time

For those relationships you'd like to change, or in which there is a boundary violation occurring, create a plan for the next encounter that details what you would like to do when you are with this person. Make sure to include a list of coping skills you will use to resource and orient yourself, specific words you will use, and actions you'd like to take. You can use the script in the next **Setting Boundaries** practice as a guide.

Embodying Practice
Setting Boundaries

Thus far, you have explored your embodied connection to others. Now it's important to practice setting boundaries with someone who has not been honoring an important boundary in your life. Use the following guidelines to create a plan to talk to this person the next time you encounter them. Make sure to include a description of the boundary violation that has occurred, what changes you would like the person to make, and what changes *you* are going to make going forward. When you're done, list coping strategies you can use to effectively set the boundary, as well as coping strategies you can use if the person does not honor your request. See the example and the boundary intention guidance below.

The next time I am with a person with whom I would like to set a boundary, I will say:

I have noticed that _____ (describe the boundary violation and the types of boundaries that have been violated).

I need _____ (describe the boundary change you'd like).

To support this, I am going to _____ (describe how you will be supporting the new boundary going forward).

I request that you _____ (describe what you would like them to do).

List your coping strategies here, including ways you will support yourself during the request and after the request:

List some options for what you will do if they do not agree with your boundary request:

For example, Soka had a coworker who often asked her to finish her shift for her at the coffee shop. It always happened the same way. Right when Soka was about 30 minutes away from clocking out, the coworker would explain that she had an emergency and needed to leave early. She would always ask Soka to cover for her and, for months, Soka had been agreeing. Although the extra hours were nice when her paycheck came, she was neglecting other important parts of her life because she was spending so much time at work. The next time Soka was at work, she followed these guidelines to set a boundary with this coworker:

"I have noticed that about 30 minutes before my shift ends, you ask me to cover the rest of your shift (boundary violation). I am often feeling tired from my shift (physiological boundary), have time commitments of my own (time boundary), feel bad for you and your emergencies (emotional boundary), and know that our manager doesn't like us to always cover for each other (professional boundary).

"I need to be able to leave work at the end of my shift (describe the boundary change you would like).

"To support this, I am letting you know now that I will be leaving at the end of my shift and will not pick up the rest of your shift anymore (describe how you will be supporting the new boundary going forward).

"I request that you get a sub when you have a lot going on so that you do not need to rely on me to cover for you (describe what you would like them to do)."

Soka planned to use grounding techniques when talking to her coworker. Her favorites were the **Grounded Breath and Centering** practice and the **Grounding and Extended Exhale** practice. If she got really activated, she planned to use the **Sensate Focus for Distress** practice. She also scheduled a therapy session for the following day so she could process how the interaction went. Last, Soka scheduled a movie night with another good friend right after her shift ended so she could remain committed to her boundary and would be rewarded for doing so. If her coworker didn't agree to her request, Soka decided she would ask the coworker to consult with the manager to problem solve the issue.

Like Soka, begin with a manageable change and take small, doable steps to set the boundary. If it feels too difficult or overwhelming, break it down into smaller steps or work with a more peripheral relationship. You might also work into the next chapter, where you will find more advanced practices for connecting with others, assessing your relationships, and being with difficult people.

Chapter 12

Advanced Practices for Being with and Working with Relationships

As you learned in chapter 2, you have an entire part of your nervous system dedicated to social connectedness and safety: the ventral vagal complex. This pathway helps you notice other people and their faces as they show emotions; it lets you attune to their voices as they signal welcoming, disinterest, or meanness; and it helps you read subtle nonverbal cues, such as eye contact and body language, that let you know *This person means well* or *This person might not be safe.* In a moment-to-moment manner, your ventral vagal system is always helping you know whether to move closer to someone or to move away. However, trauma can oversensitize this system, leading you to disconnect from it or ignore it altogether. To reconnect to your ventral vagal complex, it is important to explore your boundaries and practice maintaining them. By practicing boundary setting, you can help your connection system get back into balance.

To help you work through this process, this chapter provides a variety of advanced boundary-related practices that can help you expand on what you learned in the previous chapter. As you are ready, try out these practices when you are among others. Consider each practice to be an experiment, letting go of any expectation that it will go a certain way. That said, there will be certain relationships that function on the premise that you will not set boundaries. This means that when you begin to set boundaries, you will likely create disruption in some relationships, and in some cases, a particular relationship might end. Although this can feel like rejection, it is important to know that it is not a rejection of you—of your core self. Rather, it is a rejection of your request to have a relationship in which both people can have a sense of agency, self-determination, and the ability to define what is and is not okay for themselves.

For example, Courtney, a young woman I worked with, was in a relationship with a partner who frequently texted and flirted with other women, was often late paying rent, and did not contribute his fair share to groceries. She feared that if she asked for these actions to end, the relationship would end. Nonetheless, Courtney eventually gathered up the courage to ask for a change. She clearly told her partner that she did not feel comfortable with his interactions with other women, that she needed him to be on time with rent, and that he needed to help with his share of the chores. Painfully, Courtney's fears were correct. Unless she was willing to allow the relationship to continue as it was, there would be no relationship. He moved out. This was extremely painful for Courtney, and there were days she wished she had not insisted on setting these boundaries. However, over time it became clear that leaving that relationship created space for new, more loving and caring relationships in her life going forward.

Note that this workbook is about embodiment, so the practices included here are meant to support your own positive embodiment. Some of these practices are intended to help you set physical boundaries that protect your body, while others are intended to facilitate your ability to be with others in a more attuned way. If you are seeking more comprehensive relationship support and guidance, the following is a list of resources you might find helpful:

- Senarighi, G. (2020). *Love more, fight less: Communication skills every couple needs: A relationship workbook for couples.* Zeitgeist Penguin Random House.

- The Center for Nonviolent Communication (https://www.cnvc.org)

- Harper, F. (2020). *Unf#ck your boundaries workbook: Build better relationships through consent, communication, and expressing your needs.* Microcosm Publishing.

And one final note: If you are in a violent or unsafe relationship, this is not a good place to practice setting boundaries. Get support and find safety.

Embodying Practice
Boundary-Setting Actions*

Below is a set of nonverbal and verbal ways to set a physical boundary. To begin familiarizing yourself with this list of actions, take time to go through each one and practice each action for 5 to 10 repetitions. You can think of it like doing sets at the gym. You want to have the action sequence well rehearsed so that if you get the chance to try it out in real life, you are ready. Under the Practice Notes column, write the date you practiced, how many repetitions you did, and how confident you felt doing them (1 = *not confident* and 10 = *very confident*).

When you are done practicing, try implementing these actions in your real life. The next time someone gets close to you, notice how close is *too* close, and if they cross that line, hold the boundary. Under the Real Life Notes column, write the date you held the boundary, anything you noticed about the experience, and how confident you felt doing so.

Boundary-Setting Actions	Practice Notes (Date, number of reps, confidence rating)	Real Life Notes (Date, what you noticed, confidence rating)
Make a hard stop signal with your hands (push your hands away from your body with your palms facing out)		
Put your hand or index finger up to more softly signal stop		
Push away with hands (from table, desk)		
Cross your arms at your chest (you can add crossed legs if you are sitting)		
Set your jaw and tilt it upward, keeping eye contact		
Furrow your brow and frown (you can also shake your head no)		
Raise your eyebrows and tilt your head slightly		
Make a facial expression that says, *No, I do not want to do that*		

* Informed by Ogden & Fisher (2016).

Boundary-Setting Actions	Practice Notes (Date, number of reps, confidence rating)	Real Life Notes (Date, what you noticed, confidence rating)
Shake your head no		
Narrow your eyes (you can also tilt your head slightly)		
Purse your lips and lift your head slightly		
Scrunch your nose in an *I don't think so* or *yuck* manner		
Look away or do not make eye contact		
Move your head (or your head and body) backward		
Lean back away from the person		
Ground your feet or sitting bones, square your shoulders, and look at the person		
Tense or tighten your whole body		
Adjust your posture by pressing your feet into the floor, lifting through your belly, and drawing your shoulders back		
Turn away or walk away		
Place a hand on them to stop their approach		
Sigh with disinterest, disgust, refusal		
Laugh in an *I don't think so* manner		

Boundary-Setting Actions	Practice Notes (Date, number of reps, confidence rating)	Real Life Notes (Date, what you noticed, confidence rating)
Shift your tone of voice and pace of speaking (making it low, grounded, and slower)		
Keep moving and do not stop to talk		
Say any of the following: "I do not want to . . ." "I do not like . . ." "I am not going to . . ." "It is not okay with me to . . ." "This is not a good time . . ." "I am doing x, y, z right now . . ." "I am in disagreement with . . ." "This has not been my experience." "I think we need to agree to disagree." "I can't take this on right now." "Let's break and come back to this." "Not right now."		
Practice the above statements and align your body and facial movements with these statements		

How did you know if your boundary setting worked? What did other people do when you tried your boundary-setting actions? Which actions were not a good fit for you? What behaviors could you improve on or practice more?

_____

_____

_____

_____

_____

_____

_____

_____

—Embodying Self-Statement—
Yes and no are two of the most powerful words I can use.

—Embodying Practice—
Being with Others*

Below is a set of nonverbal and verbal ways to encourage being with others. You can think of these as proximity-seeking behaviors because they reflect actions you take when you want to be close or stay close to someone (Ogden & Fisher, 2016). To begin familiarizing yourself with this list of actions, take time to go through each one and practice each action for 5 to 10 repetitions. Similar to the previous exercise on boundaries, you want to have the action sequence well rehearsed so you are prepared for real-life scenarios. Under the Practice Notes column, write the date you practiced, how many repetitions you did, and how confident you felt doing them (1 = *not confident* and 10 = *very confident*).

When you are done practicing, try implementing these actions in your real life. The next time you want to connect with someone, use these tools to get in connection. Under the Real Life Notes column, write the date you practiced being with others, anything you noticed about the experience, and how confident you felt.

Boundary Setting Actions	Practice Notes (Date, number of reps, confidence rating)	Real Life Notes (Date, what you noticed, confidence rating)
Nod your head in affirmation and interest		
Smile with a sense of invitation, welcoming, or acknowledgment		
Tilt your head to the side and keep eye contact		
Raise your eyebrows and widen your eyes as if to say, *This is interesting* or *I am interested*		
Make or keep eye contact (you can add gently blinking your eyes)		
Open and relax your posture, with your arms open, your palms showing, or your hands relaxed		
Soften your muscles and release tension in your body (you can try this while exhaling)		

* Informed by Ogden & Fisher (2016).

Boundary Setting Actions	Practice Notes (Date, number of reps, confidence rating)	Real Life Notes (Date, what you noticed, confidence rating)
As you breathe, extend each exhale compared to the inhale		
Ground your feet or sitting bones, and orient your body and gaze toward the person		
Move or lean closer to the person		
With consent, touch the person's arm, shoulder, upper back, or hand		
Offer to hug the person (approach with your arms out and your palms facing the person)		
Reach out toward the person with your hands open, your elbows soft, and your palms up		
If you are upset and want to be closer, show your distress or need for comfort (cry and look up as if to say, *I need you right now*)		
Make a beckoning motion by gesturing your fingers toward you as if to say, *Come here*		
Mirror the other person's proximity-seeking behavior		
Stand near the person and share their gaze by looking the same way or at the same object		
Show the person something you find interesting, "Did you notice x, y, z over there?"		
Notice the other person's proximity signals and stop or step back when you see a boundary-setting signal (indicating you are getting too close)		
Use a soft, tender, pleasing, vulnerable voice (or change your voice tone)		

Boundary Setting Actions	Practice Notes (Date, number of reps, confidence rating)	Real Life Notes (Date, what you noticed, confidence rating)

Say any of the following:
    "Please sit next to me."
    "Can I touch your hand?"
    "Could I give you a hug?"
    "I like being close to you."
    "Would you come over here?"
    "Do you mind if I sit here?"
    "Can I offer you a tissue?" (if they are
        crying or upset)
    "Do you need (or want) a hug?"
    "Can I help?"
    "What do you need right now?"
    "Did you notice x, y, z over there?"		

Practice the above statements and align your body and facial movements with these statements		

How did you know if being with others was effective in enhancing connection? What did other people do when you tried these actions? Which actions were not a good fit for you? What behaviors could you improve on or practice more?

_____

_____

_____

_____

_____

_____

_____

_____

_____

_____

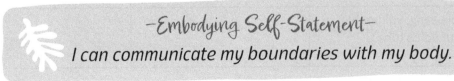

—Embodying Self-Statement—
I can communicate my boundaries with my body.

PAUSE

(**P** - Pause, **A** - Assess ➔ **USE** your resources and supports)

☐ **P**ause, check in, and acknowledge how you are feeling. This is a chance to be kind to yourself. The pace of your work is very important. Press your feet into the earth and take four gentle breaths.

☐ **A**ssess by asking yourself, *Is this a good place for a break?* If the answer is *yes* or *I don't know*, then fold over the corner of the page and take a break. This workbook is here for you for as long as it takes and for as many breaks as you need.

☐ **USE** your resources. Take a rest. Connect to your trusted friends. Contact your therapist. Practice your favorite well-being strategies. Get back to work when YOU are ready.

Embodying Practice
Positively Embodied Relationship Guidance

Having a strong social support system is key to healing from trauma. However, trauma can often cloud your ability to recognize whether it feels good to spend time and share space with a certain person. To develop a sense of positive embodiment in relationships, it is important to know what your body feels like when you are with another person. While you may think that someone else is a good person, the real tell lies beyond what you *think* about them. It lies in how your body feels when you're with them. Does it feel safe, relaxed, and open? Do you have a sense of ease and lightness? Most of the time, it will not take long before you really know, without a doubt, the nature of the relationship.

Think of a particular person in your life as you go through the features of a positively embodied relationship below. Note that the last several statements are features of an attuned sexual relationship and are only appropriate for your romantic relationships. Put a check mark by any features that you notice within the context of the relationship you are exploring.

What I notice when I check in with my body:

General Relationship Features

☐ I feel safe when we are together.

☐ I feel a sense of trust when we are together and apart.

☐ When I am with this person, my body is often in the comfort zone (scores of 1–2 on the Self-Awareness Scale).

☐ When I am with this person, I am able to stay present to and connected with my sensations.

☐ I feel open around this person.

☐ I feel like my muscles can relax around this person.

☐ My heart feels open, restful, playful, or happy around this person.

☐ I have a felt sense that this person will look out for me and that I will look out for them.

☐ I feel safe and open with this person as they are. They accept me as I am. We do not try to change each other.

☐ I do not experience any anxious belly or muscle tension when thinking about this relationship. The relationship does not come with worries or complications.

☐ I often feel sensations of safety and acceptance, affirming that we respect and even admire each other's differences.

☐ On the rare occasions that one of us has been unkind or hurtful to the other, we seek proximity to each other, communicate, and try to understand and engage in the process of making repairs.

☐ There is a felt sense of openheartedness that allows us to give each other the benefit of the doubt when exploring the motive for the other's behavior.

☐ We move and speak with mindful awareness and intention, taking the time to ground and settle our emotions before we work to understand the other's perspective, especially during disagreements.

☐ I feel lightness, buoyance, and radiating sensations in my belly and chest when I anticipate spending time together.

☐ I feel joyfully activated and excited about making plans to be together.

☐ My body feels relaxed and open, with a felt sense of knowing this person is interested in and respects my boundaries in all areas.

☐ We spend time exploring the intersectional experience of self (e.g., race, ethnicity, culture, gender identity, past trauma), how it might play a role in our relationship, and how our bodies feel and respond when having these conversations.

Sexual Attunement Features

☐ I have a felt sense of sexual agency when I am with this person and can engage in actions that meet my needs and desires.

☐ I feel safe and relaxed, with no defensive physical posturing, knowing consent and attunement are important in our relationship.

☐ Our physically intimate actions reflect the mutual valuing of each other's sexual needs.

☐ I feel that my body is safe and can be connected during intimacy with this person.

☐ I have a felt sense that I have the right to say no to sexual acts in this relationship.

☐ When we are physically intimate, agency in sexual decision-making and choice is a priority.

☐ Our sexually intimate actions demonstrate that we value the individual right to feel sexual pleasure.

☐ We spend time exploring the intersectional experience of self (e.g., race, ethnicity, culture, gender identity, past trauma) and how it might play a role in our intimacy and sexual expression and interactions.

☐ Our sexually intimate actions show that we value and practice mindful awareness as applied to body sensations and sexual pleasure.

Looking over both sections, what do you notice? Are there boxes that you didn't check that are important to you? Are there any nonnegotiables that you did not check? What is missing from this list? What lets you know if this relationship is right for you?

_____

_____

_____

_____

_____

Need-to-Know: Difficult People

Sometimes we are related to, and even love, difficult and harmful people. And for a variety of reasons, it may not be feasible or possible to cut these people out of our lives. For example, Soka's mom was a prickly person who did not protect Soka from childhood sexual abuse or her own violent relationship. Once Soka was older and had a place of her own, she was torn about whether or not to spend time with her mother, who was always texting, calling, and otherwise reaching out to her. Soka did not want to interact with her mother because she always ended up hurt by her mother's microaggressions or full-on verbal assaults. After visiting with her mother, Soka would often spend days ruminating about the things her mom said. It was exhausting, yet she felt guilty because her mother was beginning to fail physically. She also knew what a terrible childhood her mother had experienced and knew much of her mother's hurtfulness was related to the pain she had suffered as a child. Soka also knew that, in her own way, her mom loved her.

When you have people in your life like this, it is important to set boundaries around contact and make plans to protect your embodied self during (and after) the contact. For example, Soka began to set limits on how and when she would respond to texts and phone calls, as well as how often she would visit her mother and for how long. Soka also made sure to engage in regulating self-care practices before each visit and planned for a grounding and nurturing activity after each visit. By scheduling something after each visit, Soka's interactions with her mother had a hard stop.

Last, while Soka was visiting with her mom, she decided to simply notice and count her mother's hurtful comments rather than react to them. Over time, she found that her mom typically said about four hurtful things an hour, which she recorded in her journal. On days when there were 5 to 10 hurtful comments, Soka coded that with a red star for a "hurtful mom day." When it was only one or two, she coded it with a green star for a "not-so-bad mom day." The days with the typical four hurtful comments all got coded with a yellow star, which meant "typical mom day." This new approach gave Soka a sense of boundaries and personal agency, as well as some emotional distance from her mother's hurtful comments.

Like Soka, you may also have difficult people in your own life. Perhaps it's a sister or brother you love who is struggling with addiction, or maybe it's a longtime friend who is lost in grief and doesn't see the impact of her anger and hurt on those around her. I have worked with many people who deeply love a family member who is lost in addiction and lashes out at others when using and during blackouts. Creating and keeping boundaries with someone who is in addiction is a daily, exhausting process that feels rife with life-and-death consequences over which you have little control. It can also be complicated when a long-term friend's own personal tragedies and traumas shift what used to be a reciprocal and loving friendship into something that doesn't feel physically or emotionally safe.

When this happens, it is sometimes easier to simply cut a difficult person out of your life. And in some cases, that might be your choice. Yet there are often some compelling reasons why you may not want (or be able) to break ties with someone, as was the case with Soka. In these situations, it is important to develop strategies you can use to keep yourself emotionally and physically safe within the context of the relationship. These strategies can include deciding how often and how long you will spend time with the person, in what spaces that contact will occur (public or private), in what contexts it will occur (alone or with friends), and what you will do to remain connected to your own sense of embodiment and to regulate yourself before, during, and after your interaction with this person. The next practice can give you some guidance in developing these strategies.

Embodying Practice
Managing Difficult People

The following questions can help you create a plan for managing hurtful people in your life. This plan will help you set boundaries around contact and protect your embodied self before, during, and after the contact.

1. How often is it manageable for you to be in contact with this difficult person (e.g., daily, weekly, monthly, quarterly, every six months, only holidays, yearly)?

    _____

    _____

    _____

2. How long would you like that visit to be? Is it just for tea or dinner? Think back to past visits and how long you were able to stay embodied and manage this difficult person (e.g., a few hours, overnight, several nights, a week, two weeks). If they drink or use drugs, are mornings best? Choose a length that is best for your healing and well-being.

    _____

    _____

    _____

3. If you visit, where should you meet? Can you go inside the person's home, or is it better to meet publicly? If this person lives in another city, do you need to stay at a friend's house or a hotel for a longer stay? Be sure to factor in your financial boundaries.

    _____

    _____

    _____

4. Should you go alone or take a friend, family member, or partner? Is there someone you can take who will be understanding, supportive, and validating? Is that person available for the visit?

    _____

    _____

    _____

5. Before you go, what do you need to do to feel grounded, centered, and safe? Are there practices that you need to engage in? Is there a person (e.g., a therapist or sponsor) you need to meet with? When is it best to do this (e.g., right before the visit, within a day)?

_____

_____

_____

6. After the visit, what will you need to feel grounded, centered, and safe? Do you need to get a massage, meet a friend for tea, go to a pottery class, take a yoga class, go for a run with a good friend, or attend a support meeting? Intentionally set this commitment so you can end the visit at the predetermined time and say with integrity, "I need to leave. I have a commitment that I must meet."

_____

_____

_____

7. What specific behaviors are challenging for you when you visit this difficult person? Does this person verbally snap at you, engage in microaggressions, interrupt, or invalidate you? How might you be mindfully aware and intentional about this behavior? Can you count or time the behaviors? Can you rate their severity and frequency? Write out a plan to manage these difficult behaviors and review it with a trusted friend or a therapist.

_____

_____

_____

8. What are nonnegotiable behaviors that, if they occur, will cue an end to your visit? For example, this might occur if the person is using drugs or alcohol, crosses a physical or emotional boundary, has allowed other harmful people to also be present, engages in behavior they committed not to do, brings up off-limits topics, asks for money, or threatens you. Know these behaviors ahead of time and plan your exit strategy: "We talked about how it would not be okay for you to _____. I am going to end this visit now" or "I am not okay with _____. I am going to end the visit now."

_____

_____

_____

9. What level of activation will be your cue for leaving early? Check in with the Self-Awareness Scale during the visit to gauge your arousal. Does it make sense to leave if you are at a 4 or 5 and you feel things escalating? What sensations, emotions, or thoughts will let you know you have reached your limit?

_____

_____

_____

10. After the visit, review how things went and decide whether you need to change your answers to the previous questions for the next visit. Write down any changes you want to make and explain why you need to make those changes.

_____

_____

_____

Chapter 13

Connecting to Your Embodied Wisdom

—Embodying Self-Statement—
I am more than my thoughts.

This chapter is here to remind you that your integrated, embodied self is wise. So often, we think and intellectualize our way through life without listening to our embodied self. Worse, we often think too much about negative and threatening things, which reflects a negativity bias that is inherent to all humans (Hanson & Hanson, 2018). When you have a history of trauma, this negativity bias is intensified as your brain works to protect you from future trauma. You constantly think, *I am not safe* or *I am not worthy*, which activates you at the cognitive level. When you do this, you neurologically prime your emotions and body in the same direction. It's a self-perpetuating cycle in which your body and emotions tense and react, which then primes you to have further negative thinking.

Working with your thoughts in a more aware and embodied manner can help you stop this iterative cycle. Recall from chapter 1 that your thoughts are one aspect of the self over which you have some control. Therefore, the first step to break this cycle is to notice negative thinking patterns as they arise and then reframe them to more accurately reflect the present moment. This gives space to true possibility, healing, and growth. The second step is to place your thoughts in their proper context, as just a *part* of you, when considering things and making decisions.

To get better at informing your thoughts with your embodied self, this chapter is about connecting to and resourcing your embodied wisdom. When I first started as a professor, I worked with a graduate student who endeavored to trust herself more. Her mantra was "Everything I need is within me," and she often said it aloud. I love this mantra because it honors the incredible resources and wisdom held within your body. This wisdom comes from your life experiences and what you have learned from them. These life experiences include the longing and trembling matters of the heart, the punch in the stomach of utter failure, the heavy wounds of loss, and the uplifting and tingling nature of hope. All of these life experiences shift how you know what is safe and unsafe and what you value and love. It is on the other side of a deeply lived and embodied life that you see the type of knowing that is called *wise*.

This chapter includes practices to help you better notice, connect to, and listen to your own embodied wisdom. To do so, you will begin by working with embodying self-statements and then explore ways to engage in embodied decision-making. I will finish by discussing the reasons why embodiment is a fundamental right for all.

Need-to-Know: Working with Embodying Self-Statements

One way to support your nervous system is to work with embodying self-statements, which activates the thinking part of your brain and, in turn, primes your emotional and physiological systems in the same direction (Ogden et al., 2006). This approach is the basis of *top-down processing*, meaning that you work from the level of cognitions in the brain (top) to sensations in the body (down).

One caveat is that your self-statement can't be overly positive or detached from your real experience. It must be anchored in your truth. It should be something you can embody. If an embodying self-statement is characterized by artificial positive thinking, it can actually be harmful (Yeung & Lun, 2021). Therefore, when developing embodying self-statements, you want to look for solid, specific, realistic statements that can help you remember your recovery journey, remind you of your reasons for getting better, connect you to your resources, and help prime your emotional, sensory, and motor systems. These embodying self-statements align with you being embodied and whole.

Embodying Practice
Working with Embodying Self-Statements

The following are some examples of negative (or unhelpful) statements, artificial (or unhelpful) positive statements, and embodied (or helpful) statements. Look through the list and notice the differences among each phrase. You can add any statements you have used in the bottom of the table.

Negative (or Unhelpful) Statement	Artificial (or Unhelpful) Positive Thinking	Embodying (or Helpful) Self-Statements
I am not worth it.	I am, and all people are, amazing and beautiful.	I am worthy of effort and love.
I don't deserve love.	I should stay positive. Only positive vibes are welcome.	I deserve love. I am deserving.
I am broken.	Everything happens for a reason.	I can heal from harmful things.
It is not safe to feel my feelings.	Think happy thoughts. Don't give up.	I build my resources and capacity to feel my feelings.
I should have done better.	Don't worry so much, everything will work out.	I care(d) very much and did the best I could.
I can't trust anyone.	All people are inherently good. See the good in them.	I am working to choose those who are trustworthy.
I am weak.	What doesn't kill you will make you stronger.	I am learning about resources, support, and inner strength.
Everything is horrible.	It could be worse. Compare yourself to _____.	I have resources and supports when feeling overwhelmed.
I don't deserve to be safe.	I need to get over myself and have some courage.	I am working to remember that I am deserving of safety.
I don't deserve happiness.	Stop being so negative. Live, laugh, love.	Happiness is not earned. It is something I am practicing.
I don't deserve compassion.	Today is a new day. Anything is possible. #blessed	I am learning that as we grow and learn, we all struggle.
Add yours here:		

I am working on loving me ♥

When you compare the different types of statements, what do you notice? Which ones do you tend to use more? Are there times when you're more likely to use certain statements—for example, when you are at a certain level of activation? What unhelpful statements do you need to work on?

_____

_____

_____

_____

_____

Throughout this workbook, you'll notice that each chapter has included a series of embodying self-statements. Go through the previous chapters and select the ones you resonate with. As you continue to read on in subsequent chapters, continue to do the same. If you'd like, develop a few more that are uniquely yours. You want to create a collection of embodying self-statements that ring truest for you. As you work with thinking patterns in this chapter, watch for signs of negative activation and bias. If they arise, ground and center yourself, breathe gently, and access one of your embodying self-statements.

PAUSE

(P - Pause, A - Assess → USE your resources and supports)

☐ **P**ause, check in, and acknowledge how you are feeling. This is a chance to be kind to yourself. The pace of your work is very important. Press your feet into the earth and take four gentle breaths.

☐ **A**ssess by asking yourself, *Is this a good place for a break?* If the answer is *yes* or *I don't know*, then fold over the corner of the page and take a break. This workbook is here for you for as long as it takes and for as many breaks as you need.

☐ **USE** your resources. Take a rest. Connect to your trusted friends. Contact your therapist. Practice your favorite well-being strategies. Get back to work when YOU are ready.

Need-to-Know: Embodied Decision-Making

When people are tasked with making a decision, they often follow a step-by-step plan through which they consider the pros and cons of each choice, examine the possible consequences of their actions, and use this guidance for selecting the best plan forward. Although this type of process can help people make the most logical decision, it ignores the wisdom of the embodied self. Marsha Linehan noticed this limitation in 1993 when she developed the idea of "wise mind." This state of being integrates what she called "emotion mind" and "reasonable mind" into one. You can think of wise mind as your intuition. It is garnered from your felt sense, or a gut feeling or instinct. In this state of mind, you can make better choices and get closer to wisdom.

Similar to wise mind, the approach to embodied wisdom that I present here is an integration of thoughts, feelings, your gut instinct, your sense of neuroception, and your intentions. Embodied wisdom emphasizes an awareness of and orientation toward what your body is experiencing and trying to communicate to you. To allow you to connect to this wisdom, let's begin by discussing the Morita-Based Action Guide, which can help you decide on actions you want to take right here, right now.

The Morita-Based Action Guide

In chapter 6, you learned the importance of connecting to your "why"—to your values, mission, and sense of purpose. Knowing your "why" can also be incredibly helpful in present-moment decision-making because it organizes your intentions. When the present moment feels difficult and overwhelming—and it feels like acting out or shutting down are your only options—it is important to turn to your "why" and remind yourself that you (and your "why") are worth the effort.

Recall that you have very little control over the sensations and physiological reactions that occur in any given moment. You also do not have control over the feelings and feeling-based thoughts that follow a prompting event. What you *can* control is what happens next. I often remind my yoga students that embodiment practices can't stop difficult things from happening, but they can greatly reduce the likelihood you will make it worse. With awareness that something is happening and that you are having a response to it, you can begin to make a choice. For example, it is possible to physically ground your feet and breathe. This is an embodied and intentional response. Once you are aware, grounded, and breathing, you are better able to engage in further intentional thoughts and actions.

In this state, you can orient your awareness to your internal compass—to your intentions and your "why"—and decide how to respond in a way that will serve, or at least not sabotage, your intentions and larger purpose. If you have not settled on a definitive "why" yet, I often encourage my patients to use this one: *To create a life I want to be present in.* It is a beautiful placeholder to use until you get yours sorted out. The right thing to do next varies by person and can range from doing nothing to doing something that will help you stay true to the person you are working to be (Cook-Cottone, 2020).

To help you recall your "why" as you make decisions in your day-to-day life, you can use the Morita-Based Action Guide. This is a very helpful tool for making choices in the present moment and for deciding what you should be with and work with. This process was developed by a Japanese psychiatrist named Shoma Morita, who used acceptance as the main frame for his therapy.

To use the Morita-Based Action Guide, you simply bring to mind the things that are not in your control (e.g., the natural unfolding of life events, body sensations, feelings, automatic thoughts), as well as those that are in your control (e.g., your awareness, orientation, actions). Then, instead of trying to fight against or push back against that which you cannot change, you simply learn to be with and accept those experiences as they are—and then choose to act in a way that is aligned with your purpose *in spite of those experiences* (Astrachan-Fletcher & Maslar, 2009). While this can seem difficult, even counterintuitive, you do not have to act on a difficult urge or feeling simply because it is there. By connecting to your "why," you have the power to make a choice consistent with your embodied wisdom.

For example, given Soka's trauma history, she struggled to make decisions on her own and often sought out her partner to make decisions for her. Through her work in therapy, she was gradually learning to sort things out on her own. Although she was very unsure about her reasons for being, she had come to a few conclusions about what motivated her in life—about her underlying "why." With this understanding in mind, she decided to write, "To create a life I want to be present in" as her reason for being on the Morita-Based Action Guide.

Later that week, she came home to a drunk partner who began yelling at her for not having gone grocery shopping, which then quickly escalated into an argument about their financial situation. In that moment, the experience of her partner yelling at her was a life event over which she had no control. Soka then identified the body sensations she was having in that moment, which indicated that she was moving into a shutdown response. She noticed that she was feeling scared, powerless, and hopeless. Her automatic thoughts were that she deserved this and that her life was never going to be okay. In the past, she would have grabbed her purse and run to the grocery store to make the best of the moment and get her partner something to eat.

However, in that moment, Soka realized that she ultimately could not control her partner's anger, drinking, or lack of support in household tasks. While she also could not control her physiological activation, feelings, or automatic thoughts, she could control her awareness and attention. She could notice what was happening and choose purposeful actions aligned with her reason for being. She had practiced some of this with her therapist. In the moment, she focused on what she was feeling and began to engage in a grounding and centering practice. She pressed her feet into the floor, softened her knees, placed a hand on her heart, and slowed her breath. Intentionally, she called to mind her commitment to creating the life she wanted to be present in and saw that what was happening in this moment was not that. She wanted a peaceful and safe home where she could have a pet and maybe even some plants. She wanted her body to feel safe in her home. It was that night that she left for her sister's house, where she stayed for the next few months as she found her own apartment, adopted a kitten, and began growing house plants.

Soka used the Morita-Based Action Guide as an organizing framework for deciding what aligned with what she was hoping for in life and what did not. She later realized her cannabis use was also not helping her to be present, so she began to scale back and eventually quit. The next time you are struggling in the present moment with what you should do, use the Morita-Based Action Guide to work through your decision. Document the process in your journal so you can see how your decision-making processes mature over time.

Embodying Practice
Morita-Based Action Guide*

To help you make decisions that are aligned with your intention, use the following Morita-Based Action Guide to connect to your "why" and allow it to drive your actions. You can write this guide on an index card that you can put in your wallet or purse, write it down in your journal, take a photo of it, or keep it handy in the notes section of your phone for when you need it.

Things I Cannot Control	Things I Can Control
The natural unfolding of life events Body sensations Physiological reactions Feelings (Automatic) thoughts	Mindful awareness ↓ Orientation ↓ Intention ↓ (Deliberate) thoughts ↓ Muscles
Be with: The natural unfolding of life, sensations, psychological reactions, feelings, and automatic thoughts. Consider that you can simply notice, accept, and allow them as they arise and pass. →	**Work with:** Fully aware and attentive to what is occurring, ground your feet and breathe. As your body and mind settle, consider your "why." Bring your thoughts and actions in line with what matters to you and what you are working on. Act with purpose. Note that this may mean doing nothing.
My reason for being or my "why" that can help guide my choices:	

* Informed by Cook-Cottone (2020) and Astrachan-Fletcher & Maslar (2009).

PAUSE

(**P** - Pause, **A** - Assess → USE your resources and supports)

☐ <u>P</u>ause, check in, and acknowledge how you are feeling. This is a chance to be kind to yourself. The pace of your work is very important. Press your feet into the earth and take four gentle breaths.

☐ <u>A</u>ssess by asking yourself, *Is this a good place for a break?* If the answer is *yes* or *I don't know*, then fold over the corner of the page and take a break. This workbook is here for you for as long as it takes and for as many breaks as you need.

☐ **USE** your resources. Take a rest. Connect to your trusted friends. Contact your therapist. Practice your favorite well-being strategies. Get back to work when YOU are ready.

Need-to-Know: The Components of Your Inner Compass

Your inner compass is made up of three parts: (1) your felt sense or gut instinct (your belly), (2) your feeling self (your heart), and (3) your thinking self (your brain). When you are truly connecting with each part of your inner compass and all three line up, you are probably making a good decision.

You have already spent some time getting to know your sensations and your feelings. You also have a good sense of your activation level and what it means to be in (or out) of your window of tolerance. With this knowledge, you will want to engage in decision-making when you are in the comfort zone (1–2) or the low end of your growth zone (3–4). Remember that when you are too activated, the thinking part of your brain is not able to contribute effectively. This is not a good state within which to make big decisions. Big decisions include questions like: Should I go to school? Do I stay with or leave my partner? Is it time for me to quit drinking? Should I tell my friend this information I know? Is it the right time to get a pet? Do I want children? Do I need a therapist to help me through this? Should I change therapists?

Note that for some people, the process of connecting to their gut instinct and heart for guidance can trigger the protective response. Noticing this can be important. For example, if you are trying to decide about a relationship and feel activated and defensive each time you orient toward your instinct and heart, perhaps this is a signal for you. It might be helpful to explore possible similarities between your past trauma and the current situation as you proceed in the decision-making process.

When you have a big decision, complete the following meditation, which will guide you toward your inner compass. I have included an optional section that helps you consider whether your protective response is getting triggered during this process. A trauma-based protective response is not the same thing as a gut feeling or your heartfelt wisdom. If you notice this happening, pause, journal, and get support while you explore the possible association between your current decision and your past trauma.

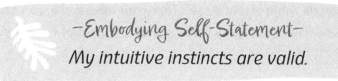

—Embodying Self-Statement—
My intuitive instincts are valid.

—Embodying Practice—
Exploring the Components of Your Inner Compass

The following meditation will allow you to take your time working through the components of your inner compass. This will help you make decisions that honor your feelings and your intuitive self, which is frequently abandoned in decision-making. When you have alignment across all components of your inner compass—across your instincts, feelings, and thoughts—this often reflects a solid decision. If there is a lack of alignment, it often means that you need more time or information, or perhaps something about this decision is not right for you.

To begin, find a comfortable seated position in a safe and private room or space. You might take a moment to look around your space, getting a sense of the doors, windows, and objects present in the room. As you are ready, close your eyes. Scan your body to assess your activation level. You will want to be between a 1 and 4 on the Self-Awareness Scale to continue this meditation practice. If you are at a 5 or above, consider doing this meditation on a different day and seek out a regulating practice or support.

If you are ready to continue, take a few moments to focus on your breath. Gently breathe in for 1, 2, 3, 4 . . . pause . . . and then breathe out for 1, 2, 3, 4, 5. Pause and repeat for three more breath cycles. Then bring your awareness to your body and briefly scan each area, moving from your toes, legs, core, shoulders, arms, hands, neck, head, and ending at your heart.

Now bring to mind a decision you'd like to make. You might verbally say it out loud or silently to yourself, *I am working to decide about* _____. Breathe and get a felt sense of your activation level. Did it change from your baseline number? Are you still below a 5? If not, take a break. If you are, then continue by scanning your body. Did anything shift? Do you notice any new sensations, areas of activation, or areas of deactivation? Is there a feeling present that you can name? You are just noticing here.

Now check in with your thinking self. What do you think you should do? Take time to slowly think through each aspect of this decision. Sometimes it can be helpful to place your hands on either side of your head. Pause and take as much time as you need. Once you have thoroughly investigated the point of view of your thinking self, breathe and get a felt sense of your activation level. Did it change from your baseline number? Are you still below a 5? If not, take a break. If you are, then continue by scanning your body. Did anything shift? Do you notice any new sensations, areas of activation, or areas of deactivation? Do your thoughts sound like feeling-based thoughts? Are they balanced and measured? Or are they global and certain? Is there a feeling present that you can name? Remember that you are just noticing. If you'd like, pause here and write down what you have noticed.

When you're done, check in with your feeling self. What do you want to do? What is your heart's desire? What do you feel about this? Sometimes it can be helpful to place your hands on your heart. Without any input from your gut or your thinking self, fully explore the point of view of your feeling self. If your feeling self could talk, what would it say? Take your time and explore this component of your inner compass. Once you have thoroughly investigated the point of view of your feeling self, breathe and get a felt sense of your activation level. Did it change from your baseline number? Are you still below a 5? If not, take a break. If you are, then continue by scanning your body. Did anything shift? Do you notice any new sensations, areas of activation, or areas of deactivation? Are any sensations moving, clenching, tensing, or letting go? Are there any feelings present that you can name? Remember that you are just noticing. If you'd like, pause here and write down what you have noticed.

When you're done, check in with your felt sense or gut feeling. What is your gut feeling about this? It might be helpful to place both of your hands on your belly. Let go of your thinking and feeling filters, and see if you can focus on your gut feeling. If your gut instinct could talk, what would it say? Take your time to explore this aspect of your inner compass. Once you have thoroughly investigated the point of view of your felt sense, breathe and get a felt sense of your activation level. Did it change from your baseline number? Are you still below a 5? If not, take a break. If you are, then continue by scanning your body. Did anything shift? Do you notice any new sensations, areas of activation, or areas of deactivation? Are you comfortable or uncomfortable? Are there any new feelings present that you can name? Is there an action urge? Is this action urge getting in the way of decision-making? Remember that you are just noticing. If you'd like, pause here and write down what you have noticed.

Now review what your thinking and feeling selves have said about this decision. Do they line up? Did your thoughts sound a lot like feelings? Why or why not? How are your thoughts and feelings different? Do you have enough information? Have you taken enough time? Which source seems to have the most information or pull? Do you have a sense of what is behind any pushiness or action urges you might notice?

Now add in your felt sense or gut feeling. Does it align with your feeling and thinking selves? Why or why not? If your gut feeling could talk to the feeling or thinking parts of yourself, what would it say? Would it give its blessing or offer a warning?

(Optional section)
Last, do you notice if there are any trauma-based reaction patterns or trauma memories present? Do you think your trauma experience is getting in the way here? Scan your body and notice. Do you notice any new sensations, areas of activation, or areas of deactivation? Is there a new feeling (or feelings) present that you can name? Are you feeling activated (above a 5)? Give yourself some compassion if you are. It might be the protective part of you jumping in to try to keep you safe. If so, you will need to take some time to work through this before making a decision. If you'd like, pause here and write down what you have noticed.

Now, bring your awareness back to your breath. Gently breathe in for 1, 2, 3, 4 . . . pause . . . and then breathe out for 1, 2, 3, 4, 5. Pause and repeat for three more breath cycles. As you are ready, close the practice by thanking your brain, heart, and belly for their work as the components of your inner compass.

If you'd like you can use the table on the following page to document what you observed during the practice. This can help you further process the components of wisdom available to you when making a decision.

Exploring the Components of Your Inner Compass

Inner Compass Component	What You Are Noticing
Your thinking self	
Your feeling self	
Your felt sense	
Your trauma memories *(Optional section)*	

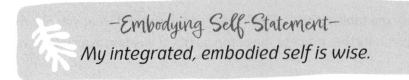

–Embodying Self-Statement–
My integrated, embodied self is wise.

Need-to-Know: Embodied Wisdom and Finding Glimmers

In this chapter, you have worked with negative thought patterns, avoided toxic positivity, and developed embodying self-statements that can help prime your emotions and body toward growth and well-being. You have also worked with two different models for integrating your body in the decision-making processes. Now, you'll focus on bringing together embodied wisdom, mindful awareness, intentional orienting, and intentional thought by finding "glimmers" in your daily life (Dana, 2020, p. 108). A glimmer is a micromoment during which your connection system is activated and you are feeling connected to yourself and others. Your body feels steady and regulated. This is your body saying, *This is good. You are on the right track!*

Because humans are primed to have a negativity bias, it can be easy to miss the moments throughout your day when your body is telling you that things are going well. Therefore, it is important to set a goal each day where you aim to notice a certain amount of glimmers. Perhaps begin with a goal of finding one per day, a moment when you feel connected to yourself and others. This moment can be really small. Perhaps it is a shared smile with a neighbor as you take your daily walk. Or perhaps it's an interaction you have with a retail associate who tells you, "Have a nice day" as you make eye contact and wish them a nice day too. It can be the moment your dog curls up in your lap at the end of the day. It is any moment when things are really aligned.

With time, your ability to find glimmers will help counterbalance the negativity bias, much like beauty seeking does. Finding glimmers is a way to orient on the positive, to prime your body and thoughts toward openness and connection.

Embodying Practice

Finding Glimmers

Whenever you notice a glimmer in your day, stop for a moment and appreciate it. Take a look around and within. Notice what is happening, who is there, and what you are doing. You might even acknowledge each glimmer when it happens by saying the word *glimmer* to yourself or by touching your hand to your heart (Dana, 2020). After you have allowed yourself to be with the experience, use this log to keep track of the glimmers you notice each day.

Date	Glimmers

Need-to-Know: Embodiment as a Human Right

As we close this discussion on embodied wisdom, it is important for me to remind you that positive embodiment is a fundamental human right. As I discussed in the introduction to this book, embodiment is something that you do not need to earn. It is something that all humans are worthy of.

The notion that embodiment is a fundamental human right was born out of the tragic and horrific events of World War II, the deadliest military conflict in history. This war was the material manifestation of destructive hate-filled ideologies, including antisemitism, racism, nationalism, the advent of the use of nuclear weapons, and a belief in war as an unavoidable solution. Ending in 1945, this horrific war was also the birthplace of the proclamation of the United Nations' Universal Declaration of Human Rights (available at www.un.org/en/about-us/universal-declaration-of-human-rights). In the wake of inhumane destruction, human beings across the globe pledged that the atrocities of World War II would never happen again. In this document, each of the human rights is listed, such as the right to live, think, speak, work, rest, learn, and see. These rights all stand on the assumption that we are born embodied and have the right to remain so. In this way, embodiment is the most basic human right from which all other human rights extend (Cook-Cottone, 2020).

One of the most inspiring philosophical developments related to embodiment also arose during this time period. Neurologist, psychologist, and existentialist Viktor Frankl (1946) detailed his experiences in the Auschwitz concentration camp during World War II in his book, *Man's Search for Meaning*. In this text, he describes his enduring embodiment and defines love and a sense of meaning and purpose as key to resilience in the face of horror, as well as within the context of a normal life. He also makes a distinction between thinking and acting. He argued that we must embody our values rather than thinking of or talking about them. He said life will question each of us, and our answers must not come in talk or meditation but in right action.

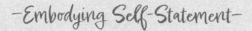

—Embodying Self-Statement—
Embodiment is a human right that is critical to our relationship with ourselves, others, and our world.

Therefore, it is from one of the worst moments in world history that humans were faced with how significant and interconnected their own embodiment is. As powerfully stated by Fannie Lou Hamer, a feminist activist in the 1970s, "No*body*'s free until every*body*'s free" (emphasis added; Brooks & Houck, 2013). How we treat and care for our own bodies and the bodies of others becomes a human rights mission. When we allow for our own embodiment to erode, become devalued, or impact the embodiment of others, we risk repeating the mistakes of the past. Fundamentally, embodiment is a basic human right, and we cannot effectively defend it for others if we do not defend it within ourselves. In this way, our own positive embodiment is a powerful and meaningful humanitarian act. Here is a short mantra to help you remember the essentials of embodiment for all:

May I know and experience embodiment.

May my embodiment serve the embodiment of others.

May all beings know and experience embodiment.

—Embodying Practice—
Loving-Kindness Meditation*

To remind you of the importance of embodiment for all, the loving-kindness meditation is an excellent way to close this chapter. This meditation takes you through a series of offerings of loving-kindness: to yourself, a loved one, a neutral other, a difficult other, and then a larger community of others. It is a lovely way to embrace our interconnectedness while still honoring our boundaries. You can either read through the script or make a recording of it to play back for yourself.

To begin, find a comfortable seat in your safe and private place. Ground your feet and sitting bones, engage your core, and extend through the crown of your head. Then soften your shoulders, jaw, and eyes. Bring your awareness to your breath, gently inhaling and exhaling.

Now begin to expand your awareness to encompass your whole body. Imagine you are surrounded by a large circle of loving-kindness, and you are at rest in the very center. Imagine the circle of loving-kindness is like a caregiver holding a young child with care, warmth, and love. This is the nature of the sphere that is around you now. As you sit within the sphere of loving-kindness, say these words:

May I be happy.

May I be well.

May I be safe

May I be peaceful and at ease.

Bring your awareness back to your breath, to your whole body, and then out to the circle of loving-kindness. Pause here and take several gentle breaths. Now bring to mind a good friend, a loved one, or someone who has shown you great kindness. Imagine that the circle of loving-kindness that surrounds you is expanding to include this person. Breathe gently and visualize yourself and this loved one within the circle of loving-kindness. Repeat these words:

May you be happy.

May you be well.

May you be safe

May you be peaceful and at ease.

Now think about someone whom you feel neutral about. You feel neither good nor bad about them. Maybe it is the person who works at the gas station or lives a few doors down from you. Hold this person in your awareness. Breathe gently and visualize yourself, your loved one, and the neutral person within the circle of loving-kindness. Repeat these words:

May you be happy.

May you be well.

* Informed by Cook-Cottone (2020).

May you be safe

May you be peaceful and at ease.

Now bring to mind a difficult person. Take a moment and get a good sense of them. Breathe and visualize yourself, your loved one, the neutral person, and this difficult person within the circle of loving-kindness. Repeat these words:

May you be happy.

May you be well.

May you be safe.

May you be peaceful and at ease.

Now it is time to expand your loving-kindness circle to include all beings everywhere. Bring to mind those who are hungry, cold, tired, and poor, as well as those who have great wealth and abundance. Bring to mind beings who are sick and those who have great health. Bring to mind all beings in your town or city, state, and nation. Bring to mind all people across the world. Bring to mind all people everywhere. Breathe and think about yourself, your loved one, the neutral person, the difficult person, and all beings everywhere within the circle of loving-kindness. Repeat these words:

May all beings be happy.

May all beings be well.

May all beings be safe.

May all beings be peaceful and at ease.

Feel the expanding loving-kindness circle as you breathe gently. Feel the expansiveness of your sphere and the possible connections with all beings. Slowly bring your awareness back to your breath and your body. When you are ready, rub your hands together, warming them gently. Raise your hands to your eyes and slowly open your eyes into the palms of your hands. Slowly lower your hands and breathe gently.

Part 3

Processing Trauma with and through the Body

Chapter 14

Remembering and Honoring Your Trauma

This chapter provides guidance and structure for you to document your trauma history. In the next chapter, you will be doing additional processing of your trauma. For now, though, the focus is on getting a brief description of the traumatic events you have endured and measuring your level of distress related to the trauma then and now. Throughout this book, you have completed foundational practices to develop your inner resources and learn about your own nervous system, stress response, and window of tolerance. You have also learned many ways to be with and work with your sensations, emotions, and relationships. You are ready.

Need-to-Know: Safety Assessment and Getting Support

To heal from trauma, your healing work should not be further traumatizing. That means you need to move slowly and cycle between effort and rest. As you explore your trauma memories, you will need to consistently check in and see how you are doing. Moving at the speed of trust means honoring the messages you are receiving from your body that say, *I need a rest, Slow down,* or *I need support.* As you work through these remaining chapters, you will want to ask yourself, *Do I push today, or do I rest and restore? Do I forge ahead or take some time to get some support? Do I feel well-resourced or do I need more practice in foundational and restorative practices?*

You can approach this work by imagining that it has two wings, much like a bird (Schwartz, 2017). One wing reflects *will* and the other reflects *surrender.* Will—or your drive to heal—is fueled by remembering your "why." Surrender is about acknowledging the enormous challenge that is inherent in the work you are doing and making time to rest, restore, and repair. With too much will, you can cause more harm. With too much surrender, you can get stuck. Therefore, each time you pick up this book, ask your body what it needs today: will or surrender? Then with a hand on your belly and a hand on your heart, breathe and listen for the answer.

> **—Embodying Self-Statement—**
> *I can take breaks.*

The importance of balancing will and surrender is illustrated by a patient named Jonathan, who experienced trauma when he was drugged and sexually assaulted in college. Although he notified authorities and an investigation was completed, no charges were filed. He often described the ensuing police response and investigation as equally traumatizing. He felt judged and invalidated. As an athlete since middle school, he approached his trauma therapy as if he was training relentlessly for a big game. He bought a self-help book and pushed himself hard. After four weeks, he felt like he was becoming even more dysregulated. He was extremely irritable around his partner and could not focus at work. He began to feel like he had experienced three assaults: the actual event, the subsequent investigation, and now his trauma work. He started to think it was better just to do nothing.

The reality is that Jonathan was pushing himself too hard. He had no real sense of a comfort zone where he could rest, repair, and restore. He also didn't have a good sense of a growth zone where he could manage his emotions, thoughts, and sensations in an effective manner. His long history of pushing himself outside of his window of tolerance in athletics had informed his attempts at healing, and he was consistently between a 7–10 on the Self-Awareness Scale. To heal sustainably, he should have been cycling between 1–2 and 3–6.

> **—Embodying Self-Statement—**
> *I can choose.*

To avoid going through the same difficulties that Jonathan encountered, know that you can choose how to move forward in these remaining chapters. If listing and processing your traumatic experience does not feel right, maybe this work is not right for you just yet. Take time to intentionally decide what the best path forward is for you. The previous chapters are specifically focused on helping you build resources and become more present and effective in your daily life. *Those chapters may be exactly what you need.*

Need-to-Know: How to Secure a Trauma Therapist

If, throughout the course of this work, you notice that you are getting pushed outside your window of tolerance or exhibiting many of the symptoms in the following **Safety Assessment** checklist, I encourage you to consider working with a trauma therapist. These steps will help you locate a therapist that is a good fit for you:

Step 1: Consider Your Preferences

Before you get started on a search, pause and think about who you might feel most comfortable talking to. Consider the characteristics that are most important to you: gender, age, experience, in person versus online, race, and ethnicity.

Step 2: Conduct a Directed Search

There are many options for accessing trauma therapists. Many cities have a local psychological association whose web page includes a search tool for finding a therapist who matches your needs. The Psychology Today and therapist.com websites also have a large directory with search options that let you narrow your search by type of therapy, insurance offered, gender, age, price, and more. There are several online therapy options, like BetterHelp and Talkspace, that can match you with a therapist too. If you have insurance, you can reach out to your insurance company for a list of in-network therapists and associated specialties. If you are a veteran, you can go through the National Center for Posttraumatic Stress Disorder (NCPTSD).

Step 3: Look for Therapist Training and Trauma Experience

Your trauma therapist should have trauma-specific training. They may have completed an internship at a trauma center or hospital, and they might have been trained in a specific trauma-treatment protocol. The following are all effective therapies that a trained trauma therapist might use. Note that this workbook is intentionally designed to work easily with these various approaches to trauma:

- **Trauma-focused cognitive behavioral therapy (TF-CBT)** involves exploring how your thoughts, feelings, and behaviors may have been affected by your traumatic experience. The treatment can occur in two ways: Exposure therapy involves gradually desensitizing you to your trauma memories by writing about them, talking about them, imagining them, and sometimes recreating aspects of them (such as associated sounds or images). Cognitive processing therapy is another form of treatment that works with trauma memories, but instead of focusing on exposure, it focuses on how the memory has affected your beliefs about yourself, others, and the world (e.g., *I am not safe, You can't trust anyone, The world is a dangerous place*) and how those beliefs shape your emotions and behaviors. Treatment involves developing more positive beliefs and coping behaviors. The TF-CBT web page has a find-a-therapist section: https://tfcbt.org/.

- **Eye movement desensitization and reprocessing (EMDR)** addresses trauma memories by asking you to focus on trauma-related body sensations, emotions, and beliefs (e.g., *I am not worthy of love*) during periods of bilateral stimulation. There are many forms of bilateral stimulation, which can include watching a light beam move from side to side, holding clickers that pulse in an alternating left-right pattern, or listening to tones that alternate between your left and right ears. For more information, visit www.emdria.org.

- **Dialectical behavior therapy (DBT)** has been accepted as an effective way to treat individuals who struggle with overwhelming emotions and interpersonal problems. The treatment teaches tools related to mindfulness, emotion regulation, distress tolerance, and interpersonal effectiveness. DBT for PTSD includes psychoeducation on trauma and also teaches you how to work with trauma-associated emotions (e.g., fear, disgust, powerlessness), question unjustified secondary emotions (e.g., guilt, shame, self-contempt), and practice radical acceptance of trauma-related facts. Exposure-based techniques are also included to address trauma-associated emotions.

- **Emotional freedom technique (EFT)** combines somatic and cognitive elements to manage trauma-related symptoms. At its most basic level, EFT involves tapping various parts of your body in a specific sequence as you bring to mind the traumatic or distressing issue for which you are seeking healing. EFT is thought to treat trauma, as well as a wide variety of other concerns, by triggering a change in the body's energy system through the stimulation of these acupoints.

- **Internal Family Systems (IFS)** is a form of psychotherapy that helps individuals access and befriend their protective and wounded inner parts. Those who practice IFS believe that the mind is made of various subpersonalities, or parts, that interact like members of a family. IFS focuses on healing the wounded parts and restoring mental balance by working with the dynamics between the parts and developing a person's core sense of self. See more at https://ifs-institute.com/.

Step 4: Go to a Session to Assess Fit

Once you have identified a therapist who aligns with your preferences and has trauma experience, go to a session. During the session, notice how you feel. Does this person put you at ease? Do they feel safe and trustworthy? When you think about going back, how does your body respond? Since you are addressing trauma, your body will hold some natural defensiveness and resistance. This is difficult work. However, do you feel something else? Does this person seem like the type of person you'd like to share these difficult experiences with? If it does not feel right, cancel your next appointment and try a different therapist. One caveat: If you notice that no therapist seems right, this might be a sign of avoidance. If you are sure that you are ready, it might be helpful to try the one that seems closest to an "okay" fit.

Once you have found a therapist who seems like a good-enough fit, simply let them know you'd like some support working through this book. When I work with patients using a workbook, I keep a copy at my office and have the patient use their own copy. It's easy for me to bookmark where they are in my copy of the book using sticky notes with the patient's initials. I also make a note in their file that indicates the page we are on and their progress.

Embodying Practice
Safety Assessment

Below is a checklist of signs that you might be outside of your window of tolerance, meaning that you are pushing yourself too hard, not adequately supported, or moving too quickly. It might also mean that working with your symptoms is a better approach for you than specifically detailing and processing the trauma experience itself. Review the checklist as you move through the remaining chapters of this workbook. Addressing trauma directly is not right for everyone, so if you have checked any boxes, stop and take whatever actions you need to in order to rest, repair, and restore. If you checked one or more of the boxes, I strongly encourage you to seek the support of a therapist.

Last, if at any point you are feeling depressed or suicidal, please seek help immediately. Contact your therapist, call a local crisis hotline, or tell someone you love and trust—someone who will actively support you and how you are feeling. Do not continue this work until you can do so with a trained mental health professional, who can help you decide whether it is the right time to do this work. If you decide to move forward, your therapist can also help you work with the Self-Awareness Scale, alternating periods of rest with periods of work, and adding restorative practices as needed.

☐ I am feeling increasingly tired each day.

☐ I notice I am not functioning at work or at home as well as I used to.

☐ As I do this work, my anxiety seems to go up and not come back down to baseline.

☐ I have been feeling depressed and overwhelmed.

☐ I am not having fun doing the things that used to make me happy.

☐ My sleep is disturbed, even more than usual.

☐ I feel alone.

☐ I feel an overwhelming resistance to moving forward.

☐ I am drinking (or using substances, overexercising, gambling, etc.) as a way of coping.

☐ I feel like I have to do everything perfectly or I will fall apart.

☐ I feel like my life is becoming unmanageable.

☐ I have had self-harm, suicidal, or homicidal thoughts or behavior in the past six months.

☐ I don't have supportive people in my life.

☐ I currently do not feel safe.

☐ I do not have daily structure in my life right now.

—Embodying Self-Statement—
I can ask for help.

Embodying Practice
Use Your Resources

In the previous chapters, you worked to develop your resources (chapter 5), created a container to hold any overwhelming experiences (chapter 9), and practiced dozens of embodiment practices. In the box below, list the resources, specific type of container, and embodiment practices you will use when needed going forward. Also recall how you will ask for help using your support signal (chapter 3). Finally, list the contact information for trusted loved ones and other sources of professional support. You might find it helpful to have your encouragement letter to yourself and your vision board and mission statement nearby (chapter 5).

My resources are (include symbols or talisman for your refuge and protector):

My container is:

The embodying practices I will use are:

My signal for support is:

Contact information for at least two trusted loved ones:

1. _____

2. _____

Contact information for my therapist or other forms of support (e.g., minister, yoga therapist):

1. _____

2. _____

―Embodying Practice―

Your List of Distressing and Traumatic Experiences

The next step is to create a list of the events you have found very distressing or traumatizing in your life. You can think of these as your worst experiences (Shapiro, 2017). Document each of these events in your journal, or you can use the log on the following page. For your list, there is no need to go into detail. Simply give each experience a brief label. Here are some examples: car accident, beaten by father, leg surgery, death of mother, bone marrow transplant, house fire, witnessed shooting, domestic violence (mom and boyfriend), principal (or priest) touched me, sexual assault, or police arrested sister in home. Write enough so you know which experience you are referring to. You will have an opportunity to expand later.

If there was recurrent trauma that occurred over a period of time, like abuse, note the time it started and ended, rather than documenting each incidence. If there were more serious experiences within that timeframe that stand out in your mind, it can be helpful to specifically note those. For example, my patient Anna experienced sexual abuse from her older cousin from ages 6 to 11. During that time, however, there was a specific occasion during which Anna's cousin threatened to harm her little sister if she told anyone about the abuse. There were also two other occasions during which the abuse escalated. Anna added those three specific experiences to her timeline, in addition to the overall abuse.

―Embodying Self-Statement―
Remembering can be a way to honor my past.

For each event, record your age at the time of the trauma (as close as you can get to the month and year of the experience), then use this expanded Self-Awareness Scale to rate your distress at the time of the event and your distress as you recall the experience in the present moment.

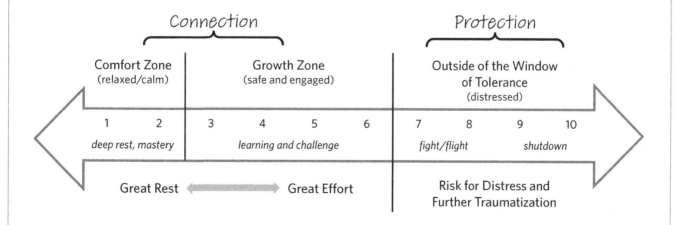

This is the beginning of honoring what you have experienced. Although there are several spaces here to document your list of traumatic experiences, some people will only have one or two experiences, while others will have many. Remember to take breaks, get support, and use your inner resources and container as you need to.

Experience	Age and Date (month/year)	Distress Then	Distress Now

Moving Through and Honoring Your Body

It can be difficult to work through traumatic experiences when your body is primed to mobilize into a state of fight or flight, immobilize into a state of shutdown, or freeze into a state of attentive immobility. When this happens, movement and stillness that you generate while being connected to yourself and your body can be regulating. In fact, body and movement-oriented interventions can be helpful in PTSD recovery. Therefore, while the following embodiment practice is not a trauma-processing practice per se, it can help you honor your body's resilience and strength as you move through the experience of listing your traumas.

This practice has two phases: (1) move through and (2) rest and honor. Note, if you feel you are moving out of your window of tolerance at any point, remember to take a break and return to the practices you identified on the **Use Your Resources** worksheet before moving forward.

Moving Through

Find a place where you have some privacy and space to move (a circle of about five feet). It is helpful to wear clothes that allow you to move freely, such as comfortable shoes or no shoes with your socks off. Make sure there are no other distractions present—turn off the TV or radio and silence your phone.

To begin, get into a standing position and make sure you are settled into your safe place. Then take a moment to scan your location, noticing the doors, windows, or landscape, and address anything that might interfere with your practice.

In the center of your space, place your feet a little more than hip distance apart. Then begin to gently rock side to side. You can let your hands flow freely by your sides or wrap them arm under arm just below your chest. Bring your awareness to your feet on the floor as one foot and then the other presses. You can track this with your words, saying or thinking, *My feet can connect with the earth.* Repeat this for one to two minutes, moving and reminding yourself, *My feet can connect with the earth.*

Next, add a bit of a twist, releasing your hands and allowing them to swing. Keep your feet where they are. As you twist to the left, release your right heel and let your arms swing to the left. When you swing to the right, lift your left heel and let your arms swing to the right. You might notice the twisting and swinging sensations in your body and the air on your arms and hands as they move from side to side. Swinging and twisting gently side to side, you can track your movements with your words, *I can move my body.* Repeat this for one to two minutes or so, moving and reminding yourself, *I can move my body.*

Pausing at the center, bring your hands to your sides and take a few breaths. Notice your feet on the floor. Notice your knees and allow a gentle softness or bend. Notice your hips, shoulders, and jaw. Allow for the release of any tension or holding. Slowly begin to walk around your space, letting your feet move one ahead of the other with your arms swinging naturally at your side. You can play with your footsteps by making them smaller or bigger. You can create different types of walks, such as a business-person walk, a toddler walk, a someone-with-big-floppy-shoes walk, or a stuck-in-the-snow walk. Play around a little bit and create different kinds of walks. Tip toe. Stomp your feet. Walk lightly. Walk with heavy feet. As you play, you can track this with your words, *I can move my body*. Repeat this for one to two minutes or so, moving and reminding yourself, *I can move my body*.

When you are ready, return to a regular and then a slow walk. You might try synchronizing your breath with your footsteps, breathing in step, step . . . and breathing out step, step. As you breathe and walk, you can track this with your words, *I can move my body*. Repeat this for one to two minutes, reminding yourself, *I can move my body*.

Come back to the center of the room and pause. Take your feet back to hip distance apart, pressing them into the earth with your knees soft. Notice your hips, shoulders, jaw, and eyes. Allow for softness and the release of tension or holding.

Breathing in, lift your hands up toward the ceiling. During a deep exhale, fold forward, allowing your hands to move to the floor. Repeat this several times. Do this at a softness or intensity that feels okay with your body. As you breathe in and raise your arms, track your movements with thoughts like *Rising up*, *Reaching up*, or *Nourishing*. As you exhale and fold forward, track your actions with your thoughts, thinking something like *Letting go* or *Releasing*. Find the words that make sense for you as you reach up (breathing in) and fold forward (breathing out). Depending on how it feels, you can repeat this up to 10 times.

Coming back to standing, begin to slowly rock back and forth. You can let your hands flow freely by your sides or wrap them arm under arm just below your chest. Bring your awareness to the feeling of your feet on the floor as one foot and then the other presses. You can track this with your words, saying or thinking, *My feet can connect with the earth*. Repeat this for one to two minutes, moving and reminding yourself, *My feet can connect with the earth*.

When you're done, find a comfortable seat, and support your legs and back as needed. Your body is well grounded and you are safe. Next, place one hand on your stomach and one hand over your heart as you focus on breathing in and out. Breathe using your typical breathing pattern for three breaths, then begin to slowly extend the inhalation and exhalation by counting—inhale 1, 2, 3, 4 . . . exhale 1, 2, 3, 4. Inhale 1, 2, 3, 4 . . . exhale 1, 2, 3, 4. Then allow your breath to return to normal. With your hand over your heart, bring your awareness to your heart and notice any sensations there or the feeling of your heartbeat. Maybe remind yourself that this does not need to be any certain way.

Honoring Your Body

For this next step, you might want to take a moment to adjust your position so you feel well supported and comfortable. Rest your hands in your lap. As you are ready, soften your gaze or close your eyes. From a distance, imagine you can see your trauma list, the experiences you and your body have endured. Now, move your awareness back to you, right now. Imagine a sphere of loving-kindness all around you. Imagine your protector is there, making sure you are safe. Acknowledge to yourself, to your body, all that it has endured to get to this point: *You have been through so much. I see you. You are resilient and strong.*

Then bring your awareness to your feet. Imagine a sense of loving-kindness all around your feet and say to them, *You have been through so much. I see you. You are resilient and strong.*

Move your awareness to your legs and hips. Imagine that same loving-kindness all around your legs and hips and say to them, *You have been through so much. I see you. You are resilient and strong.*

Move your awareness to your hands. Imagine the energy of loving-kindness surrounding your hands and say to them, *You have been through so much. I see you. You are resilient and strong.*

Move your awareness to your arms and shoulders. Imagine that radiant loving-kindness all around your arms and shoulders and say to them, *You have been through so much. I see you. You are resilient and strong.*

Move your awareness to your neck and head. Imagine the sphere of loving-kindness on your neck and head and say to them, *You have been through so much. I see you. You are resilient and strong.*

Move your awareness to your belly, lungs, and heart: the core of you. Imagine loving-kindness radiating all around your center as you breathe, as your heart beats. You might want to move your hands, placing one hand on your belly and one hand on your heart, as you breathe. Say to your belly, lungs, and heart, *You have been through so much. I see you. You are resilient and strong.*

Finally, expand your awareness to your whole body. Allow the sphere of loving-kindness to surround your whole body. Breathe a few gentle breaths here. Close the practice by saying to your whole body, *You have been through so much. I see you. You are resilient and strong.*

—Embodying Self-Statement—
I can honor my body's resilience and strength.

Next Steps

In the next chapter, you will be processing your trauma memories—*if* it feels right for you to move forward. Take a moment and see how it has felt for you to list your trauma memories here. What is your feeling of safety like? Do you feel that it is best for you to move on? Or do you need more support? Consider reviewing your readiness with your therapist or secure a therapist to help you decide.

PAUSE

(**P** - Pause, **A** - Assess → **USE** your resources and supports)

☐ **Pause**, check in, and acknowledge how you are feeling. This is a chance to be kind to yourself. The pace of your work is very important. Press your feet into the earth and take four gentle breaths.

☐ **Assess** by asking yourself, *Is this a good place for a break?* If the answer is *yes* or *I don't know*, then fold over the corner of the page and take a break. This workbook is here for you for as long as it takes and for as many breaks as you need.

☐ **USE** your resources. Take a rest. Connect to your trusted friends. Contact your therapist. Practice your favorite well-being strategies. Get back to work when YOU are ready.

Chapter 15

You and Your Body Healing: Doing the Trauma Work

—Embodying Self-Statement—
My body knows how to heal.

As you work through your trauma in this chapter, you will have increasing access to the sensations of embodiment: sensing, feeling, knowing, and connecting (Ogden & Fisher, 2016). However, the embodied healing process is not linear, meaning that it isn't something you do once and are done with. Rather, the process of being with and working with trauma is an ongoing, interactive, and circular process that involves befriending your body, providing it with safety and care, developing your resources, knowing your "why," and learning to be with and work with your sensations, emotions, and relationships. All of these embodied actions, which you have been working on throughout this book, have prepared you to process trauma.

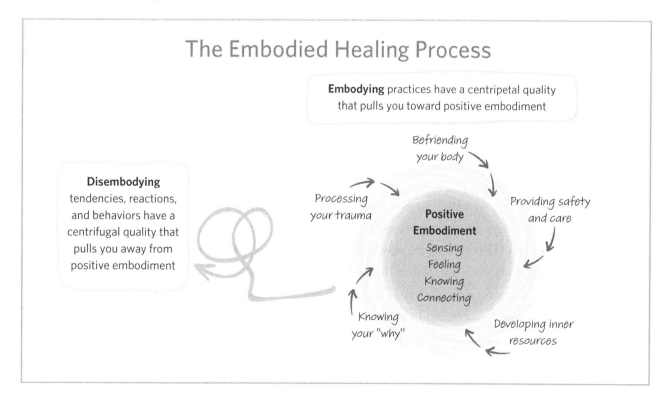

To facilitate this healing process, this chapter provides a unified practice protocol that helps you process your traumatic memories. This will be done using practices that keep you in a state of connection and allow you to develop positive embodiment. To do this, you will need to remain aware of any defensive tendencies, reactions, and behaviors aligned with being in a state of protection and disembodiment. You will be using the Self-Awareness Scale to track your physiological state throughout this process. Use of this scale, while honoring the experiences of both yourself and your body, is critical. Positive embodiment and connection promote healing, while reactive, protective, and disembodied states keep you stuck and facilitate further traumatization (Ogden & Fisher, 2016; van der Kolk, 2014).

Need-to-Know: Healing and Processing Trauma Memories

Recall that trauma memories are often stored in your body as sensations, feelings, thoughts, physiological states, and associated action urges. They don't fit neatly into a story or your understanding of who you are (van der Kolk, 2014). Rather, they often appear as isolated visual flashbacks and sensations that unpredictably move through your body. For example, during a first kiss, you might suddenly feel like you are in physical danger of being sexually assaulted, your heart might start racing and your body gearing up to fight, and you might think, *I am being assaulted* as you push your romantic partner away. These memories can also show up as extreme physiological and behavioral reactions to internal or external triggers. For example, in response to the sound of a siren, you might experience the rapid beating of your heart and the urge to run—and then actually start running while the thought *I am not safe* runs through your mind.

Healing requires bringing all of these pieces together into one coherent narrative that integrates the current context, provides an accurate assessment of safety right here and now, and gives you a felt and embodied understanding that the trauma happened in the past. This can be done for each trauma memory. Further, it is helpful to simultaneously explore and challenge what each memory means in terms of your understanding of yourself. This integrating work can help weave these memories into your overall experience of yourself and create a different experience for you. For example, recovery and healing can look like this: *This is our first kiss. Being this close to someone can be triggering for me. I choose this, have done my trauma-processing work, and have skills I can use to stay present and connected. For now, I will orient toward the sensations in the here and now. I will pause, communicate my boundaries, and use my practices as I need to.*

My years of experience in researching trauma and working with trauma survivors have taught me that there are multiple pathways to recovery. Some forms of therapy begin by working with the narrative, or story, of your trauma. This type of therapy explores how your trauma narrative is interwoven into your understanding of who you are. Other therapies begin by focusing on the physiological states and sensations that are held as nonverbal memories in your body. I think both approaches are helpful in their own ways, within certain contexts, and for particular patients. Ultimately, healing and recovery happens as you practice being with and working with each aspect of the trauma as it is embodied across the layers of who you are.

The big question is *Will it be helpful for me to reprocess my trauma?* Across research, it still remains unclear if it is best for everyone to reprocess their trauma as part of healing. For some, going through what happened again can be destabilizing and potentially retraumatizing. In this case, taking a *symptom-processing path*—in which you explore ways to be with and work with the sensations, feelings, thoughts, physiological states, and action urges that come up in your day-to-day life—may be a better fit. This is what you have done in the preceding chapters. For others, trauma processing can be a highly effective way to learn how to be with and work with the symptoms as they present. In this case, taking a *traumatic memory–processing path*—in which you reprocess the trauma memory while activating your associated thoughts, emotions, sensations, physiological states, and action urges—can be effective. For others yet, the right thing to do is to get professional support from a trauma therapist in navigating either path.

There is no one right path for everyone. Rather, there is a time, place, and pathway (or set of pathways) that will be right for you. Ultimately, your body knows how to heal. You decide what is right for you. If you are not sure if you should move forward, revisit the **Safety Assessment** checklist in the previous chapter.

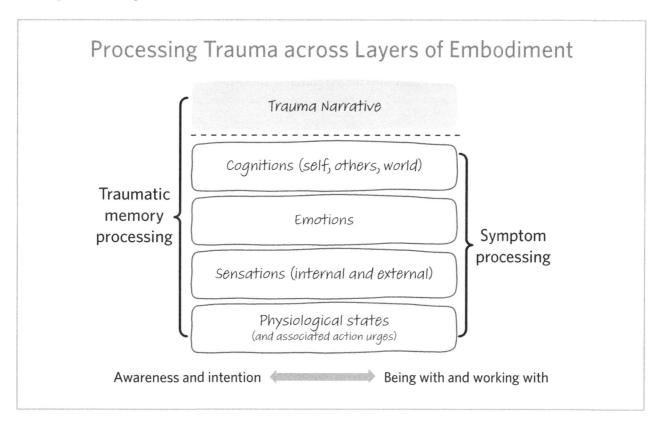

This chapter provides step-by-step guidance to help you process and integrate your traumatic experience using the *traumatic memory–processing path*. The techniques presented here reflect an embodied approach that integrates techniques from several different modalities, including somatic experiencing, somatic and sensorimotor psychotherapy, emotional freedom technique (EFT), trauma-focused cognitive behavioral therapy (TF-CBT), eye movement and desensitization reprocessing (EMDR), and yoga therapy. You'll find specific physical postures and practices to help you be with and work with the experience, as well as several supportive practices, such as self-holding, that honor and support your experience.

These integrating practices are built over three core sessions. For each traumatic memory, you will move through the three sessions, potentially repeating the third session as needed. Each session and each step will take you through a different form and level of processing. Each person will respond uniquely, with some sessions and steps being a better fit than others. As you work with these processing practices, take time to journal and assess what is right for you. Last, for some, this level of processing will not feel like or be enough. For others it may feel like or be too much. In both cases, a trauma therapist can be extremely helpful. This book is not meant to replace the deeper work than can be done with a therapist.

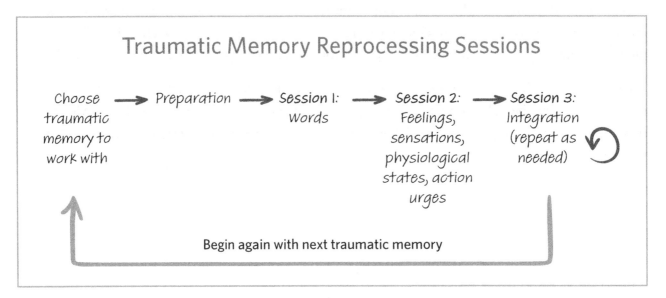

Session 1 (Words): This session focuses on developing the trauma narrative and associated self-statements. Here you will complete a centering mudra practice, select a trauma memory to work with, represent the memory using words, write the memory as a story or narrative, explore trauma-based cognitions versus healing-based cognitions, and complete a closing mudra practice.

Session 2 (Feelings, Sensations, Physiological States, and Action Urges): This session focuses on detailing the feelings, sensations, physiological states, and action urges associated with your trauma. You will write a here-now and then-there script, practice self-holding techniques, free draw, integrate feelings and sensations into your trauma narrative, and do some grounding yoga.

Session 3+ (Integration): This session, which can be repeated as needed for each memory, focuses on integrative traumatic-memory processing. Here you will be with and work with your trauma memory, practice a healing self-tapping exercise, and complete a closing mudra practice. The practices in this section are repeated for four cycles for each traumatic memory.

As you move through this process, you will want to move between the comfort zone and the growth zone, while remaining inside your window of tolerance. The goal is to practice being with your experience as a challenge rather than an overwhelming distress. Dosage (how much) and pace (how fast or slow) will help you stay within your window of tolerance. Remember that this work is most effectively completed while in a state of connection, not protection.

Preparation Procedures

Before you begin, it might be helpful to go back and read the letter you wrote to your inner protector in chapter 5. You might also want to update your letter and keep it at hand during this work. Your inner protector will likely find this work difficult (because it is) and become defensive (because that is your inner protector's job). Tell your inner protector that you will be moving at the speed of trust, that you have lots of resources, and that you have a plan for support. Ask your inner protector if there is anything it needs, wants, or would find helpful as you move forward in your journey. Your protector is a very hard worker and may have some good ideas, so take some time to put some of these ideas into practice.

Then go through the following guidelines to prepare for your trauma-processing sessions:

- Go through the following TP-PAUSE (Trauma Processing: Pause, Assess, and USE your resources) practice. I encourage you to complete the gentle breathing practice in the TP-PAUSE a few times before you begin the processing work.

- Familiarize yourself with the following centering mudra practice, which you will use to begin this processing work.

- Gather any materials you need in your place to practice, including a writing utensil, your journal, and a water bottle for hydration. For support, bookmark the following practices: **Use Your Resources** (chapter 14), **A Letter of Encouragement to Future You** (chapter 6), **Envisioning Your Future** (chapter 6), and **Developing a Personal Sense of Mission** (chapter 6).

- Make sure you have time set aside for this processing work. This includes making time for setup, for about one hour of processing itself, and for transitioning back into your day-to-day life. A quick 20 minutes at your lunch hour won't work and doesn't honor the potential emotional and physical fatigue you may experience after. Look for a 90-minute to 2-hour block of time you can set aside for each session, followed by a restful, easy schedule. Remember, your pace is part of the healing process. Even healing interventions can do harm if you move too quickly.

- About an hour before you start, have a light meal or snack.

- Let your loved ones or therapist know that you are going to be doing this work and that you may reach out if you are overwhelmed or need support.

—Embodying Self-Statement—
It is okay to pause and take care of myself.

Embodying Practice
TP-PAUSE

The TP-PAUSE (Trauma Processing: Pause, Assess, and USE your resources) is an advanced form of the PAUSE practice that you have been using throughout the book. This is a more formal version that you can use when you feel like you might need to take a break. It allows you to assess how you are doing and decide what is best for next steps.

TP-PAUSE (Trauma Processing: **P**ause, **A**ssess, and **USE** your resources)

Pause: Take a moment to orient yourself to your body in the present moment. Remember, this is a chance to be kind.

Assess: What is your number on the Self-Awareness Scale? Jot it down, as well as the zone you are in (comfort, growth, outside of the window of tolerance).

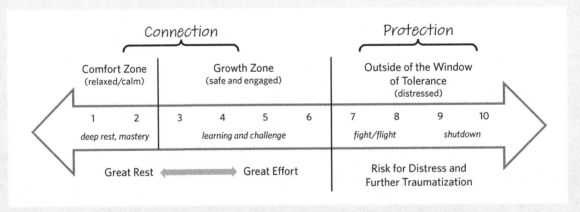

My number is _____. My zone is _____.

USE your resources:
Recall that pendulation is a process in which you practice moving back and forth between distressing experiences of the past and grounding experiences in the present. This process will help you notice where you are (and are not) feeling distress in your body, what the distress is like, and how it changes as you notice. The following is an abbreviated version of the pendulation practice you learned in chapter 5:

- Scan for distress: Bring your attention to your body. Do you feel any distress? If so, where is it? What does it feel like? Take a moment to experience this sensation. If it feels overwhelming, focus on the very edge or a small part of the sensation.

- Scan for neutral or calm feelings: Scan your body for places that feel neutral, calm, or grounded. This is a place that is free from distress or not part of the distress you are feeling. Some people call this an oasis spot. This place can be anywhere in your body. To find it, slowly move outside of the area where you are feeling the distress, moving past its edge. If you are struggling to find a spot, check your hands, feet, fingers, or toes. If it is really hard, hold or touch your talisman and notice the point of contact with your skin.

- Be with the distress: Now, slowly move your awareness back to the place in your body where you were feeling the distress. Experience it as fully as possible.

- Be with the neutral or calm feeling: Shift your awareness back to the area without distress. Experience it as fully as possible.

- Pendulate: Continue to slowly move your awareness from the distressing feeling to the neutral or calm feelings, orienting your awareness back and forth.

- Notice: As you pendulate, notice the area of distress. Notice any shifts in its intensity or size. You may notice a spontaneous deep breath, a shiver, or other body movement as your body relaxes and you release energy.

Once you feel complete with the pendulation process, take a moment to assess where you are on the Self-Awareness Scale. Jot down the number and the zone you are in, and also note whether your activation increased or decreased in response to the pendulation:

My number is _____. My zone is _____. My activation is _____ (increasing/decreasing).

Now, bring to mind your safe place, your inner resources, and your sense of mission and purpose. Engage in 60 to 90 seconds of gentle breathing. Note that other calming techniques presented later in this chapter (e.g., self-holding, grounding yoga) can be substituted here:

- Gentle breathing: Soften or close your eyes. Place a hand on your belly and a hand on your heart. Breathe gently through your nose, stilling and softening your shoulders and chest. Emphasize expanding your belly as you inhale and contracting your belly as you exhale. Breathe even more gently and softly until you can barely notice your belly moving. Bring your awareness just to your nose and your nostrils as the air moves slowly and gently in and out. As needed, soften your shoulders, jaw, and eyes. Once 60 to 90 seconds have passed, return to your normal breath pattern. Notice the rise and fall of your belly for about 30 to 60 seconds.

When you are done, take a moment to assess where you are on the Self-Awareness Scale. Jot down the number and the zone you are in, and also note whether your activation increased or decreased in response to gentle breathing:

My number is _____. My zone is _____. My activation is _____ (increasing/decreasing).

Look back to your ratings at the beginning, middle, and end of this TP-PAUSE practice. Have they changed? Are you in the comfort or growth zones? Did the resourcing practices change your ratings? If so, in what direction?

This is a decision-making point where you can decide to take a longer break, reach out to a support person, or keep going. Decide what is best for you.

- <u>Take a break and get support</u> if you are currently outside of your window of tolerance (or your scores are increasing or staying the same).

- <u>It is okay to keep going</u> if you are within your comfort or growth zones, have shown positive responsiveness (i.e., rating went down).

- <u>Do what is right for you</u> no matter your scores. If you feel you need a break, take one.

If you decide to take a break for the day, take a moment to place the work you have been doing today in your container. Then close with one more session of gentle breathing.

A Centering Mudra: Hands at Heart Center

Begin this process with a centering mudra practice. Mudras are hand movements that are often used to represent concepts such as earth, grounding, and grace. Bringing the palms of your hands together at your heart center is one form of this practice that is used across many traditions. In yoga, this is referred to as *anjuli mudra*. There are several interpretations of what this mudra represents. The word *anjuli* means a gesture of reverence, honor, and respect. With your hands in this posture, you might notice you can press your thumbs into your sternum and feel your body move with your breath and heartbeat.

In a safe and quiet space, find a seated position. Press your body, legs, and sitting bones into the earth below you. Engage your belly and lengthen your body up through the crown of your head, simultaneously softening your shoulders, jaw, and eyes. If it feels right, close your eyes.

Gently breathe in and out as you bring your hands together, with your palms facing each other and your thumbs at your sternum. Allow for a space between your palms, sealing your hands together at their heels, little fingers, fingertips, and thumbs. As you breathe, consider that in this space between your palms is the seed of a lotus flower. Lotus flowers grow from the murky bottom of ponds and blossom once they break through the water and open toward the sun. For this reason, it is often said, "No mud. No lotus." Imagine that this seed is the seed of possibility.

With your hands at heart center, gently press the outer surface of your thumbs into your sternum just enough to make contact. Breathe here, perhaps noticing your body move and your heart beat as you gently breathe in and out. As you breathe, with your hands at heart center and the lotus seed of possibility present, consider adding the thought *As the lotus flower knows its way to the sun, my body knows how to heal.*

Breathe and repeat, *As the lotus flower knows its way to the sun, my body knows how to heal.* Consider allowing the notion of honor, reverence, or respect for the inherent and natural processes of growth and healing. Gently breathe here for several breath cycles. As you are ready, slowly release your hands (and your lotus seed of possibility) and bring your awareness to the room.

Session 1: Words

Begin this session with the previous **A Centering Mudra: Hands at Heart Center** practice. Once you feel grounded and ready, move to the first step.

Step 1: Select Your Memory

When you are done with the previous centering practice, take a moment to reference **Your List of Distressing and Traumatic Experiences** from chapter 14. To help build competence with this process, choose a traumatic experience that has low "distress now" and "distress then" scores. You want something that generally feels like it will be the most manageable for your first session. As you continue, you will work your way through your remaining trauma memories, identifying the next most manageable memory on your list.

Note, for traumatic experiences that occurred over a period of time (e.g., ongoing conflict with a partner), it can be helpful to select an incident that you feel best represents the series of traumatic experiences rather than go through each incident separately. For example, one of my patients, Candice, was working with traumatic memories associated with her experience of domestic violence, which occurred several times a week for about four years. During this time, her mother's boyfriend would drink and become aggressive just after dinner time. Candice estimated that these incidents occurred hundreds of times. For this part of her processing work (and after she had worked through the process with some less intense memories), she chose to work with one particularly distressing event during which her mother was knocked unconscious and eight-year-old Candice called 911, hoping to save her mother's life. That evening, Candice was placed in emergency foster care for three months. Her mother was taken to the hospital, treated, and returned home, only to remain in the relationship for two more years.

Step 2: Represent What You Remember with Words

Once you have selected a memory, describe the event in a few words to help you recognize this specific memory right away. Then bring to mind the image or picture that represents the worst part of the experience. Imagine yourself back in that moment and, as you do so, write out the details of the traumatic experience as you recall them. It's okay if you have trouble remembering what happened in sequence. Just write down what you recall.

Describe memory in a few words:

Details you remember:

TP-PAUSE (Trauma Processing: **P**ause, **A**ssess, and **USE** your resources)

Follow the script earlier in the chapter.

Step 3: Write the Memory as a Timeline, Story, or Narrative

Now organize the memory into a timeline as best you can. Describe what you were doing before the incident, the incident in the order you recall it occurred, and what happened directly after the traumatic experience. As you write, use the first-person pronoun "I" and tell the story from your point of view at that time, as if it were happening in the present tense. For example, *I am sitting in my room reading, and I hear loud and angry talking. I walk downstairs to see what is happening.*

Once you are done, circle the section that corresponds with your image of the worst part of the experience. If you notice that writing this out feels overwhelming, return to the TP-PAUSE practice. Then consider some of these options as you continue with this work: (1) dictate the event into your phone to bring your words into written form, (2) complete this section with a therapist or trusted loved one, or (3) wait until you feel ready and focus on growing your resources in the previous chapters.

TP-PAUSE (Trauma Processing: **P**ause, **A**ssess, and **USE** your resources)

Follow the script earlier in the chapter.

Step 4: Explore the Cognitions Aligned with the Trauma Memory

Read over the trauma narrative you wrote in the previous step, then complete the following sentence stems as you would answer them during or immediately after the experience. If it helps, focus on the worst part. For example, as Candice focused on the night where she called 911, she came up with the statements *I am nothing*, *No one is safe*, and *The world is cruel*.

Think of the statements that come to mind for you as you recount your trauma narrative. You might have more than one belief in each area, so write down anything that comes to mind.

I am _____.

Other people are _____.

The world is _____.

Now reread your (1) trauma narrative and (2) self, other, and world statements. From the point of view of you right now, where you are in a safe place recalling the past, do you notice any bias in these thoughts? Are they too harsh? Do they match up with thoughts you have when you're outside your window of tolerance (**Exploring Outside of the Window of Tolerance** practice in chapter 3)? Do they look or sound like feeling-based thoughts (**Exploring Your Feeling-Based Thoughts** practice in chapter 9)? If so, what feelings? For example, Candice noticed that her trauma-based cognitions in this step were related to the experience of not being protected from domestic violence as a child. They were harsh, negative, and associated with sadness, hurt, and fear. Write what you noticed about your trauma-based cognitions in the following space.

Step 5: Explore Self, Other, and World Cognitions Aligned with Healing

As you are here, safe and on a path toward healing, what self-statements might offer support or empowerment while witnessing yourself back in the midst of the traumatic experience? What could you say to yourself then to let your past self know they are seen and heard? For example, as Candice looked back to her trauma narrative, she added the statement *I am brave* in relation to her ability to call 911 at age eight. Write your positive self-statement here.

I am _____.

When you are done, do this for your other and world statements as well. How might you finish these sentences in a way that feels true and empowering? For example, as Candice recounted that difficult night, she remembered the heroic EMS responders who worked to save her mother from her internal bleeding. She remembered how she was able to take comfort from the kind social worker who brought her a warm blanket as she sat in the social services office, awaiting her foster care placement. She added those notes to her trauma narrative and also added the following other and world statements: *Other people can be thoughtful and kind* and *The world is complicated*. For Candice, it didn't feel true to write something positive about the world. However, she thought that describing it as complicated was a fair portrayal. As for you and Candice, it is important to write what feels true for you.

Other people are _____.

The world is _____.

When you are finished, complete the following closing mudra practice to bring session 1 to a close.

—Embodying Practice—
Closing Hands to Heart

Find a comfortable seated position, making any adjustments as needed, and press your body, legs, and sitting bones into the earth below you. Engage your belly and lengthen your body up through the crown of your head, simultaneously softening your shoulders, jaw, and eyes. If it feels right, close your eyes.

Gently breathe in and out as you bring your hands together, with palms facing each other and your thumbs at your sternum. As before, allow for a space between your palms, sealing your hands together at their heels, little fingers, fingertips, and thumbs. Remember that in this space between your palms is the seed of a lotus flower.

With your hands at heart center, gently press the outer surface of your thumbs into your sternum just enough to make contact. Breathe here, perhaps noticing your body move and your heart beat as you gently breathe in and out. As you breathe, with your hands at your heart center and the lotus seed of possibility present, consider adding the thought *As the lotus flower knows its way to the sun, my body knows how to heal.*

Breathe and repeat, *As the lotus flower knows its way to the sun, my body knows how to heal.* Consider allowing the notion of honor, reverence, or respect for the inherent and natural processes of growth and healing. Gently breathe here for several breath cycles. As you are ready, slowly release your hands (and your lotus seed of possibility) and bring your awareness to the room.

Session 2: Feelings, Sensations, Physiological States, and Action Urges

Begin this session with the **A Centering Mudra: Hands at Heart Center** practice. Once you feel grounded and ready, move to the first step.

Step 1: Explore Feelings, Sensations, Physiological States, and Action Urges

Make sure you are seated comfortably and feel well supported. Using a cushion or folded blanket, place your back to the wall or against a firm chair. Collect any supportive resources you need near you, and bring to mind your traumatic experience from the point of view of that moment. Recall the image that represents the worst moment of the event (from Session 1), as well as the self, other, and world statements you were thinking at the time.

Feelings. When you concentrate on the experience, what feeling comes up? If there is a mixture of feelings, locate the predominant one to work with first. Some common feelings associated with trauma are sadness, anger, agitation, anxiety, betrayal, hurt, fear, loneliness, numbness, powerlessness, shock, guilt, and shame. Take a moment to write the name of the feeling in the space provided. If you are not sure, write down the sensations you notice.

Sensations. Where do you notice the feeling in your body? Scan your body, beginning with your chest and belly, then moving to your hips, legs, feet, shoulders, arms, and hands. Then scan your neck, jaw, eyes, and head. Locate where in your body you notice the feeling most intensely. Pause here and simply be with the experience of the feeling. Notice if the feeling is hot, warm, or cold. Is it tingly, clenched, tight, or painful? Is it heavy or intense? Does it radiate or contract? Is it still, or does it move? Is its size stable, or does it get bigger or smaller? Breathe gently and notice. Then describe any sensations you notice in the space provided.

Physiological state and action urges. Notice your level of activation using the Self-Awareness Scale and assess your number and zone. As you notice your feelings, sensations, and physiological state, acknowledge any urges you have to move, walk, run, reach, lift up, push away, draw toward, let go, push down, or any other form of movement. You don't need to act on the urges; simply notice and acknowledge them.

Describe feelings:

Describe sensations:

Describe physiological state and any related observations:

My number is _____. My zone is _____.

Describe action urges:

As you complete this step, you may notice physical sensations arising as if the trauma were happening right now. If so, simply notice these sensations and remember that it is you, here today, who is noticing sensations related to a memory from the past. If you are still feeling overwhelmed, it can be helpful to complete the following three practices to help you be with and work with these experiences.

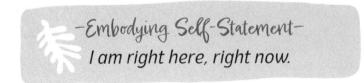

— Embodying Self-Statement —
I am right here, right now.

Here-Now and Then-There Script*

The following script can ground you in the present moment when your feelings or sensations make it seem as if you are reliving the trauma all over again. This script will remind you that you are in the present—right here, right now—where you are safe and well-resourced. If, after completing this practice, you still feel overwhelmed, take a break and connect to your inner resources or a part of your body that is free from distress. Then practice pendulating back and forth between the source of distress and the place in your body where you feel neutral or calm.

Right now, I am noticing these feelings (e.g., scared, anxious, sad, numb):

_____

_____

_____

Right now, I am noticing these sensations (e.g., heart beating, shaking, muscle tension):

_____

_____

_____

Right now, I am noticing these action urges (e.g., to push away, check out, shut down, engage in an escape or avoidance behavior, confront someone):

_____

_____

_____

These feelings and sensations are occurring because I am remembering (describe the traumatic experience in a few words):

_____

_____

_____

At the same time, it is now (time, date, and year):

_____

* Adapted from Rothschild (2017).

In this moment, I can look around and know I am in this space (name the room or space you are in):

_____

_____

_____

In this moment, I can look around and see these four things (describe four things you see around you):

_____

_____

_____

_____

_____

_____

So I know that this is not happening (briefly name the traumatic experience):

_____

_____

_____

_____

_____

_____

_____

It is not then, and I am not there. I am right here, right now.

TP-PAUSE (Trauma Processing: **P**ause, **A**ssess, and **USE** your resources)

Follow the script earlier in the chapter.

Self-Holding

Self-holding is a healing practice that can help you be with your experiences as you move through this trauma work. It combines comforting touch with a self-hug to bring about a calming shift in your body.

To begin, close your eyes or gently soften your gaze. Then place your hands on the area where you are noticing the feelings, sensations, or action urges most intensely. Gently press your hands on the area, hand over hand. Engage in gentle, slow breathing here. If you'd like, you can gently move your hands in soft circles. Breathe here and notice.

Next, take your right hand, place it under your left arm (holding your side just under your arm), cross your left arm over the right, and place your left hand on your right shoulder like you are giving yourself a hug. Then gently squeeze in toward your body. Self-hugs can help remind you that your body is a container and that the feelings and sensations are not as overwhelming because they are being contained or well held (Levine, 2010b). Breathe here and notice.

Now place one hand on your forehead and the other on your upper chest. Notice what happens in your body between your hands. You might notice an energy flow, a temperature change, certain feelings, or other sensations. Keep your hands in place until you feel some kind of a shift. When you are ready, take the hand on your forehead and move it to your belly, keeping the hand on your chest in place. Again, simply breathe and notice what happens in the area of your body between your hands.

In this process, offer your body the experience of being seen and listened to. When you are ready, use the figure on the following page to draw or write about what you noticed. You can include arrows to show shifts in energy or movement or use colors to represent different types of sensations or aspects of feelings. This process can help you symbolically represent the experience of your body. In this way you are saying, *Body, I see you. Body, I hear you.*

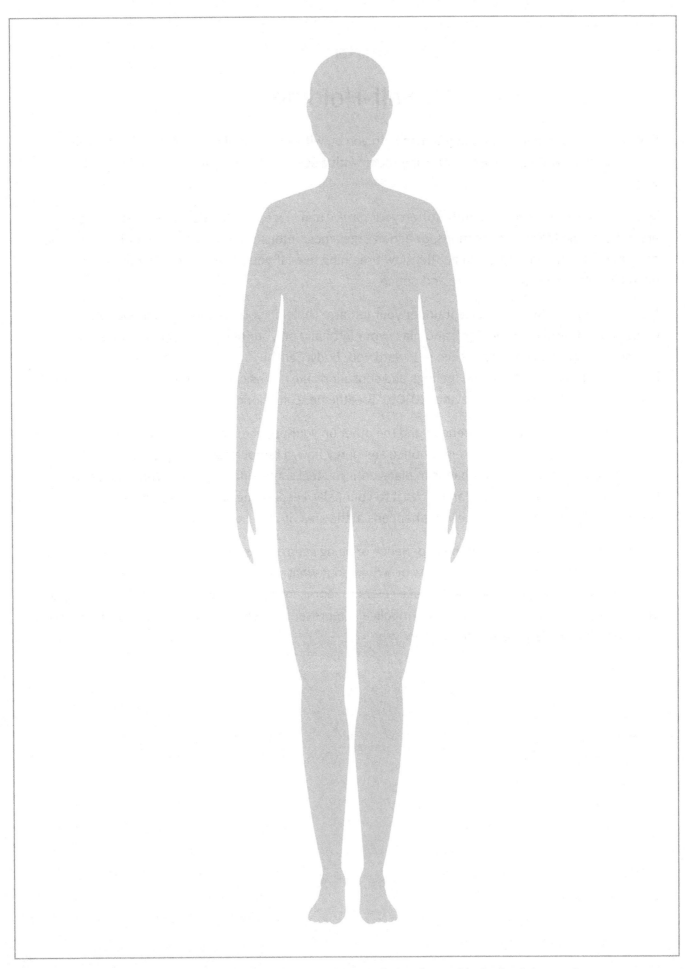

Free Drawing

Free drawing is another technique for being with your experiences. Bring to mind the image of the worst part of your traumatic memory, the associated feelings and sensations, and any action urges that you noticed in your body. Then, in the space provided or in your journal, draw how you experience these feelings, sensations, or urges. Let go of any need for your drawing to be or look a certain way. Use colors you are drawn to. Maybe a few. Set your timer for 5 to 10 minutes and just draw whatever comes to mind. It can have form or no form, color or no color. There is no right way to do this. When you are done, write what you notice about your drawing and what you noticed about yourself as you were drawing. There is no further processing or contemplation required.

TP-PAUSE (Trauma Processing: **P**ause, **A**ssess, and **USE** your resources)

Follow the script earlier in the chapter.

Step 2: Write an Integrated Traumatic Memory Narrative

For this step, you will be rewriting your trauma narrative while incorporating the sensations and emotions you felt at the time. To do this, read through your initial narrative slowly, allowing yourself time to reflect and remember these additional aspects of your experience. Consider both your sense of interoception and exteroception, or what you noticed on the inside and outside during the traumatic experience.

For example, Candice reworked her narrative by adding the anxiety she felt in her belly when her mother's boyfriend got home from work. She also added the whole-body feeling of fear that ran through her when she heard yelling and loud thuds in the house as a child. Finally, she added how she felt frozen the night she called 911 with the phone in her hand, barely able to breathe as she waited for help.

When you are finished, close this session with the following two embodying practices to help you move toward or deeper into the comfort zone.

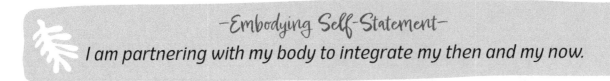

—Embodying Self-Statement—
I am partnering with my body to integrate my then and my now.

—Embodying Practice—
Exploring Sensations and Action Urges

The sensations and action urges associated with a traumatic experience can often feel a bit like a pressure cooker. If you take the lid off too fast, what is suppressed inside can explode (Porges et al., 2019). But if you mindfully notice, feel, and work with those sensations and action urges—staying within your window of tolerance—you can slowly release the pressure without additional harm. Therefore, as you engage in this practice, consider it a way to slowly release the experience and move with mindful awareness.

Begin in a standing position with your hands resting at your sides. Then bring to mind your traumatic experience as you complete the four movements below. Be mindfully aware of your sensations, feelings, and action urges as you move.

Up: Press into your sitting bones, engage your belly, and extend through your spine. As you breathe in, lift your hands in front of you to shoulder height, your palms facing down with your elbows somewhat extended but still bent.

Out: Now extend your wrists so your palms are facing forward and away from you. On your exhale, push your hands away, extending fully through your elbows.

In: Then turn your palms toward you, and slightly overlap your hands so there is a sense of holding. On your inhale, bend your elbows and draw your soft, inward-turning hands toward your heart.

Down: On your exhale, press your hands down, allowing your elbows to extend and your hands to separate and move down to the sides of your body.

Repeat this series of movements for several sets: inhaling up, exhaling out, inhaling in, and exhaling down. As you do this, notice what each direction feels like. Which direction feels most aligned with the action urges you experienced? If you feel drawn toward one, a few, or all of the movements, notice that. If you feel aversion to one, two, or all of the movements, notice that as well.

Now consider movement of your feet and torso. Would you like to walk forward, backward, or to one side or the other? Do you feel like you'd like to twist or bend to one side or the other? What ways do you feel like moving: not at all, a lot, slow, or fast? Are there remnants of being frozen, so you desire to take a step? Are there remnants of reactive, undercontrolled movement, so you desire to ground and center yourself as you stand still? Move (or do not move) mindfully—from the ground and core outward—as feels right for you right now.

Now bring to mind the up, out, in, and down movements of your hands and arms, as well as the forward, back, side-to-side, and twisting movement of your feet and torso. Pause and notice. If you feel compelled to extend or combine any of those movements into a larger action sequence, do that. Express the movements from your core outward. Allow the movements to evolve or settle, considering that this a chance to partner with your body, to express your experience. Stay within your comfort and growth zones, using your resources if you feel the need for nurturing, connection, and validation.

When you are ready, settle into a steady standing posture with your feet hip width apart, your knees softened, your core engaged, and your shoulders and jaw relaxed. End with several sets of the initial hand movement: inhaling up, exhaling out, inhaling in, exhaling down. When you are ready, transition to the following grounding yoga practice.

—Embodying Practice—
Grounding Yoga

Grounding yoga practices are well suited for moving yourself toward the comfort zone after working with the sensations, feelings, and action urges associated with trauma. As you practice, continually bring your awareness back to your breath and body. Breathe with an intention to be right here, right now with your body and your yoga practice. If any of these yoga postures or practices do not feel calming to you, move to the next one or select a different calming or grounding practice from those you have learned.

Seated mountain pose: Sitting in a chair, place both feet on the ground about hip distance apart. Place your hands, palms down, on your thighs. Draw back into your chair so your back feels well supported. Press your feet into the floor and your sitting bones into the seat of the chair as you draw your belly in and lift up through the crown of your head. Soften your shoulders, jaw, and gaze. Breathe gently here, slightly extending your exhale. As you breathe, move your awareness from your grounded feet and sitting bones to the drawing up through your spine. Now bring your awareness to the softening of your shoulders and jaw, then back to your feet. Repeat this cycle of awareness four to six times.

Shoulder rotations and softening: Still seated in the chair, allow your hands and arms to relax by your sides. Begin by drawing your shoulders forward, then up by your ears, then back as you draw your shoulder blades together, then down away from your ears. Continue this rotation four times, inhaling as your shoulders move forward and up, and exhaling as your shoulders move back and down. As you move your shoulders, allow your arms and hands to follow naturally. When you are ready, change the direction of your rotation, drawing your shoulders back, then up by your ears, then forward expanding your back, and then toward the floor. You can add in your breath, breathing in as your shoulders move back and up, and out as your shoulders move forward and down. Complete four cycles in this direction. As you feel complete, place your hands on your thighs and soften your shoulders away from your ears. Let tension go with each exhale. Breathe here for four to six gentle breaths.

Reclined twist: Now lie on your back on a blanket or yoga mat. With your legs extended, draw your right knee in toward your belly. Then, gently draw your right knee over to the left side, creating a twist in the right side of your body as your right hip comes up and off the mat. You can place your left hand on your right knee and extend your right hand to the right, taking your gaze over the right side. Breathe gently here, softening into your hip with each exhale. This is a soft gentle stretch. After about four to six breath cycles, extend your legs on the mat once again. On your next exhale, draw your left knee into your belly and then gently take it over to the right side of your body, allowing your left hip to leave the floor. Notice the stretch through the left side of your body. Breathe here, allowing a softening in your hip as you exhale. If it feels okay, breathe here for four to six breath cycles. When you're done, take a few breaths with both legs extended on your mat.

Supine rest: Still lying on your back, bend your knees and place your feet on the floor a little more than hip distance apart. Let your knees gently rest together at your centerline. It may also be comfortable for you to place your feet together and let your knees move to open toward the floor. Choose what feels right for you. Place one hand on your heart and one hand on your belly. Breathe gently, trying to pause at the end of each inhale and exhale for two counts. Breathe in 1, 2, 3, 4 . . . pause 1, 2 . . . breathe out 1, 2, 3, 4 . . . pause 1, 2. Do this for four to six breath cycles. Close by gently breathing in again.

Easy sitting pose with hands at heart center: Sit up on your mat (or on a chair), cross your legs (or ankles if in a chair), and bring your hands together, with your palms facing each other. If it feels right, offer gratitude for your body, for your body's natural tendency to heal, and for your work today.

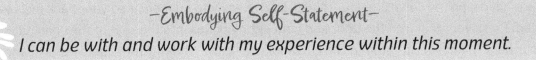

—Embodying Self-Statement—
I can be with and work with my experience within this moment.

Session 3: Integration

As mentioned earlier in this chapter, you may use this session several times to process your trauma memory, depending on your level of activation and the pace you are taking. You might also consider doing this step with a therapist or a safe person. Pause and see if that feels right for you.

Step 1: Draw Together Your Complete Trauma Narrative

Your complete trauma narrative comprises these components:

- A brief title that represents the traumatic experience, the date it occurred, your age at the time, and your distress then and now

- A story or timeline of the trauma with your sensations, feelings, and action urges at the time (then) and now

- Self, other, and world statements that align with the worst parts of the traumatic experience

- Self, other, and world statements that align with healing and recovery

In the space below, draw together these steps to create your complete trauma narrative.

Trauma experience title:

Date it occurred and your age at the time:

Your distress: _____ (then) _____ (now)

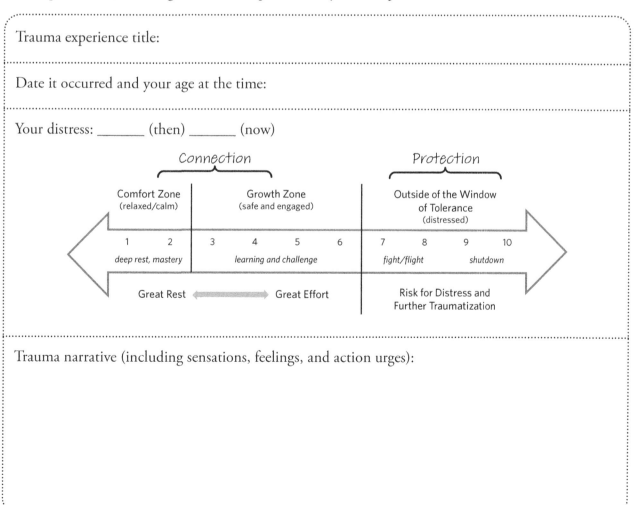

Trauma narrative (including sensations, feelings, and action urges):

Trauma narrative (continued):

Trauma-based statements:

I am _____.

Other people are _____.

The world is _____.

Healing-based statements:

I am _____.

Other people are _____.

The world is _____.

Step 2: Be with and Work with Your Trauma Memory

In this step, you are giving the trauma memory and the associated thoughts, feelings, sensations, and action urges a chance to be seen, heard, and responded to. Please read through this step so you have a sense of the process before you begin. You will complete anywhere from one to four cycles of being with and working with your traumatic memory. For each cycle, you will use the processing table (page 297) to record your level of activation on the Self-Awareness Scale before processing and after processing. Keep this session to a maximum of four cycles. If you feel like you need more time to process your trauma memory, repeat session 3 on a different date. See Processing Table example on page 300.

Before you begin, record your "before processing" activation level on the processing table. You should only go forward if you are in the comfort or growth zone. If you are already outside of your window of tolerance, complete the TP-PAUSE exercise again until you are back in connection mode, or get support and stop for the day.

If you are ready to proceed, make sure you are in a comfortable seated position and feel well supported. Place your feet on the floor, press your sitting bones into the chair, and breathe gently. Now bring to mind the following:

- The title of the trauma

- The image of the worst part of the trauma

- The predominant feeling associated with the memory and associated thoughts, feelings, body sensations, and action urges

- The self, other, and world statements that align with the memory

It can be helpful to describe and speak these aspects of the memory out loud. Begin by being with the trauma memory and its associated thoughts, feelings, sensations, and action urges. Gently breathe and just notice. Do not force anything, letting go of the need for this to be a certain way. You might say to yourself, *I am noticing this feeling (or this body sensation, thought, or action urge)*. If you are within your comfort or growth zones, do this for about 6 to 12 gentle breath cycles.

If you notice that you are moving outside of your window of tolerance, add gentle breathing. If it is helpful, cross your arms and gently pat yourself on each shoulder, alternating sides in a slow, rhythmic manner. Or place your palms on your thighs, one on each thigh, and gently tap one hand and then the other. You can also gently rock from side to side. If (or as) uncomfortable sensations or feelings arise, notice them. If it feels right, place your hands where you feel the sensation or feeling, press softly, and gently circle your hands. Do this for about four to eight gentle breath cycles.

Step 3: Practice Self-Tapping

Once you are done with the previous step, transition into the following tapping exercise, which is a practice for working with trauma that can help regulate distress.

Before you begin tapping, you will need to develop a setup phrase to use throughout the practice. To create a setup phrase, recall one of your healing self-statements from session 2 and choose the one that seems to fit best right now. For example, Candice chose the self-statement *I am brave*. Once you have selected a healing self-statement that resonates with you, use the following template to create a setup phrase:

"Even though _____ (name traumatic experience), I also know

that I _____ (name healing self-statement)."

For this practice, Candice created the following setup phrase: *Even though my mom and her boyfriend didn't protect me from their domestic violence, I also know that I am brave.* If you'd like, you can use a more general phrase, such as *Even though this thing happened, I deeply and completely accept myself* (Church, 2019, p. 95). Write your healing self-statement in the processing table.

Now you are ready to begin self-tapping. Using the pinky-finger side of your hand, tap your small intestine and lower belly area while saying your setup statement three times.

Then, using two or more fingertips, tap each of the following areas five to seven times while repeating the title of your traumatic experience (e.g., *I wasn't protected* or *I was assaulted*). You can use one hand or both hands as needed. For the areas that have a twin point on the other side (e.g., eyebrows, collarbones, underarms), you can do one side using one hand, or both sides at the same time using two hands (Church, 2019).

- Inside edge of your eyebrow (at the start of the eyebrow, near bridge of the nose)
- Outside of your eyes (outside edge of your eye socket)
- Under your nose (at the philtrum)
- Your chin (center)
- Under your collarbone (hollow point under the collarbones)
- Under your arm (approximately four inches below the armpit)
- Top of your head (in line with ears)

Repeat this tapping sequence two to three times. End with the full set up statement, "Even though _____ (name traumatic experience), I also know that I _____ (name healing self-statement)." Then record your "after processing" rating on the processing table.

TP-PAUSE (Trauma Processing: **P**ause, **A**ssess, and **USE** your resources)

Follow the script earlier in the chapter.

Processing Table

Traumatic experience title:				

Healing self-statement:				

	Cycle 1	Cycle 2	Cycle 3	Cycle 4
Activation level Before processing				
Activation level After processing				

What you noticed (sensations, feelings, thoughts, action urges):

Cycle 1:

Cycle 2:

Cycle 3:

Cycle 4:

Step 4: Continue with Processing or Close the Session

You have now completed one processing cycle. At this point, you can decide to continue with another processing cycle or close the session. If you continue with further processing, make sure to record your experience on the processing table for each cycle. Since it can be helpful to see an example of someone else's table, you can find a copy of Candice's completed processing table at the end of this chapter.

Alternatively, you may feel that you are ready to close the session. You can close the session for a few reasons:

- You have completed a processing cycle and ended in the comfort zone.
- You have completed four cycles and feel it is time to stop.
- You were in the growth zone and making your way to the comfort zone and are ready to stop.
- You are at your time limit (no more than 90 minutes).
- You have moved outside of your window of tolerance and are in need of further grounding and calming practices or support.

Take a moment and review your processing table. Reflect on each aspect and journal what you have noticed, what was difficult, where you felt strong and well-resourced, and what you might need now. If you are in need of grounding, calming, or further support, move directly to those procedures. Otherwise, continue the closing process. If you have anything remaining from your session that you would like to place in your container until the next session, go to chapter 8 and complete the container practice before you close this session.

—Embodying Practice—
A Closing Mudra

Find a comfortable seated position, making sure your feet can touch the ground below and you feel well supported. Consider taking your shoes off and letting your bare feet touch the floor.

Direct your awareness to your legs and feet. Bring in the intention of grounding. Imagine that you have roots that reach through your legs and the bottoms of your feet, connecting you to the earth. With each inhalation, draw strength from the earth, like a tree bringing stability, support, and strength. With each exhalation, offer loving-kindness to the pace of your healing, the work you have done in the session, and your inner resources—just as a tree releases oxygen into the air. During each inhalation, you draw strength from the earth, and with each exhalation, you offer loving-kindness and deep appreciation filling the space around you..

Now place your hands on your thighs, with your palms facing upward. Then touch the tip of your ring finger to your thumb. This is the earth mudra. In yoga therapy, the earth element is considered grounding, stable, solid, and enduring (Wheeler, 2022). As you breathe, consider these qualities of the earth element and allow them to be present. Gently breathe here for four to six breath cycles.

With the strength of your inner refuge, your protector, your symbol, and your talisman, bring to mind your healing self, other, and world statements. Consider that even though you have been through so much, your healing statements can also be true. Holding your hands in earth mudra, repeat each statement.

I am _____.

Other people are _____.

The world is _____.

Close your practice by bringing your hands to heart center. Offer thanks to yourself for the work you have done, and offer compassion to yourself for the work left to do.

As you complete your session, take care of your space by putting any resource objects in a safe and secure sport. If you used a yoga mat, roll it up and store it away. Put away your journal. Fold any blankets. Use this ritual of taking care of the objects within your safe place as part of your closing routine.

Think of this chapter as a structure you can use with each of your trauma memories. Working from the least distressing to the most, you can move through your trauma memories at the pace that is right for you. Monitor your well-being as you go, and take a break and secure support and professional help as needed.

Example: Candice's Processing Table

Traumatic experience title: *The night I called 911*

Healing self-statement: *Even though my mom and her boyfriend didn't protect me from their domestic violence, I also know that I am brave.*

	Cycle 1	Cycle 2	Cycle 3	Cycle 4
Activation level Before processing	*6*	*6*	*5*	*3*
Activation level After processing	*5*	*4*	*3*	*2*

What you noticed (sensations, feelings, thoughts, action urges):

Cycle 1:

I felt tension throughout my whole body and a sinking heavy feeling in my belly that felt like it pulled me down. I felt fear and like I was shutting down. I didn't notice any action urges, but I felt weak during some parts of the processing.

Cycle 2:

I still felt tension throughout my body. I also noticed the floor beneath me and my feet. My belly had the same sinking feeling. I think it is a dread-like feeling: "Oh no, this is happening again. How bad is it going to be?" I reminded myself I was right here, right now. The tapping helped me feel calm and present. I felt an action urge to get out of there. I felt my legs wanting to move. I remembered feeling that way when they would start fighting.

Cycle 3:

I felt less tension. I think I am getting used to the story. It doesn't seem to shake me. I started hearing myself better when I said my healing self-statement—like I believed it. I felt my feet on the floor and the cushion underneath me. I would feel that feeling in my belly, but it was less intense and it wasn't pulling me down. I don't think I felt an action urge.

Cycle 4:

I hardly felt any tension. I began to feel lifted up through my chest, especially when I said, "I am brave." It felt so true.

Chapter 16

Embodied Life:
Posttraumatic Growth and Joy

-Embodying Self-Statement-
I have the resources and skills I need.

Perhaps one of the most important questions in the trauma recovery process is *What will my life look like when trauma is no longer getting in the way?* Imagine your work through each chapter in this book as a beautiful and difficult hike through the inclines and valleys of healing. Here you are at the summit. Some people might think, *I am done. Here I am at the top.* I know for my friends who are avid hikers, this would be the exact spot where they begin planning their next hike. Just like those avid hikers, getting to this point is not really the end of the trail, and it is most certainly not the end of hiking. Perhaps it is more accurate to say that this is your beginning. Being here at the summit means you are an accomplished hiker, one who knows more about the nature of things, knows where the beautiful and tough spots are, and has the skills, gear, and support to keep hiking.

In this chapter, we will review what you have learned and practiced and what you have noticed as you have healed and grown. We will add to your resources by exploring how play and creativity can bring joy in both structured and spontaneous ways. We will also consider what you might do if you are triggered as you explore play, creativity, and joy. Finally, we will end by exploring the concept of posttraumatic growth and what might be possible for you!

Need-to-Know: What You Have Learned

In this book, you have learned and implemented practices that offer you and your nervous system structure and predictability in day-to-day life. These skills and practices tend to cluster in two areas: mindful self-care and a sense of mission and purpose. Second, you have developed on-the-ready practices that allow you to negotiate challenges as they arise, whether it be an argument with someone you love, an old trauma memory, or sensations that enter your consciousness. You are prepared for whatever today brings you. These skills tend to cluster in two areas: honoring trauma and growth, and growing your "be with" and "work with" skills.

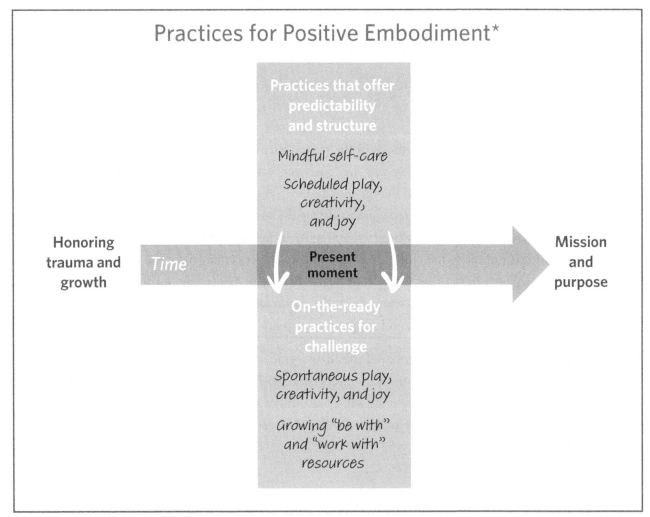

* Adapted from Cook-Cottone (2020)

Structure and Predictability through Mindful Self-Care

Mindful self-care helps you plan ahead and structure the ways in which you will be taking care of yourself. You plan your present moment as a pathway to your future well-being. For example, this morning I practiced yoga and then walked my dog. This did not happen spontaneously. I planned it last night. In fact, I plan something each morning for my self-care, so no matter where I am in the world, no matter what I am doing, I start my day with meditation and then some form of movement. My nervous system can count on me doing that every day. I set up my *future me* for success.

In what ways do your mindful self-care practices offer your nervous system a sense of structure and predictability? What have you noticed?

Structure and Predictability through a Sense of Mission and Purpose

Your sense of mission, purpose, and meaning also provides structure, as it gives you direction—a way forward from the past into the future. Having a sense of mission and purpose is like having a map you created yourself, designed to take you exactly where you want to go.

For example, my patient Rosalind grew up in a very chaotic home, in which there was little food and the heat and gas were often turned off without notice. A teacher at school noticed Rosalind's distress and befriended her. She connected Rosalind with the school social worker, who was able to get Rosalind's family connected to community resources and support systems. The teacher also helped Rosalind write about her circumstances through poetry and short stories. Even when Rosalind moved on to the next grade, this teacher kept in touch, reading her poetry and writing, and offering feedback and praise.

Back then, Rosalind's sense of meaning began to unfold as she was driven to tell the story of what it was like to live in poverty. This evolved into her admission into a respected literature program in college and eventually to the publication of her poetry. Rosalind decided to go to graduate school to become an English teacher so she could help children like her cope through writing and self-expression. When things were difficult in graduate school, she connected back to her younger self, who was eking out her first poem and feeling so very seen and heard as her teacher read it. This memory remained a touch point for Rosalind's sense of "why" and helped her keep going during tough times. Her mission and purpose served as a guidepost, offering structure as she embodied her way forward.

In what ways does your sense of mission or purpose (your "why") offer your nervous system a sense of structure and predictability? What have you noticed?

Dealing with Challenges: Honoring Trauma and Growth

All human beings have a personal history on their timeline of life. Trauma can cause this timeline to become disintegrated and fraught with dysregulation and distress. *Trauma work* brings together the past with the present so it becomes part of the evolution and development of you. This work requires integrating your memories and sensations, spending time with your feelings, and listening to and honoring the experiences of your body so you can grow moving forward. You have done this work so that when the past comes up, you know what to do. You also know that you have the capacity to do it.

For Rosalind, honoring her past self and struggles meant thinking back to her younger self and acknowledging her ability to connect to a teacher, even though she had been let down by so many adults. She also felt so much loving-kindness for her courage in creating and sharing her poetry and writing.

In what ways has the ability to honor your trauma and growth served your well-being and resilience? What have you noticed?

Dealing with Challenges: "Being with" and "Working with" Skills

At this point in your journey, you have developed and implemented skills to be with and work with difficult experiences. You now have a plethora of ways to manage distress, ride the wave of emotions, and handle things well into the reaches of your growth zone. You even know what to do if you get outside of your window of tolerance. You have also created a tremendous set of resources that you've internalized along the way.

In her work with the social worker at school, Rosalind learned "be with" and "work with" skills to manage her difficult feelings about her mom and to work with anxiety about sharing her poetry and short stories. As she got older, she used these skills when she didn't feel like she fit in at college and when she challenged herself to perform at poetry readings. She also used these skills to apply for graduate school and to navigate the interview process.

In what ways have your "be with" and "work with" skills served your well-being and resilience? What have you noticed?

PAUSE
(**P** - Pause, **A** - Assess ⟶ **USE** your resources and supports)

☐ **P**ause, check in, and acknowledge how you are feeling. This is a chance to be kind to yourself. The pace of your work is very important. Press your feet into the earth and take four gentle breaths.

☐ **A**ssess by asking yourself, *Is this a good place for a break?* If the answer is *yes* or *I don't know*, then fold over the corner of the page and take a break. This workbook is here for you for as long as it takes and for as many breaks as you need.

☐ **USE** your resources. Take a rest. Connect to your trusted friends. Contact your therapist. Practice your favorite well-being strategies. Get back to work when YOU are ready.

Need-to-Know: Play, Creativity, and Joy

Here you are at the summit, with your backpack full of resources and your heart ready for the next thing: happiness. Recovery is not just about the absence or management of symptoms; it is about cultivating a grounded, open heart with the capacity for happiness. Happiness is about experiencing positive emotions (e.g., joy, elation, vitality, pleasure, cheerfulness), having a sense of meaning and purpose in life, and being satisfied with your quality of life (Steptoe, 2019). Play and creativity are two ways to explore happiness and find your pathway to joy. Take a moment right here and consider that play, creativity, and joy may be as important to your recovery as trauma work. This is your next exciting journey.

Trauma often takes away any sense of spontaneity, pleasure, creativity, and joy, which is why a big component of recovery involves creating a life you want to be present in. I assert that a life you want to be present in is especially wonderful if it includes play, creativity, and joy. Importantly, play and creativity are more than just activities; they are a state of mind (Brown, 2009). They can be lighthearted and whimsical, or intellectual and informative. They can be self-directed or other-directed. When you play and create, you can discover new ways of thinking. You develop things that have never been created before and move in new ways. Importantly, in play you also practice distress tolerance as you experience the discomfort of developing new skills and behaving in new ways (Proyer, 2017; Walia, 2019).

When you play, create, and allow yourself to experience pleasure and joy, you activate a sequence of experiences for your nervous system that support your happiness and well-being. Your body feels good. You nervous system is engaged, you feel connected, and your level of activation moves up and down in service of your play and creativity (not as a reflection of defensive reactivity). You experience pleasant, even exhilarating emotions. Your body is then primed to support all kinds of positive thoughts (Ogden & Fisher, 2016). Think of a time when you were playing or creating. How might you finish these sentence stems when you reflect on that time: *I am . . .* , *Other people are . . .* , and *The world is . . .* ? It's very likely that you answered with statements that were positive and suggested a sense of connectedness to yourself and others.

Developing Play, Creativity, and Joy*

There are many ways to play and cultivate joy, ranging from very structured group experiences, like dance and art classes, to less structured experiences you can engage in alone and in private, like playing an instrument or doing a puzzle. Play and creativity can also be things you plan as well as things you experience in the moment. In what ways could you expand your play and creativity? Below is a list of ideas. Put a check mark by any you'd like to try. Then choose three activities from each section and set a date to try out the experience.

Group or Dyad

☐ Play group sports (e.g., soccer, pickleball, tennis, volleyball, group hiking)

☐ Play a board game

☐ Play active group games (e.g., large-size Jenga, corn hole, tag)

☐ Play card games

☐ Take a dance class

☐ Play video games with friends

☐ Host a dinner party

☐ Host a mystery theater party

☐ Build and do an obstacle course

☐ Run or hike with friends

☐ Visit a bird sanctuary or nature preserve

☐ Attend a concert

☐ Sing in a choir or a band

☐ Visit a theme park

☐ Go out dancing

☐ Go golfing with friends

Individual

☐ Play arcade games

☐ Play a video game

☐ Do a puzzle

☐ Start a collection (e.g., coins, stamps)

☐ Go roller-skating or skateboarding

☐ Go skiing

☐ Jump on a trampoline

☐ Go horseback riding

☐ Learn magic tricks

☐ Practice hula-hooping

☐ Do word games

☐ Hike a new route

☐ Go to the park

☐ Swing on a swing

☐ Dance to great music

☐ Take guitar or voice lessons

☐ Play golf

☐ Attend dog training classes with your pet

* Informed by Brown (2009) and Ogden & Fisher (2016).

Group or Dyad	**Individual**
☐ Check out local meetups	☐ Cannonball jump into the pool
☐ Attend a large sporting event	☐ Play racquetball
☐ Do a bad-joke contest	☐ Build a sandcastle
☐ Plan a skit night	☐ Play with your pet
☐ Start an improv band with kitchen-based instruments (e.g., spoons, pans)	☐ Experiment in the kitchen
	☐ Juggle a soccer ball
☐ Do yoga, puppy yoga, or even goat yoga	☐ Try a new yoga posture or sequence
☐ Go jet skiing, snow skiing, or water skiing with friends	☐ Exercise in a new way

I would like to try the following three things by this date: _____

1. _____

2. _____

3. _____

Ideas for Creativity

Group or Dyad	**Individual**
☐ Take a cooking class together	☐ Color or paint
☐ Be a participant at an improv club	☐ Play an instrument or write music
☐ Join a band or orchestra	☐ Take music lessons
☐ Join a themed daily journaling club	☐ Make a reel or TikTok video
☐ Take acting classes	☐ Try out a pottery class
☐ Make a charcuterie board (and have a charcuterie board contest)	☐ Take up photography, videography, or embroidery
☐ Do creative hair braiding	☐ Garden
☐ Scrapbook together	☐ Make candles or jewelry
☐ Have an essential oil party (a themed party where you share and try out various essential oils while engaging in relaxing activities and discussions)	☐ Get creative with makeup
	☐ Polish your nails using nail art
	☐ Dye your hair a unique color
☐ Take a poetry or creative writing class	☐ Journal
☐ Tell campfire stories	☐ Create essential oils
☐ Have a talent show night (or a not-so-talented talent show night)	☐ Make a terrarium
	☐ Create a vision board

	Group or Dyad	**Individual**

Group or Dyad

☐ Volunteer to be on a theater stage crew

☐ Write a fictional story with someone, taking turns to write sections and creating off each other

Individual

☐ Write a fictional story

☐ Make a scrapbook

☐ Start a blog or podcast

☐ Dress up in a fun outfit

☐ Make a webpage

I would like to try the following three things by this date: _____

1. _____

2. _____

3. _____

PAUSE

(**P** - Pause, **A** - Assess → **USE** your resources and supports)

☐ **Pause**, check in, and acknowledge how you are feeling. This is a chance to be kind to yourself. The pace of your work is very important. Press your feet into the earth and take four gentle breaths.

☐ **Assess** by asking yourself, *Is this a good place for a break?* If the answer is *yes* or *I don't know*, then fold over the corner of the page and take a break. This workbook is here for you for as long as it takes and for as many breaks as you need.

☐ **USE** your resources. Take a rest. Connect to your trusted friends. Contact your therapist. Practice your favorite well-being strategies. Get back to work when YOU are ready.

Need-to-Know: Play and Creativity Can Be Activating

Play and creativity give your nervous system a chance to practice being happy, connected, *and* activated. This is why embodied practices like dance, yoga, and theater can be so therapeutic. I've seen these effects in real time when teaching yoga. When students are trying a new pose, or a familiar pose is challenging, I can see and feel uncomfortable and challenging sensations arising—priming their emotional and cognitive systems to react in a negative way. There is a wobbliness, a falling out of a pose, or the intensity of a muscle working. Uncomfortable emotions, like frustration, discouragement, and anger, can begin to arise in alignment with these uncomfortable sensations, leading students to have negative thoughts like *I am uncoordinated, I have no skill, I am not strong*, and even *I don't like this pose or yoga.*

It is during these moments that I remind students that the sensations associated with their heart beating and body working are a really good thing. I cue them to simply notice the sensations and label them just as they are and let go of judging. For example, *I notice my heart beating deeply and quickly, I feel contraction in my leg as it works*, or *I notice my muscle is burning but not hurting*. Sometimes I encourage them to pause and place their hands on their hearts, just to feel their hearts working hard to support them. I remind them, "Your heart is meant to beat, meant to work hard in support of your play, creativity, and work, and—yes—even yoga."

Later, when they are in a restorative or restful pose, I encourage students to notice this same heart beating at a slower rate, still making sure their whole body is nourished. Through this process, students can practice being with and working with the layers of the self as they move from a neutral to an activated state (mobilization) and then to deactivation (immobilization) while staying within their window of tolerance. In this way, yoga is a beautiful practice for learning how to stay in connection mode (a ventral vagal state).

—*Embodying Self-Statement*—
I can be activated and stay within my window of tolerance.

However, when people are in recovery from trauma, sometimes the experience of activation, even if it occurs during play or creativity, can be triggering in itself. If your body could talk to you, it would say, *Oh no! I am activated. I must be in danger. I better start mobilizing and going into protection mode.* Therefore, it is important to move forward with play and creativity in small recursive circles. If you notice yourself become activated and your body priming itself to go into protection mode, remind yourself that there is a difference between being activated or deactivated during the experience of play and creativity versus having the same experience while in protection mode. Ground your feet, gently breathe, and ask yourself, *Am I connected to myself and others? Can I find that connection?* If you are within the window of tolerance, you will be able to say yes. But if you can't connect or find the connection, you are likely outside of your window of tolerance and will need to bring yourself back into the window.

On the following page, you'll find a plan you can use to bring yourself back into the window of tolerance and manage any activation that may occur during the experience of play and creativity. One of my husband's favorite sayings is "Success is when preparation meets opportunity." Therefore, before you engage in a playful or creative activity, take the opportunity to prepare this plan so you can turn to it if needed.

—Embodying Practice—

Planning for Activation

Use the guide below to develop a plan for managing possible activation during creativity and play. It might be helpful for you to review chapters 2 and 3 to detail the ways you can recognize activation in your body. Then use chapters 5 through 9 to help you select resources and practices you think will be most helpful.

1. **Notice you are outside of your window of tolerance.** How will you know when your stress response system is activating and you are moving into protection mode? How will you know if you are at risk of losing connection with yourself and others? What body sensations, emotions, and thoughts would you notice?

   Body sensations:

   Emotions:

   Thoughts:

   Action urges (if any):

2. **Access your thinking (cognitive) resources.** What word, phrase, or symbol can you bring forward to help you reconnect to yourself and others? (Remember your inner refuge, protector, and other resources.)

3. **Access your physical resources.** What embodying practices will you engage in if you are feeling your protection system activated? (Remember your resources, such as your inner refuge, your protector, grounded breath, sensate focus, and subtle breathing.)

Need-to-Know: Using Play and Creativity for Continuous Growth

Sometimes, when you have been in protection mode for so long, it can feel like you are not allowed to play, create, or have joy. For example, my patient Elizabeth had an extremely difficult childhood and grew up in an alcoholic family, in poverty and uncertainty. She had progressed well in therapy addressing her trauma history, but she still had a lingering issue. She spent much of her life afraid of being happy, and despite her progress, that fear was still there. Her nervous system functioned as if happiness was threatening. It kicked into protection mode all too easily whenever she began to feel a little joy. She typically responded by withdrawing and isolating in order to keep her system regulated. Sometimes she drank alcohol to cope. This repetitive process of trying to be happy, being activated, getting scared, isolating, and drinking wasn't working anymore for Elizabeth, so she decided to work on this issue, just like she worked on her trauma.

As Elizabeth dipped her toe into the possibility of feeling happy and safe, she decided to take a break from alcohol and work through some very specific challenging experiences. For example, it was very difficult for Elizabeth to get a massage, which is something she had been wanting to do to release tension. However, the experience created so much anxiety for her that it created more stress than relaxation. Her happiness-during-massage plan started with a two-pronged approach: (1) working with embodying self-statements and (2) working with embodied physical practices. Her goal was to work her way toward being present and allow for happiness when getting a massage.

Working with Embodying Self-Statements

For Elizabeth, the first step in experiencing happiness without fear involved working with her belief system. Because of her traumatic past, Elizabeth held negative thoughts like *I am not allowed to feel happy*, *Something bad is going to happen*, and *Happiness is for other people, not me*. After exploring her thoughts (as discussed in chapter 9), she created embodying self-statements that felt true to her struggle and that aligned with what she hoped for herself.

Table 16.1. Elizabeth's Embodying Self-Statements

Negative (or Unhelpful) Statement	Artificial (or Unhelpful) Positive Thinking	Embodying (or Helpful) Self-Statements
I am not allowed to feel happy.	Let it go. Just be happy. Find happiness.	I have permission to feel all my feelings, even happy ones.
Something bad is going to happen.	Look at the bright side. You have to stop being negative.	I know how to assess and work with automatic fear.
Happiness is for other people, not me.	Things could be way worse. Think of _____.	I am working on my worthiness and capacity for joy.
I can't tolerate happiness.	Don't worry, be happy.	I can work toward allowing happiness in my life.

To reinforce these embodying self-statements, Elizabeth established a short, daily meditation practice using a simple meditation app on her phone. At the end of the practice, she recited her four embodying self-statements. She then began reciting them when she felt even the mildest distress. She knew that by practicing these statements every day, they would be more accessible to her when she was in distress. She also added them to the notes section on her phone and wrote them on an index card she kept in her purse. This was her plan for using her thinking practices to prime her emotions and orient toward her sensations in a positive and powerful direction.

Working with Embodied Physical Practices

Her next step was to create a manageable embodied experience that would help her prepare for getting a massage. She researched the instructions for doing a self-massage and planned to do so on Friday nights as part of what she called "mindful self-care night." This night would include listening to her favorite soothing music, drinking turmeric and ginger tea, indulging in a self-massage, and taking a bath. She would then eat a takeout salad and watch a movie.

As Elizabeth put her plan into motion, she rehearsed, practiced, and applied her embodying self-statements. She spent several weeks working on her self-massage. As she approached the possibility of getting a massage from someone else, she decided to start small and booked a pedicure that included a foot and lower leg massage. It took her several months, but she was ultimately able to enjoy a 50-minute massage without feelings of anxiety or fear. She now had another access point to relaxation and happiness.

Elizabeth's story is a wonderful example of how you can use play and creativity to move from healing to the possibility of flourishing. Thinking about your own recovery and healing process, what are your experiences with playfulness? Do you leave room for fun, or is this something you need to explore like Elizabeth? Are there still behaviors you engage in, like drinking alcohol or overworking, that are getting in the way of your ability to find joy? What self-statements show up for you when you work to find joy and happiness, and what are some embodying self-statements that can move you in the right direction?

Consider the body feelings and sensations that you'd like to experience, and explore playful or creative activities that might help you cultivate those feelings. For example, if you seek community and active engagement, check out some local exercise or yoga workshops. If you want to meet sober friends, go to a recovery meeting or sober bar. If you want to expand your self-expression, take an art lesson. If you want to feel nurtured, take a weekend day (call it spa day!) and invite over a few friends to make it happen. Like Elizabeth, this might feel so new, so outside of your comfort zone, that it will take work and commitment. If there are joyful activities that you'd like to engage in but they seem too overwhelming, take a slower start. For example, if you'd like to join a tennis league but it feels too scary, can you start with individual lessons? If you'd like to start painting but you feel too perfectionistic, can you go with a trusted friend to a fun paint night?

You, too, can set up manageable experiences that help you experience the capacity for joy. Your beautiful healing body deserves and is worthy of joy, care, and happiness. On the following pages, you'll find Elizabeth's self-massage practice, as well as instructions for making massage oil, but feel free to experiment with what works for you. I encourage you to try these two practices. Patients are often very surprised at how nurturing and relaxing the process is. If it feels like a lot to massage your whole body or use oils, try massaging just your hands, feet, or both using your favorite moisturizer.

—Embodying Self-Statement—
My body can feel happiness and joy.

—Embodying Practice—
Make Your Own Massage Oil

It can be fun to make your own massage oil for your self-massage. To do so, you will need a small glass jar with a lid, carrier oil, and an essential oil. Good carrier oils include sweet almond oil or jojoba oil, as they are both good for moisturizing the skin. Calming essential oils include chamomile, lavender, rose, frankincense, bergamot, ylang ylang, and jasmine.

To begin, decide whether you want to make a small batch or a large batch of oil. A small batch uses 2 tablespoons of carrier oil, while a larger batch uses ¼ cup of carrier oil. Once you have decided how much oil to make, add essential oil to the carrier oil at about 2 percent dilution. That means you will add 12 drops of essential oil for a small batch and 24 drops for a large batch. If you are combining essential oils, remember to stay within the recommended totals. Do not add more than these amounts.

Secure the lid and shake to combine. You are ready for your self-massage!

Embodying Practice
Self-Massage

This self-massage practice will empower you to be the source of your own nurturing and relaxation. It represents a structured and dedicated time that you can devote to taking care of yourself. It is also a very healing practice that can reduce muscle tension, increase circulation, and support overall well-being. Plan to set aside about 30 to 45 minutes for this practice. Before starting, create a relaxing space where you feel safe and well supported. You might light a candle or diffuse essential oils. If you'd like, put on some music that supports relaxation. When you're ready, follow the instructions below to complete your self-massage, starting at your head and neck and gradually working your way through the body, ending with your feet.

Materials

- Massage oil
- Tennis ball

Tips

- Massage each area for about 30 to 60 seconds, as this will prevent your skin and muscles from becoming irritated.
- Explore and find the right pressure for each area. What works for one area might not work for the next.
- Use the massage oil as you'd like, placing a small amount in your hands and rubbing your hands together to distribute it evenly. Reapply as needed.
- Remain aware of your breathing. Work to keep your breath steady and gentle.
- Do not massage anywhere you feel pain. If you have pain, consider reaching out to a physical therapist or your doctor.
- If you are feeling sick, save your massage for another day.

Head and Neck

Get into a comfortable seated position, and press your feet and sitting bones into the floor and chair. Lift up through your core, straightening your back and neck. Reach the crown of your head toward the ceiling. Soften your shoulders away from your ears.

Decide if you'd like to use the massage oil in your hair. If you do, place a small amount in your hands and rub your hands together to distribute it evenly. With your hair loose, run your hands through your hair or along your scalp from front to back using the tips of your fingers. Begin by smoothly drawing your fingers across your scalp with downward pressure. If it feels good, add a tiny bit of circular motion.

Now press your fingers into your scalp at either side of the center part at the front of your scalp. Massage by pressing your fingers into your scalp and rub in small circles, making your way across your scalp. Work from front to back and side to side. Then move your hands so that your fingers are on the area behind your ears, palms facing your ears. Repeat the circular motion there, moving down into your neck.

Move to the base of your skull, at the back of your head, and place your pointer and middle fingers in the center. Allow your fingertips to touch. Then draw them outward along the back edge of your skull. You can do this in smooth drawing-out movements or gentle circular movements. See what feels best.

With your fingertips, run your fingers from your skull down to your neck. Add small circular motions. Begin under your ears to your shoulders. Then move slowly toward the center from skull to shoulders.

Shoulders and Arms

Make sure that you are grounded, your core is engaged, and your shoulders are soft. Then tuck your chin to your chest and stretch through your neck. Bring your chin back to neutral.

Reapply oil to your hands as needed. Now place your fingers on your shoulders where they connect to your neck. Press and then draw your fingers outward to where your shoulders meet your upper arms. You can add small circles if you'd like.

Lift your elbows and reach your fingers farther down your back to the area between your shoulder blades. Rub your fingers in small circles.

Take one hand and glide it over the opposite arm, moving up and down from your shoulder to your wrist, to warm up the skin. Then use your fingers and thumb to gently squeeze your muscles on this arm, working from top to bottom and then bottom to top, spending about 30 to 60 seconds on each muscle. When you are ready, switch sides.

Upper and Lower Back

Place the tennis ball on the floor and lie on the floor with your chest up. If it feels good, place a rolled towel or small pillow under your head for support. Then place the tennis ball between your shoulder blades and slowly move your upper body so you are rolling the ball and massaging any spots of tension. Continue for about 60 seconds.

Now move to massaging your lower back. Sit on a chair with your feet grounded and lean slightly forward. Reapply oil to your hands as needed. With the knuckles of your hands, rub your lower back from the base upward in a smooth motion on either side of your spine. Repeat this for about 60 seconds. See how it feels to change the pressure by going deeper or lighter. Then, at the base of your lower back, beginning at the center, press your knuckles into your back and draw your knuckles outward on both sides. Repeat this motion, moving from inside to outside, for about 60 seconds. As you do this, you can move up and down your back.

Hands

From a grounded seated position, reapply oil to your hands as needed, then place your right hand in your lap and use the palm of your left hand to apply some pressure to your right hand, stroking from your wrist to your fingertips on your palm and on the top of your hand. Repeat three to four times.

Place your left thumb in your right palm and your left fingers on the back of your right hand. Squeeze gently and then massage your right hand at its base using small circles. Move through the palm to the pinky finger, massaging the knuckles up to the fingertip. Repeat this with each of the fingers, finishing with your thumb. Close by returning your left thumb to the center of your right hand and your left fingers on the back of your right hand, and squeeze gently. Then switch hands and repeat this process.

Hips, Legs, and Feet

Sit on the floor with your legs extended, and rotate your body onto your left hip so your right hip is lifted. As you rotate, allow your legs to bend gently on the floor. Support yourself with your left hand and arm on the floor. Reapply oil to your hands as needed. Then use your right knuckles to massage your right hip, pressing in circles. Focus wherever you feel holding or tension. Then, from your hip to the outside of your knee, press your knuckle in and allow it to glide down the side of your right leg. If you'd like, add small circles. Repeat this several times and then switch sides.

When you're done, sit with your legs extended again, making sure both sitting bones are square to the floor. Focusing on one leg at a time, massage your thigh muscles by rubbing them in gentle circles and then running your fingers or knuckles down the length of the thigh. Notice which movement you prefer. Repeat around the knee area and the calves, reapplying oil to your hands as needed.

Still seated on the floor, or in a chair if you prefer, bend your knee, lift one foot into your hands, and draw your foot toward the center of your body so that you have access to the sole of your foot. Your toes should be facing away from you and your heel toward you. Your pinky toe should be facing the floor, and your big toe side should be facing up. Rest your other leg on the chair or floor. Place your thumbs on the bottom of your foot near the heel and your fingers on the top of your foot, squeezing your foot. Press your thumbs into the sole of your foot and use your thumbs and fingers to massage in gentle circles into the bottom side of your foot, working your way from the heel to your big toe. Do the same movement through each toe. Then switch to the other foot.

Close by holding your feet, one at a time, and gently squeeze your feet with your fingers at the top of the foot and your thumb at the sole.

PAUSE

➤ **PAUSE** ◄

(**P** - Pause, **A** - Assess ➤ **USE** your resources and supports)

☐ **P**ause, check in, and acknowledge how you are feeling. This is a chance to be kind to yourself. The pace of your work is very important. Press your feet into the earth and take four gentle breaths.

☐ **A**ssess by asking yourself, *Is this a good place for a break?* If the answer is *yes* or *I don't know*, then fold over the corner of the page and take a break. This workbook is here for you for as long as it takes and for as many breaks as you need.

☐ **USE** your resources. Take a rest. Connect to your trusted friends. Contact your therapist. Practice your favorite well-being strategies. Get back to work when YOU are ready.

—Embodying Self-Statement—
I am always learning and growing.

Need-to-Know: Posttraumatic Growth

As Elizabeth looked back on her traumatic childhood, she realized how far she had come. She was no longer in a persistent protective mode, reacting and overreacting to her daily life. Although she could never say she was glad that any of her trauma happened, she could see she had grown in some important and positive ways through her trauma work. Instead of holding disdain for her body—viewing her body as unworthy and problematic—she had come to befriend, respect, and trust it. She had also discovered what true happiness felt like. Her life shifted from one of protection to one of loving, kind, compassionate, and joyful connection. Elizabeth had created a life that she truly wanted to be present in, an experience known as posttraumatic growth.

Posttraumatic growth refers to the positive psychological change that can occur after a challenging or traumatizing event. After trauma, some people feel compelled to reassess their goals and priorities, as they see new possibilities and develop new interests. Sometimes trauma survivors view social relationships differently. For example, they may realize they can count on others, connect more closely to their loved ones, and feel more compassion for others. For some, there is a newfound appreciation for their own personal strengths and for the beauty of life. Some people report having a new understanding of spiritual matters, believing that the trauma helped them see a bigger picture, tap into their mission and purpose, and connect with a higher power (Tedeschi & Calhoun, 2004; Wu et al., 2019).

The process of posttraumatic growth is different for everyone, with some people taking 6, 12, or more months to experience this phenomenon. For others, posttraumatic growth happens more quickly (Wu et al., 2019). The takeaway is that just like your healing, posttraumatic growth will happen on its own timeline.

Embodying Practice
Embodying Posttraumatic Growth

This practice will take you through the process of examining how your priorities, strengths, relationships, spirituality, and overall appreciation for life have shifted since beginning your trauma work. From this reflective summit of having worked through the chapters in this book, take a moment to think about what you have noticed as you have engaged in these healing and integrating practices. Allow for all possibilities to arise, including your own pace of change.

To begin, make sure you have set aside about an hour for this practice. Then find a place where you feel safe and can move your body freely. You might move any chairs or small tables to the side of the room to give yourself space. Keep this workbook or your journal and a writing utensil nearby so you can process each experience. Have a blanket or yoga mat nearby for the closing part of the practice.

Personal Priorities

Stand in the center of your space and bring to mind what is important to you—your personal priorities—and consider how they have changed and evolved as you have done your trauma work. Press your feet into the floor below you. Slightly soften your knees, engage your core, and reach through the crown of your head. Soften your shoulders and jaw. Place your hands on your heart. Consider your most important priority. Take a moment to be with this priority. Scan your body and the space around you. What sensations do you notice inside of your body and around you as you bring to mind your priority and how it may have evolved? Breathe gently and notice. Now release your hands. See if there are any feelings or action urges present. Pause and be with what is there. Then ask yourself, *What way would my body like to move?* Take a few moments and allow your body to move through any action urges or movement sequences it would like. As you are ready, come back to a grounded standing pose and close with a few gentle breaths. If you have two or more priorities, take some time to work through each one.

> List your priorities, then write what you noticed when being with each one (e.g., sensations, feelings, thoughts, action urges).

Personal Strengths

Place your hands on your heart. Now bring to mind your strengths: the ones you have always had and the new, earned ones. Earned strengths are the ones you have developed on your healing journey. How have your personal strengths changed and evolved as you have done your trauma work? Take some time to be with each strength. Stand in a grounded position and say the name of the strength out loud. Scan your body and the space around you. What sensations do you notice inside of your body and around you? Say the name of the strengths again. Breathe gently and notice. Now release your hands. See if there are any feelings or action urges present. Pause and be with what is there. Then ask yourself, *What way would my body like to move?* Take a few moments and allow your body to move through any action urges or movement sequences it would like. As you are ready, come back to a grounded standing pose and close with a few gentle breaths.

List your personal strengths, then write what you noticed when being with each one (e.g., sensations, feelings, thoughts, action urges).

Relationships

Place your hands on your heart. Bring to mind your relationships with others, specifically your most important relationships. How have these relationships changed and evolved as you have done your trauma work? Take some time to be with your experience of self within the contexts of your important relationships. Stand in a grounded position and scan your body and the space around you. What sensations do you notice inside of your body and around you? If you'd like, describe the sensations aloud. Breathe gently and notice. Now release your hands. See if there are any feelings or action urges present. Pause and be with what is there. Then ask yourself, *What way would my body like to move?* Take a few moments and allow your body to move through any action urges or movement sequences it would like. As you are ready, come back to a grounded standing pose and close with a few gentle breaths.

> List any changes to your relationships, then write what you noticed when being with each relationship (e.g., sensations, feelings, thoughts, action urges).

Spirituality

Place your hands on your heart again and consider your spirituality. Allow for whatever comes to mind. In what ways has your spirituality changed or evolved through your trauma work? Take some time to be with your experience of spirituality. Stand in a grounded position and scan your body and the space around you. What sensations do you notice inside of your body and around you? If words come to you, say them out loud. Breathe gently and notice. Now release your hands. See if there are any feelings or action urges present. Pause and be with what is there. Then ask yourself, *What way would my body like to move?* Take a few moments and allow your body to move through any action urges or movement sequences it would like. As you are ready, come back to a grounded standing pose and close with a few gentle breaths.

> List any changes to your spirituality, then write what you noticed when being with your spirituality (e.g., sensations, feelings, thoughts, action urges).

Appreciation for Life

Place your hands on your heart again and bring to mind your life as it is right now. How has your life changed and evolved as you have done your trauma work? Have there been shifts in appreciation or gratitude? Take some time to be with your experience of appreciating and valuing your life. Stand in a grounded position and scan your body and the space around you. What sensations do you notice inside of your body and around you? If words come to you, say them out loud. Breathe gently and notice. Now release your hands. See if there are any feelings or action urges present. Pause and be with what is there. Then ask yourself, *What way would my body like to move?* Take a few moments and allow your body to move through any action urges or movement sequences it would like. As you are ready, come back to a grounded standing pose and close with a few gentle breaths.

Describe how your appreciation for life has changed, then write what you noticed when being with this sense of appreciation (e.g., sensations, feelings, thoughts, action urges).

To close this practice, take 5 to 10 minutes to move in any way you'd like. Then lie down on the floor using your blanket or yoga mat. Place one hand on your belly and one hand on your heart. Notice any lingering energy from the thoughts, sensations, feelings, action urges, and movement sequences you experienced. Imagine this energy softly settling into the floor as you gently breathe. Imagine your hands can radiate loving-kindness and gratitude. Allow this energy to radiate into your heart and throughout your body. You might say to your body, *I am here.* As you are ready, slowly close the practice by moving into a seated position and taking a few gentle breaths.

Writing Your Hero(ine)'s Journey

You can consider your journey to trauma recovery as a hero(ine)'s journey, in which you have hiked through dark, treacherous lands to reach the top of a mountain where new possibilities lie (Schwartz, 2020). From this summit, you can see the lay of the land. You can look inward, outward, and forward. To honor this journey and recognize all of the work that got you to right here, right now, I encourage you to write your own story of this journey.

For example, when I turned 40, I decided it was time for me to write my journey, to be in control of my own narrative. I took the summer and interviewed the people close to me, documenting dates and events, and pulled together a narrative of my childhood, adolescence, and young adulthood. I made sense of the difficult and traumatic experiences I had endured, and I connected those moments to who I had grown to be. I found meaning.

The story of your hero(ine)'s journey can be a journal entry documenting your experience, or it can be a project like the one I completed the summer I turned 40. It can be something as grand as a memoir. It doesn't need to be perfect or even what some would call well written. It just needs to be yours. It will not be carved in stone, so you can edit it as it evolves and as you grow.

To write your hero(ine)'s journey, consider these writing prompts:

My hero(ine)'s journey began (time, place, weather, context) . . .

Let me tell you what I have learned . . .

At the top of this mountain, I look back and see . . .

I once knew this kid who . . .

What I want my younger, more vulnerable self to know is . . .

When I was able to look back and forward, I saw . . .

I didn't realize it then, but now I know that I am strong in these ways . . .

Then take some time to write your hero(ine)'s journey in a way that feels right to you.

The Next Loving Thing*

The following is a beautiful practice that you might consider adding to your resource repository as you venture off on your own. It involves connecting to the earth (and to yourself) and bringing forth the word *loving*, which creates access to your connection system and increases the likelihood that your next action will be something loving and kind to yourself and others.

To complete this practice, the next time you feel overwhelmed, disarmed, shutdown, or unsure, take a moment to ground your feet and connect to your heartbeat. Gently breathe here for several breath cycles. Then lift your eyes and look around you. Say to yourself, *I can do the next loving thing*. Be with the moment or take action from that orientation. For example, you might choose to rest, maintain calm awareness, acknowledge yourself or others, or complete a resource practice. It can be almost anything as long as you do not abandon or defer your needs. The next loving thing must include your body. It must include you.

> *—Embodying Self-Statement—*
> *My embodiment is a journey toward integrated*
> *and attuned self-determination.*

---

* Informed by Levine (2010a).

In Closing: Keep Working on Love

One of my mother's favorite books, as well as mine, is Richard Bach's (1970) *Jonathan Livingston Seagull*. In this book, there is a powerful scene in which it is time for the mentor to say goodbye to his student. Anxious and distraught, the student asks how he will know what to do when his mentor is gone. His mentor responds, "Keep working on love."

Love is the emotion of connection. It is not passed down through genetics, like the color of your eyes or the shape of your toes. It is not granted only to those deemed worthy. It is not something to be given and taken away. *Love is a practice.* It is what you have been working on throughout this whole book as you have been with and worked with the most challenging aspects of being you.

As you read these final paragraphs, take a moment to acknowledge all you have done and how far you have come in your courageous journey. Your work has enhanced your resources, increased your competencies and skills, and strengthened your resilience. I wish all of these practices could make it so that nothing difficult ever happens again. But life does what it does, and no matter how much work you've done, it can still bring you to your knees. When it does, you will know what to do. Go back to the basics, call in your resources, ground yourself and gently breathe, place your hand on your chest, and find your heartbeat. Then remind yourself, *Keep working on love.*

I leave you with the following offering that I like to say at the end of a meditation or yoga practice. I find that it orients my awareness toward seeing love, healing, and growth in my own life and in others.

May my life be filled with love, healing, and growth.

May this love, healing, and growth serve the healing and growth of others.

May all beings know love, healing, and growth.

References

Astrachan-Fletcher, E., & Maslar, M. (2009). *The dialectical behavior therapy skills workbook for bulimia: Using DBT to break the cycle and regain control of your life.* New Harbinger.

Bach, R. (1970). *Jonathan Livingston Seagull: A story.* Scribner.

Brooks, M. P., & Houck, D. W. (2013). *The speeches of Fannie Lou Hamer: To tell it like it is.* University Press of Mississippi.

Brown, S. (2009). *Play: How it shapes the brain, opens the imagination, and invigorates the soul.* Avery.

Bullock, B. G. (2016). *Mindful relationships: Seven skills for success.* Handspring.

Chernin, K. (1999). *The woman who gave birth to her mother: Tales of transformation in women's lives.* Penguin.

Church, D. (2019). *Emotional freedom technique: The EFT manual.* Energy Psychology Press.

Cook-Cottone, C. P. (2015). *Mindfulness and yoga for self-regulation: A primer for mental health professionals.* Springer.

Cook-Cottone, C. P. (2020). *Embodiment and the treatment of eating disorders: The body as a resource in recovery.* W. W. Norton.

Cook-Cottone, C. P., & Guyker, W. M. (2018). The development and validation of the Mindful Self-Care Scale (MSCS): An assessment of practices that support positive embodiment. *Mindfulness, 9*(1), 161–175. https://doi.org/10.1007/s12671-017-0759-1

Dana, D. (2020). *Polyvagal exercises for safety and connection: 50 client-centered practices.* W. W. Norton.

Dinsmore-Tuli, U. (2021). Yoga nidra healing. In D. Finlayson & L. C. Hyland Robertson (Eds.), *Yoga therapy foundations, tools, and practice: A comprehensive textbook* (pp. 405–417). Singing Dragon Press.

Durant, W. (1926). *The story of philosophy.* Garden City Publishing.

Fisher, J. (2021). *Transforming the living legacy of trauma: A workbook for survivors and therapists.* PESI Publishing.

Frankl, V. E. (1946). *Man's search for meaning.* Beacon Press.

Grabbe, L., & Miller-Karas, E. (2018). The trauma resiliency model: A "bottom-up" intervention for trauma psychotherapy. *Journal of the American Psychiatric Nurses Association, 24*(1), 76–84. https://doi.org/10.1177/1078390317745133

Grabovac, A. D., Lau, M. A., & Willett, B. R. (2011). Mechanisms of mindfulness: A Buddhist psychological model. *Mindfulness, 2*, 154–166. https://doi.org/10.1007/s12671-011-0054-5

Guidi, J., Lucente, M., Sonino, N., & Fava, G. A. (2021). Allostatic load and its impact on health: A systematic review. *Psychotherapy and Psychosomatics*, *90*, 11–27. https://doi.org/10.1159/000510696

Hanson, R., & Hanson, F. (2018). *Resilient: How to grow an unshakeable core of calm, strength, and happiness.* Harmony Books.

Juarascio, A., Manasse, S., & Espel, H. (2016). Acceptance and commitment therapy for anorexia and bulimia nervosa. In A. F. Haynos, E. M. Forman, M. L. Butryn, & J. Lillis (Eds.), *Mindfulness and acceptance for treating eating disorders and weight concerns: Evidence-based interventions* (pp. 26–44). Context Press.

Kabat-Zinn, J. (1994). *Wherever you go, there you are: Mindfulness meditation in everyday life.* Hyperion.

Kabat-Zinn, J. (2012). *Mindfulness for beginners: Reclaiming the present moment—and your life.* Sounds True.

Levine, P. A. (2010a). *Healing trauma: A pioneering program for restoring the wisdom of your body.* Sounds True.

Levine, P. A. (2010b). *In an unspoken voice: How the body releases trauma and restores goodness.* North Atlantic Books.

Lewis, M. (2016). *The biology of desire: Why addiction is not a disease.* PublicAffairs.

Linehan, M. M. (1993). *Skills training manual for treating borderline personality disorder.* Guilford Press.

Mazza, J. J., Dexter-Mazza, E. T., Miller, A. L., Rathus, J. H., & Murphy, H. E. (2016). *DBT skills in schools: Skills training for emotional problem solving for adolescents (DBT STEPS-A).* Guilford Press.

McEwen, B. S. (1998). Stress, adaptation, and disease: Allostasis and allostatic load. *Annals of the New York Academy of Sciences*, *840*(1), 33–44. https://doi.org/10.1111/j.1749-6632.1998.tb09546.x

Mehling, W. E., Acree, M., Stewart, A., Silas, J., & Jones, A. (2018). The Multidimensional Assessment of Interoceptive Awareness, Version 2 (MAIA-2). *PLoS ONE*, *13*(12), Article e0208034. https://doi.org/10.1371/journal.pone.0208034

Miller, R. C. (2015). *The iRest program for healing PTSD: A proven-effective approach to using yoga nidra meditation and deep relaxation techniques to overcome trauma.* New Harbinger.

Mischke-Reeds, M. (2018). *Somatic psychotherapy toolbox: 125 worksheets and exercises to treat trauma and stress.* PESI Publishing.

Myers, N. (n.d.). *Yoga of 12-step recovery.* https://y12sr.com

Neff, K., & Germer, C. (2018). *The mindful self-compassion workbook: A proven way to accept yourself, build inner strength, and thrive.* Guilford Press.

Nummenmaa, L., Glerean, E., Hari, R., & Hietanen, J. K. (2014). Bodily maps of emotions. *Proceedings of the National Academy of Sciences*, *111*(2), 646–651. https://doi.org/10.1073/pnas.1321664111

Ogden, P., & Fisher, J. (2016). *Sensorimotor psychotherapy: Interventions for trauma and attachment.* W. W. Norton.

Ogden, P., Minton, K., & Pain, C. (2006). *Trauma and the body: A sensorimotor approach to psychotherapy.* W. W. Norton.

Ortony, A. (2022). Are all "basic emotions" emotions? A problem for the (basic) emotions construct. *Perspectives on Psychological Science, 17*(1), 41–61. https://doi.org/10.1177/1745691620985415

Osher, D., Cantor, P., Berg, J., Steyer, L., & Rose, T. (2020). Drivers of human development: How relationships and context shape learning and development. *Applied Developmental Science, 24*(1), 1–31. https://doi.org/10.1080/10888691.2017.1398650

Perry, B. D., & Winfrey, O. (2021). *What happened to you? Conversations on trauma, resilience, and healing.* Flatiron Books.

Pipher, M. (1994). *Reviving Ophelia: Saving the selves of adolescent girls.* Riverhead Trade.

Porges, S. W. (2017). *The pocket guide to the polyvagal theory: The transformative power of feeling safe.* W. W. Norton.

Porges, S. W. (2018). Polyvagal theory: A primer. In S. W. Porges & D. Dana (Eds.), *Clinical applications of the polyvagal theory: The emergence of polyvagal-informed therapies* (pp. 50–69). W. W. Norton.

Porges, S., Ogden, P., Booker, L., Eger, E. E., & Schwartz, R. C. (2019). *The healing trauma summit: Volume 3. Transform trauma with advances in neuroscience, spiritual psychology, and embodied approaches to healing.* Sounds True.

Proyer, R. T. (2017). A new structural model for the study of adult playfulness: Assessment and exploration of an understudied individual differences variable. *Personality and Individual Differences, 108,* 113–122. https://doi.org/10.1016/j.paid.2016.12.011

Rilke, R. M. (2012). *Letters to a young poet.* Watchmaker Publishing.

Rothenberg, R. L. (2020). *Restoring prana: A therapeutic guide to pranayama and healing through the breath for yoga therapists, yoga teachers and healthcare practitioners.* Singing Dragon Press.

Rothschild, B. (2017). *The body remembers: Revolutionizing trauma treatment* (Vol. 2). W. W. Norton.

Schwartz, A. (2017). *The complex PTSD workbook: A mind-body approach to regaining emotional control & becoming whole.* PESI Publishing.

Schwartz, A. (2020). *The post-traumatic growth guidebook: Practical mind-body tools to heal trauma, foster resilience and awaken your potential.* PESI Publishing.

Schwartz, A. (2022). *Therapeutic yoga for trauma recovery: Applying the principles of polyvagal theory for self-discovery, embodied healing, and meaningful change.* PESI Publishing.

Shapiro, F. (2017). *Eye movement desensitization and reprocessing (EMDR) therapy: Basic principles, protocols, and procedures* (3rd ed.). Guilford Press.

Siegel, D. J. (1999). *The developing mind: How relationships and the brain interact to shape who we are.* Guilford Press.

Smith, H. L., Sriken, J., & Erford, B. T. (2019). Clinical and research utility of the highly sensitive person scale. *Journal of Mental Health Counseling, 41*(3), 221–241. https://doi.org/10.17744/mehc.41.3.03

Spence, J. (2021). *Trauma-informed yoga: A toolbox for therapists*. PESI Publishing.

Steptoe, A. (2019). Happiness and health. *Annual Review of Public Health, 40*(1), 339–359. https://doi
.org/10.1146/annurev-publhealth-040218-044150

Tedeschi, R. G., & Calhoun, L. G. (2004). Posttraumatic growth: Conceptual foundations and empirical
evidence. *Psychological Inquiry, 15*(1), 1–18. https://doi.org/10.1207/s15327965pli1501_01

van der Kolk, B. (2014). *The body keeps the score: Brain, mind, and body in the healing of trauma*. Viking Press.

Walia, C. (2019). A dynamic definition of creativity. *Creativity Research Journal, 31*(3), 237–247.
https://doi.org/10.1080/10400419.2019.1641787

Wheeler, A. (2022). *The gold zone: The 2000-year-old art and science of creating a wonder-full life*. Optimal State.

Wu, X., Kaminga, A. C., Dai, W., Deng, J., Wang, Z., Pan, X., & Liu, A. (2019). The prevalence of moderate-
to-high posttraumatic growth: A systematic review and meta-analysis. *Journal of Affective Disorders, 243*,
408–415. https://doi.org/10.1016/j.jad.2018.09.023

Yeung, J. C., & Lun, V. M. C. (2021). Uncritical use of non-evidence-based self-help materials induces
victim-blaming on depressed individuals. *The Journal of Positive Psychology, 16*(4), 492–502.
https://doi.org/10.1080/17439760.2020.1752780

Acknowledgments

I would like to begin by acknowledging those moments in life when I found the capacity to be with and work with what was there, those moments when I didn't, and those moments when I couldn't. Those moments were my greatest teachers that inspired me to write this book.

I would also like to acknowledge Chloe Cottone, for brainstorming concepts and ideas and being my biomedical consultant, and Maya Cottone, for reading and reviewing each word, practice, and concept in this book, some of them more (much more) than once.

Thank you to Carly Pershyn for reading the book and providing valuable feedback. A big thank you to my editor, Jenessa Jackson, for your attention to detail, thoughtfulness, and ability to help me say what I wanted to say even better than I said it. Thank you, as well, to Emily Dyer, who took my academic graphics and created beautiful, warm, and inviting images that effectively conveyed my ideas, and also brilliantly created the lovely cover of this book.

Finally, thank you to Karsyn Morse for believing in the concept of this book and taking my idea to PESI and to Kayla Church who shepherded it the rest of the way!

About the Author

Catherine Cook-Cottone, PhD, C-IAYT, is a psychologist, yoga therapist, and professor at the University at Buffalo (SUNY). As a psychologist and yoga therapist she treats individuals with trauma, anxiety, and disordered eating focusing on pathways to positive embodiment. Her research explores embodied self- regulation (i.e., yoga, mindfulness, and self-care) and psychosocial disorders (e.g., trauma and eating disorders). She has dedicated decades to creating and assessing trauma-informed mindfulness and yoga trainings, prevention programs, and interventions worldwide including service as a consultant for the United Nations Foundation. She received the American Psychological Association's presidential citation for service for her yoga-based prevention and intervention work. At the University at Buffalo, Catherine teaches masters and doctoral level courses in mindful therapy, psychopathology, self-care and service, and advanced counseling techniques. She is co-author of the Mindful Self-Care Scale (MSCS), the Collective Care Scale (CCS), and co-editor in chief of *Eating Disorders: The Journal of Treatment and Prevention*. Catherine has written ten books and over 100 peer reviewed articles and book chapters. She also, and perhaps most importantly, joyfully and courageously, embodies being a wife, mother of two incredible young women, an equestrian, and lover of all animals big and small.

Made in the USA
Monee, IL
10 May 2024

58312799R00195